CAPTURING SUNLIGHT

Skills & Ideas for Intensive Grazing, Sustainable Pastures, Healthy Soils, & Grassfed Livestock

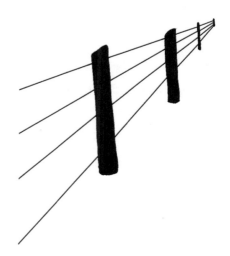

Woody Lane Ph.D.

ISBN: 978-0-983-32382-2 (trade paperback)
Library of Congress Control Number: 2017918554

Lane Livestock Services
240 Crystal Springs Lane, Roseburg, Oregon 97471
www.woodylane.com

Front cover design by Kristen Phillips, Denton, Texas

Copy editing by Karen Cristobal, Salem, Oregon

Editing and formatting by Self-Publishing Services LLC, Missoula, Montana

This book is dedicated to:

The three forage discussion groups of Oregon ranchers, farmers, and other agriculture specialists who have been a major part of my professional activities. For more than twenty years, our monthly meetings — consisting of ranch visits, pasture walks, and technical discussions — have opened up worlds of excellent information, shared experiences, and practical insights.

UVFSG	*Umpqua Valley Forage Study Group*, Douglas County
FANG	*Forage And Nutrition Group*, Curry and Coos counties
WVGANG	*Willamette Valley Grazing And Nutrition Group*, five counties in the Willamette Valley

In more than 600 meetings, members generously shared their knowledge and experiences with each other and with me. Again and again, the questions and comments discussed in these meetings became the germinal ideas for many of my writings.

It has been my great pleasure and honor to be the facilitator of these three groups.

Thank you, everyone.

Previous books by Woody Lane:

From the Feed Trough: Essays and Insights on Livestock Nutrition in a Complex World

Available at Amazon, Barnes & Noble, Apple, and more.

"The light which puts out our eyes is darkness to us.
Only that day dawns to which we are awake. There is more day to dawn.
The sun is but a morning star."

Henry David Thoreau, *Walden*

Knowledge is power —
the power to make good decisions,
and better decisions more often.

Woody Lane

Contents

Section 3: Soils, Soil Fertility, Fertilization

Section 4: Forage Growth & Storage

Section 5: Forage Quality

Section 6: The Science & Business of Grazing

Section 7: I Wonder . . .

Section 8: Intensively Managed Grazing Systems – A Textbook

Preface

This book is about the forages and animals that capture sunlight to feed the world.

I've wanted to write this book for a very long time. My training and postgraduate degrees are in animal nutrition, particularly with ruminants. The concepts of voluntary intake, rumen fermentation, fiber digestion, rate of passage, rumen turnover time, TDN, net energy, etc. have all been part of my everyday vocabulary since I began my formal graduate studies at Cornell.

It seemed like a natural progression that my interests evolved to include the primary natural source of nutrition for ruminants: forages. Especially pastures, which entails the concepts and principles of grazing and also the corollary topics of forage management and stocking density and soil fertility and hay and silage and . . . well, the list goes on. Over the years, these topics have become central in all the courses and workshops I teach and the consulting services I offer.

These topics also appear in my writings. For more than twenty years, I've written a monthly nutrition column in *The Shepherd* magazine titled "From The Feed Trough . . ." While many of these essays have been, of course, about nutrition, many have been about forages and grazing and related topics. Sixty-two of these essays appear in this book. These articles range from grazing management to pasture walks to soils to business decisions to the forage nutrition of dinosaurs. Dinosaurs?!! Well, the big dinosaurs were herbivores, similar, in a way, to cattle and sheep, and they had to obtain their nutrients from plant fiber just like our cattle and sheep.

The final section of this book is a bit different— it's a practical, no-nonsense textbook on grazing management, especially on improved pastures. I first wrote it as part of the "Forages Chapter" in the *SID Sheep Production Handbook* by the American Sheep Industry Association. Although it was

X

originally targeted for the sheep industry, this section is not about sheep; it's about forages and how to manage them in an improved pasture system. The principles apply to all grazing livestock: beef cattle, dairy cattle, goats, sheep, bison, llamas, alpacas, horses, wildebeests, impalas, capybaras, gnus . . . the possibilities are vast.

There are some folks I would like to acknowledge and thank. I want to thank the people who published *The Shepherd* magazine for more than 35 years: Guy and Pat Flora and Kathy and Ken Kark. They were a great pleasure to work with. They were always supportive and professional. They honored good information based on science, they supported and encouraged me as a writer, and they put up with my occasional offbeat sense of humor. They are friends in the truest sense, and my life is richer in knowing them and working with them.

This book is about forages. It's about plants and soils and grazing and nutritional value. It's about walking through pastures and feeling the earth and knowing that we can create food and fiber in a sustainable way from forages. It's about the miracle of fiber and the rumen and our skills to manage this system. It's about knowing that forages exist because of sunlight.

Sunlight is free. Plants, through their magnificent system of photosynthesis, use the sun's energy to create carbohydrates that they combine with nitrogen compounds to form proteins. Forages grow in nearly all climates, and lush pastures properly managed are sustainable and environmentally friendly. But plants also represent a conundrum. A high percentage of the forage dry matter is fiber, mostly cellulose and hemicellulose. Although humans can certainly consume plants, humans do not have the digestive enzymes to digest most of the plant fiber.

But ruminants do. Ruminants — cattle, sheep, goats, and others — house microbes in their rumen. These microbes digest fiber through the process of fermentation, and the host ruminant lives on the products of this fermentation. Ruminants then provide meat and milk and other products for humans.

In essence, raising ruminants on forage is a sustainable way of using sunlight.

Woody Lane
Roseburg, Oregon
November 2018

Section 1

Capturing Sunlight

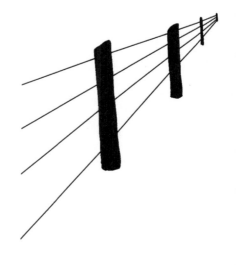

Ruminant

Are we lucky *or what?*

We raise sheep or cattle or goats or reindeer or yaks. Usually, we are very busy with daily chores and don't have much time to contemplate the larger world of mammalian physiology. But let's stop for a moment and consider this: these animals are *ruminants*, and we are indeed lucky to raise one of the marvels of evolution — a creature ideally designed to harvest sunlight.

Sunlight . . . a free and unlimited source of energy captured by green plants and converted into leaves and stems and roots. Much of the world's landmass is covered by plants that we call "forages" (grasses and legumes and other broadleaf plants). Ruminants are astonishingly effective in their use of forages; they are walking connoisseurs of green plants. In one sense, a ruminant is a mammal that has evolved to contain a large colony of fiber-digesting microbes in a gastrointestinal sac just upstream from its true stomach (*abomasum*) and small intestines. In another sense, we may consider that the rumen microbes have guided evolution to house them in a safe and secure environment, in a mobile four-legged platform that can provide a steady source of substrates and seek out new sources of food for them. Clever devils.

Officially, *ruminant* means one who ruminates, and *ruminate* means to chew one's cud. (This most assuredly does *not* mean someone who chews tobacco.) Of course, our common livestock species — sheep, goats, cattle, deer, bison — are all ruminants, but so are wildebeest, pronghorn antelope, water buffalo, gazelles, and the smallest antelope, the dik-dik. And the largest ruminant? The giraffe. Whoa — chew cud?!! *That's* food for thought.

Is a rumen absolutely essential for animals to eat forage? Not at all. Horses are not ruminants, and they do a fair job of grazing forages. And so do elephants, and they would be largely offended if someone called them ruminants. (Have you ever seen an elephant ruminate?) And so do capybaras, the world's largest rodents, who live in South American rivers and really enjoy an afternoon of grazing green plants. Not one of these animals is a ruminant. So . . . if a rumen is not absolutely required for grazing, what makes it so special?

It is special because of its many functions, which all work together to support a ruminant's ability to obtain nutrition from plants and compete efficiently in the evolutionary race. Let's consider its four major functions.

The first, and primary, rumen function is *fiber digestion*. Plant cells contain fiber, one of the main characteristics that make them plant cells. In terms of tonnage, fiber also constitutes the largest amount of nutritional plant material on Earth, making it a convenient food source if it could be used.

Fiber is actually a complex matrix of large molecules like cellulose, hemicellulose, and lignin. Let's ignore lignin because it is not digestible unless someone attacks it with strong acids or dynamite. The other two major fiber components — cellulose and hemicellulose — are *only* digestible if an animal has the *cellulase* enzymes that split those internal molecular bonds.

This is a good news-bad news situation. The bad news is that no mammals have this enzyme in their digestive tract. The good news is that some bacteria *do* produce this enzyme, and the rumen is essentially a large container for these bacteria. The rumen, therefore, is a place of fiber digestion where bacteria break fiber down in a process called *fermentation*. The products of this fermentation are small molecules called *volatile fatty acids (VFAs)* which are then absorbed by the animal and used for energy and other metabolic needs.

Ruminants also chew cud, which is really a novel way of recycling fiber through a crushing machine (the mouth) so that it becomes easier for the rumen microbes to digest it. And the act of chewing cud causes the ruminant to produce lots of saliva, much more than humans and other non-ruminant animals. This saliva contains buffers and other compounds that help maintain a favorable rumen environment for the microbes that ferment the fiber.

In addition, the anatomical position of the rumen — at the beginning of the gastrointestinal tract, upstream from the true stomach and the small intestine — means that many products of rumen fermentation and all the bodies of dead rumen microbes ultimately travel downstream into the lower tract where they can be digested and absorbed by the animal.

All this points to one thing: ruminants are designed to extract maximum energy from the most common feedstuff — fiber — in the most efficient way possible.

The second rumen function is *to convert nonprotein nitrogen into proteins*. To be technical, rumen microbes can convert many forms of *nonprotein nitrogen (NPN)* into amino acids that the microbes then use to manufacture their own proteins. These microbial proteins ultimately pass into the lower tract where they are broken down into amino acids which are then absorbed by the animal, who uses them to synthesize its own animal proteins. What is NPN? Things like nitrates, loose amino acids, and other nitrogenous compounds that plants accumulate in their leaves, sometimes in large amounts. Also, and this is very important, a common NPN feed ingredient is *urea* — the same urea that we use as a fertilizer. If we include urea in a protein supplement along with molasses, rumen microbes can convert that urea nitrogen into amino acids, just like they do with plant NPN compounds. If you read the feed tags on some protein supplements and protein "licks," you'll often see the word "urea."

The bottom line is that ruminants can convert nonprotein nitrogen — that humans cannot use — into animal protein that humans can use. Urea and nitrates into lamb chops and steaks. It's something to ruminate on.

The third rumen function involves *vitamins*. Specifically, the B-vitamins: compounds like thiamine, biotin, niacin, pantothenic acid, etc. Just like our livestock species, rumen microbes need these vitamins for their own metabolic processes. But these microbes don't worry about taking one-a-day pills; they simply manufacture their own B-vitamins in the rumen. Eventually, these vitamins pass out of the rumen into the lower tract, where they can be absorbed into the blood by the host animal.

Yes, you read that right — *we don't need to include B-vitamins in ruminant rations because the rumen microbes usually make enough for everyone.* There is, uh, one minor wrinkle: vitamin B_{12}. Although rumen microbes can indeed manufacture their own vitamin B_{12}, this molecule is built around an atom of cobalt. Without cobalt, the microbes cannot make B_{12}. But in practice we can easily overcome this problem by routinely including cobalt in our trace mineral mixtures. We don't need to feed vitamin B_{12} to ruminants, just cobalt. This strategy provides enough cobalt to the microbes, and they can do the rest.

Finally, the fourth rumen function is *detoxification*. The plant world is a dangerous place, and many plants, including some of our common forages, can contain all sorts of toxic compounds. But before those compounds can be absorbed into the blood, they must pass through the rumen, and the rumen can act as an effective barrier. Rumen microbes can degrade those toxic molecules or alter them so they are no longer toxic or are less toxic. Here are some examples: nitrates, some phytoestrogens from legumes, some mycotoxins from moldy hay, toxic amino acids such as mimosine from the *Leucaena* tree, etc. Also, the rumen contains so much fluid that it dilutes some toxins below the critical threshold that would otherwise cause toxic symptoms. In a larger perspective, the rumen helps make life safer for ruminants, so they can continue to consume forages.

The rumen is indeed something very special. Fiber, nitrogen, vitamins, toxins — all facets of a very complex organ that gives ruminants a real survival edge in a ruthless world.

But this topic — being a ruminant — kind of brings up the sensitive issue of corn. Corn and other grains are actually packages of starch; they don't contain significant amounts of fiber. So . . . if ruminants are some of the best utilizers of fiber on the planet, it is interesting that much of our modern agriculture is based on feeding them starch. But maybe this is a good place to end this month's article.

First Published: June 2011

Author's Note: This is the magic: Sunlight is an endless, free supply of energy. All green plants capture this sunlight. Legumes also capture nitrogen from the air. The main product of plants is fiber, which represents the largest tonnage of nutritive feedstuff on Earth. Humans are very limited in their ability to digest fiber, but ruminants are exquisitely designed to do this in the most efficient and environmentally sustainable way. Ruminants, therefore, effectively convert sunlight and atmospheric nitrogen into meat, milk, wool, and other products that humans can use. A magnificent equation we can be proud of.

Section 2

Grazing Techniques

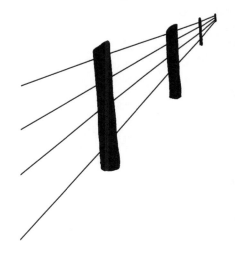

Disconnected Height and Mass

I'm a nutritionist, so I have a simple question: how many inches of grass does a ewe need to meet her daily nutrient requirements?

Let's say we want to graze a flock of 100 ewes with their new lambs on a 5-acre field. We must answer two basic questions: (1) when should we put our animals onto that field, and (2) when should we take them off? We go to our reference books or "how-to" fact sheets and see guidelines for different types of forage species. For example, a typical recommendation for tall grasses such as orchardgrass or tall fescue would be to initiate grazing when the forage height is 8–10 inches and then remove the animals at 2–4 inches. Shorter forages like Kentucky bluegrass have correspondingly lower numbers. This seems straightforward enough . . . until we really start to think about it.

Maybe the guidelines in those reference books are not necessarily the guidelines we need.

Hmmm . . .

Let's step back for a moment. When I balance a diet or calculate the amount of feed needed to support a group of animals, what is the numerical basis of my calculations? Let's put it another way: what fundamental unit of measurement do I use to balance a diet? The answer is simple: it's the number of pounds or kilograms or tons or whatever. In other words, *weight*. When I balance a ration, I do my calculations in units of *weight* (also known as *mass*). Once I estimate an animal's intake in pounds, I can easily calculate the amounts of forage or corn or byproducts that should be included in the ration. Weight is my fundamental unit of measurement for solving the practical problems of nutrition.

9

Yet, the standard published guidelines for grazing management are given in terms of *height*.

"Houston, we have a problem." A complete disconnect.

If the nutritional needs of livestock are listed in *pounds* and the grazing guidelines are listed in *inches*, how can I properly combine these two systems to manage animals and forages together on the same pasture? Again, the simple answer — I can't. But there is a solution, it's just not the one we are used to.

Instead of trying to match apples and oranges, we can turn everything into apples. Instead of managing a pasture in terms of *height*, we can manage it in terms of *mass*. Once we begin thinking in terms of mass, all our measurements and calculations become easy — everything is in pounds. Of course, we do need to overcome 200 years of traditional thinking, as I believe that even Thomas Jefferson used rulers to measure his grass and move his fence. (Just kidding. I don't think he had good electric fences in 1804.) But in other countries like New Zealand, farmers have long used measurements of pasture mass to manage grazing successfully. We can learn from their experience.

Back to our 100-ewe example. Let's say those ewes average 150 lb, which gives us a total flock weight of 15,000 lb. If we assume a daily dry matter intake of 5% body weight (a reasonable estimate for early-lactation ewes on young vegetative grass), then our flock would consume 750 lb of dry matter each day ($= 15,000 \ x \ 0.05$). So here are two practical questions: (1) how many days can our flock graze that 5-acre pasture? And (2) if we wanted to go on a 2-week vacation, how many acres should we allocate to provide enough feed for our flock? Two straightforward, routine questions. But before we can answer them, we need one more piece of information: we need to know the amount of forage in the field.

This number is not exactly obvious. The amount of forage in the field is not the same as the amount that our animals will eat, at least not if we want that forage to grow back again for hay production or additional grazing. We need to recognize that a field actually contains *three* types of forage amounts (mass). The largest amount is the *Total Mass*, which includes *all* the forage from the ground up, everything. The second amount is the *Residual Mass*, which is the amount remaining when the animals leave the pasture. Generally, we don't want this amount to equal zero, unless we are trying to turn a useful pasture into a putting green. The concept of Residual Mass is critical, because it represents the starter forage that will grow back after grazing. Residual Mass is actually a target, a goal. We aim for a certain amount of Residual Mass based on our management plan. A smaller Residual Mass usually translates to a slower recovery of the pasture; a larger Residual Mass usually results in a quicker recovery. Finally, the third type of forage amount is the *Available Mass*, which is simply the difference between the Total Mass and the Residual Mass. The Available Mass is the amount of forage that our animals will actually consume. *This* is our prime working number. When our animals graze the forage down to the Residual Mass, we move them off the field. Simple.

By convention, we generally express these values as pounds of dry matter per acre.

Now back to our two practical questions. Let's say that we've already made some forage measurements (we'll save the descriptive details for the next few chapters and also the textbook section at the end of this book). Our measurements show that our pasture contains a Total Mass of 2,500 lb per acre. Let's set our target Residual Mass at 1,000 lb. That gives us an Available Mass of 1,500 lb per acre. Now we have enough information to guide our grazing decisions.

Practical Question #1: Our field contains an Available Mass of 1,500 lb per acre, which means that the entire 5-acre field contains 7,500 pounds of grazeable forage. Since the flock has a dry matter intake of 750 lb/day, our animals can remain in that field for 10 days (= 7,500 ÷ 750). What would happen if we keep them there for 15 or 20 days? Well, they certainly won't stop eating. Our sheep will continue to graze and reduce the Residual Mass to a smaller and smaller amount. This will result in a long lag period for forage regrowth and also probably have other negative effects on species composition, weed invasion, etc. Here's another management point: ten days in a single field will be long enough for animals to graze the *forage regrowth*, especially if the field is fertile and contains fast-growing forages. So we might want to throw an electric netting fence across the field to split it into two 5-day grazing sessions, but that is a topic for another time.

Practical Question #2: Two weeks is 14 days. (We will not skimp on our vacation.) With a daily intake of 750 lb, our flock will require 10,500 lb of dry matter for that period (= 14 x 750). Recall that our Available Mass is 1,500 lb/acre. Our final calculation includes the dry matter intake of the sheep, the number of days, and the amount of Available Mass in the field. The answer for Practical Question #2, therefore, is that we need to reserve 7 acres for our entire vacation period (= 750 x 14 ÷ 1,500). If we reserve fewer acres, our sheep will leave a much smaller Residual Mass. If we reserve more than seven acres, the sheep will have the luxury of consuming some areas of the field more than others, and the forage will show higher levels of variability, which makes it hard to manage. It's a perfectly nice logic.

This logic, however, does have its limitations. Setting aside 7 acres gets the sheep through our vacation, but setting aside 30 acres does not automatically force the boss to give us a longer vacation.

Nonetheless, by basing our calculations on animal weights and forage weights, we've successfully answered both Practical Questions. What a relief. We are no longer trying to fit the square peg of pasture height into the round hole of animal nutrition. Recently, after returning from a vacation in New

Zealand, a local rancher reported that one of the main tools New Zealand graziers carry in their pockets is a calculator. Now we can see why.

>—<

First Published: March 2010
Author's Note: This is the absolute basis for good pasture management. Knowing the amount of forage in a field gives us objective numbers. We can then proactively manage that field and make better decisions. Better forage cover, fewer weeds, more persistent forages, higher yields . . . the list goes on. There will be lots more detail in subsequent chapters, but you get the idea.

Opening a Door

Spring in Douglas County, Oregon: the hills are a vibrant, rich green, as green as the fabled Irish countryside, and the valleys are filled with a lush carpet of grass and clover growing at 80 lb per day or more . . .

Huh? Isn't forage growth measured in inches? Well . . . no, not for grazing. Inches are too imprecise; inches don't give us information about forage density, maturity, or carrying capacity; and inches can't be applied anywhere else. Also, animals eat *pounds* of feed, not inches. *Pounds* are the numbers we need for good grazing decisions. So let's look at forage management in a new way — by the numbers.

Whenever we want to formulate a grazing plan for a specific paddock, *before we put the animals in it,* we should always do one thing: we should estimate how much forage is really out there. This is not hard. Just take a sample (or a few samples, as defined by your time and energy). Here, we use a simple wooden frame, 12 inches long and 11.5 inches wide, inside diameter (the reason for this weird measurement is actually arithmetic convenience. I explain this rationale in other chapters). We place the frame on the ground and cut off everything inside it with a pair of good garden shears. Right to the ground. Then we'll weigh the sample, dry it in a regular oven or microwave until it is dry, and weigh it again. We stop drying it when its weight stabilizes, which occurs after an initial 5-minute period in a microwave plus successive 2-minute periods. Remember to put an open glass of water in the microwave. A tip: first warn the rest of the family about your intentions. The fragrance of drying forage should not catch them by surprise.

Our sample gives us the total amount of forage dry matter in 138 square inches. Let's say that our dried forage sample weighs 34 grams (we use a gram scale for accuracy, convert to pounds, and correct for the tare weight of the paper bag). Letting our calculator go to work, this equates to 0.07815 lb per

13

square foot. This is a nice value but not really very useful, unless we are raising a herd of slugs. But because an acre contains 43,560 square feet, we can convert this number to a total dry matter/acre of 3,404 pounds (= 43,560 x 0.07815). Now *that's* a number that we can use.

It's a good beginning. Now we must adjust this value for the realities of grazing because we never let our animals eat *all* the grass in a paddock, not unless we want to batter our fields into a desert. Generally, we open a gate, allow the animals into a paddock, and then pull them off when they graze it down "low enough." This leftover *residual forage* is the amount remaining when the animals leave.

So now we have a fundamental equation for grazing: *the amount of forage available to our grazing livestock is the difference between the total forage and the residual forage.* This amount is called, not surprisingly, the *available forage.* Therefore, good grazing management is quite simple: we measure the total mass, decide on the residual, and let the sheep and cattle do the rest. There are, of course, a *few* other details . . . but we'll get to them later. First, let's return for a moment to our much-maligned height measurement because height is what we see.

In New Zealand, where farmers have made a few zillion measurements on forage height and mass, they've devised a general rule of thumb for their type of pasture: the lowest inch of forage contains approximately 1,000 pounds of dry matter per acre, and every additional inch contains 500 pounds (translated from the metric). Now don't rush off to take those height measurements just yet — remember: *those numbers apply only to a very specific type of pasture managed in a very specific way.* Those numbers were derived from well-managed New Zealand pastures composed primarily of perennial ryegrass and white clover, pastures that are very dense, heavily fertilized, and intensively grazed.

Frankly, very few pastures in North America are like that. Our pastures generally differ in forage species, grazing management, and fertilizer use. The New Zealand rule of thumb, however, gives us a handle, a rough idea about a possible relationship between forage height and forage mass.

We've checked the accuracy of this relationship here in Douglas County in western Oregon. Many of our improved pastures seem to average 800/300 — that is, 800 pounds in the first inch and 300 pounds for every inch above that. Eight inches of forage clearly means different things in different places: 4,500 pounds/acre on lush New Zealand-type pastures, and 2,900 pounds/acre on many local pastures.

Why? Well, our local pastures contain different forages than perennial ryegrass and white clover. They also contain orchardgrass, tall fescue, bentgrass, subterranean clover, foxtail, and an occasional thistle or two — and these species have different growth forms than perennial ryegrass. Also, we haven't fertilized our pastures as heavily or grazed as tightly as many New Zealand farmers, so our swards aren't as dense. This 800/300 relationship is only a general average, however, and there is quite a bit of variation. Some pastures probably range from much less than that up to, in the very best swards, nearly 1000/500.

So what does this mean? Simple. Pasture weights give us information about forage density and growth. Weight (mass) values allow us to discuss pasture management intelligently with *anyone* in the world and learn from *their* management. For example, if I hear that a successful Irish sheep farmer puts his lactating ewes onto a perennial ryegrass paddock at 3,500 lb/acre and aims for a residual of 1,200 lb/acre, I know exactly what he did. I can also assess his management in terms of my own pastures.

And more. With those weight numbers, I can infer how he managed his livestock, what grazing options he faced in that paddock, and how that sward may respond to the next grazing cycle. Compared to that, inches, ahem, just don't measure up. More next month . . .

First Published: June 1997
Author's Note: I wrote this chapter and the next chapter in the 1990s, when the concepts of intensive grazing were just getting off the ground in the United States. Compared to my later articles and also the textbook section at the end of this book, these two chapters may seem a bit elementary, but I have included them because they describe the situation clearly and succinctly, and I enjoyed the writing.

Animals and Acres

In every grazing workshop, someone asks, "How many sheep can I put on my pasture?" Or "How much space does my flock need for grazing?" Or "How long can my flock graze in a 10-acre field?"

These are really all variations of the same question. Let's discuss two main concepts of pasture growth and then describe a method for calculating reasonable answers to these questions.

Main Concept #1: Forage grows in stages. When grasses and clovers first come out of the ground, the tiny plants spend their time and energy collecting sunlight, transporting sugars down to the roots, and constructing more solar panels, which we call leaves. Since young plants only have a couple of tiny leaves, this process takes time. Once enough photosynthetic machinery is in place, however, the carbohydrate assembly line kicks into high gear. Then, with enough sunlight and root-supplied nutrients, these plants make lots of sugars and protein, build more leaves, and grow profusely. Finally, the forage plants become tall enough to shade out their lower leaves, which then turn brown. At that point, new plant growth just about equals senescence, so the net effect is little or no additional high-quality tissue. From a grazier's perspective, these plants may still be healthy, but the pasture is actually gaining very little nutritional mass.

These stages, or "phases," are called *Phase I, Phase II,* and *Phase III.* For any pasture, we can identify the phase by measuring the amount of dry matter in an acre. As I described last month, pasture height is not the best measure of growth. We really need to describe a pasture in terms of pounds of dry matter. Here's a practical rule of thumb with most of our common forages: Pastures with less than 1,000–1,200 lb/acre are in Phase I; pastures containing more than 3,500–4,000 lb/acre are usually in Phase III; everything in between is Phase II. These are rough estimates, of course.

17

Different types of pastures have different numbers. Height can certainly be misleading. Species that specialize in prostrate growth like Kentucky bluegrass, Gala grazing brome, and some varieties of white clover, birdsfoot trefoil, and perennial ryegrass contain more of their biomass in the lower inches of growth than upright forages like tall fescue, orchardgrass, and ladino clover.

Phase I is a preparatory phase, a lag phase. Plants in Phase I are young and highly nutritious, but their growth is very slow. Phase II is the grow-like-gangbusters phase. Plants in Phase II are larger and robust and still have high nutritional value. Phase III is the inefficient, too-tall-for-good-grazing phase. Hay is almost always Phase III forage. But in the opening paragraph, those initial questions were about grazing, which is definitely not the same as making hay.

In an ideal system of sustainable, controlled grazing, we want to keep our pastures oscillating between the high and low ends of Phase II. If possible, we should put animals into a paddock *just before* the plant mass reaches Phase III and take them off *just before* the plant mass is reduced to Phase I.

Main Concept #2: My *5-Day Rule:* don't keep animals in a tightly fenced paddock for more than five days. Reason? Because grazing animals eat the most delectable forages first. Consider some of the new, improved forage varieties that have been bred for palatability and quick growth. Five days after they are munched, if given water and nutrients, these plants will begin to send out new shoots. These are *precisely* the forages that we want in our pastures. But if our animals are still in that paddock, what do you think they will eat? Animals will spend all day searching for those new shoots. Yummy! But removing leaves from these plants so quickly puts them under severe stress, and that ultimately exerts a steady selection pressure *against* the very species that we want to encourage. The answer is really simple: move livestock *before* they can eat those new shoots.

Now the main question: how large an area do we need for our sheep? Let's approach the problem in logical steps: how many sheep are in the mob? How much do the animals weigh? How much do they eat (dry matter intake, DMI)? And how much forage dry matter is available for grazing? Then we match the answers, find a balance, and stir in the 5-day constraint.

Our hypothetical flock consists of 25 adult Targhee ewes and their month-old lambs, mostly twins. Let's guess that the ewes weigh approximately 175 pounds. A reference table in the *SID Sheep Production Handbook* lists an expected DMI at 6.6 lb, which is 3.8% of their body weight. But that DMI is based on including some grain in the ration. In reality, I would expect that ewes on pasture would consume (and also stomp and soil) approximately 5% of their body weight, or maybe even 6%. Let's use 5% for this example, which means that the total daily DMI of the entire flock, including stompage, would be 219 pounds (= 25 x 175 x 0.05).

On the pasture side of the equation, our field is composed of smooth brome, orchardgrass, and white clover, with a total mass of 2,800 lb of dry matter per acre. We'd like to move the sheep off the pasture at the low end of Phase II, so let's decide to leave a residual of 1,200 lb. By subtraction, therefore, our pasture contains 1,600 lb of available DM per acre. If our ewes use 219 lb/day, one acre of this pasture will last the flock 7.3 days (= 7 days, 7 hours, 20 minutes, and 30 seconds). This is longer than our 5-day rule. One acre, therefore, is clearly too large.

In five days, our sheep would use 1,095 lb of DM (= 5 x 219), which is available from 0.68 acres of pasture. But if we wanted to move our sheep after only 3 days (more reasonable) and still leave 1,200 pounds of residual, then our flock would need only 657 lb of DM (= 3 x 219), which equates to only 0.4 acres. For a three-day movement, that's where we could put our temporary electric fence.

Pasture management: fire up the calculator, move fence, and watch the sheep graze. But maybe I should add one note of warning. Although your attention may be focused on pasture weights and grazing areas, and you may be staring intently at your calculator, just remember that before you move the electric fence, first turn it off.

First Published: July 1997
Author's Note: Numbers and calculations — they are the backbone of our logic and our grazing decisions. One strength of this system is that we can apply these concepts to any grazing animals: sheep, cattle, goats, dairy cows, yaks, bison, etc. Horses, of course, are similar, but they come with some practical behavior restrictions about crowding them too much. Similarly, I wouldn't want to crowd a pride of lions either.

Regrowth

When I teach my course on pasture management to livestock producers and get to the topic of grazing, the ranchers ask very practical questions, such as: when should I open the gate to let the animals into a field? When should I move the animals off? How long is too long?

These questions and their permutations may be endless, but the principles they invoke are not. So, here, briefly, I'll cover one crucial principle of good grazing.

[Important disclaimer: Here I'm talking about *improved* pastures, or at least *improvable* pastures. Grazing livestock in open range country is a different universe entirely.]

Crucial Principle: The 5-Day Rule. Have you ever carefully watched grass grow? *Really* watched it? Let's say that you have a pasture with good fertility and sufficient water, a pasture containing forage with excellent genetics for rapid recovery and a high growth rate. After animals graze this forage (or after equipment cuts it), how many days pass before you can see the little, bright-green shoots of regrowth? Hmmm. Well, next time look carefully. In my fields, I've seen that bright young regrowth within 4 or 5 days.

Now let's think about this. If a sheep or goat or cow is still wandering around that field during this period looking for something to eat, and it comes across these new, bright-green shoots — what will it graze? Will our animal choose to avoid this new vegetation and instead munch on older grass, or will it happily graze our new shoots and look for more? The answer is obvious.

But let's pursue this concept a little further. When our grazing animals preferentially select these new shoots, they effectively put selection pressure *against* the very plants we *want* in our pasture — i.e., the valuable forage plants that show new growth and recover quickly after defoliation. In addition, the

21

new palatable regrowth may come from plant reserves, and this type of grazing management systematically lets our animals destroy those reserves before the plants can fully recover. And if we allow our animals to do this for weeks or months, over time, the only forages that will thrive in those fields will be plants with slower regrowth and lower palatability. Including awful weeds like thistles and toxic plants that are *really* less attractive to our livestock.

Hence my 5-Day Rule: *Do not keep animals in a paddock for more than five days.* Fewer days is usually better, but that choice depends on the management details in each farm or ranch. Dairy farmers, for example, move animals twice each day anyway, so, for them, a 12-hour move makes sense. Graziers with other species of livestock may move animals every 1–4 days based on their specific production system and their strategies for managing time and labor. But never more than five days.

In other words, we should always protect the forage regrowth in a pasture. I repeat: *we protect the regrowth.* In fact, as good graziers, we should become fanatical about protecting the regrowth. A grazing period of five days or less gives us a management tool to do this.

The 5-Day Rule implies lots of things, especially about some traditional approaches to grazing. First, look at any classic textbook on forages, such as the books assigned to university students for their agronomy courses. Those textbooks list all types of grazing techniques that are each carefully named and defined (which students must memorize for their exams), such as "creep grazing" and "forward creep grazing" and "first-and-second grazing" and "put-and-take grazing" and "multi-species grazing" and others.

But in light of our 5-Day Rule, all of these grazing techniques and memorized jargon comes down to this: *animals should be off the field within five days.* Period. It's all about regrowth. No matter which livestock species we use, or how we select their subgroups, or how skillfully we design the sequences for one subgroup to follow another — the basic axiom is that everyone must be off that field before the plants begin any significant regrowth.

And when we keep this principle in mind, all the various grazing techniques actually become variations of the same theme. Sure, we can graze the lighter animals first and then follow up with heavy breeding stock. Or design a clever creep-grazing system that allows very young stock to graze ahead of their mothers. Or top off a pasture with one mob, and then "clean it up" with a follow-up mob, etc.

Even the popular concept of multi-species grazing falls neatly under the same principle. Start with sheep, follow with cattle. Or start with cattle, follow with chickens. Or start with goats and follow with sheep. Whatever. Just get the last group of animals off the field within five days. The rest are just details and preferences.

Which brings us to the important grazing concept of *set-stocking*. Most folks think they know about set-stocking — that it's a type of grazing management system in which animals are left in a field for a hundred years, and they demolish all the forage in that field. While that scenario may be true, it's not quite the full story. Viewed in the light of our 5-Day Rule, the concept of set-stocking takes on a whole new and insidious meaning. *Set-stocking really means that animals will consume young regrowth.* Which means that set-stocking isn't only defined by weeks or months on the same field, but rather it can be defined by *days*—a few extra days that allow animals the opportunity to eat our field's most valuable forage, its regrowth.

Which means that set-stocking can actually occur on a fertile pasture in only seven days. Which implies that forages can be damaged by leaving livestock on them a few extra *days*, not just the classic weeks or months that most people think about.

But, you say, my field is too big! It takes my flock (herd, mob, pod, etc.) at least 14 days to graze all the forage in that field!

Actually, there is a straightforward answer to this problem: *electric fencing.* Set a temporary electric fence across that field to reduce its size. Aim for a size that allows the animals to consume the feed in only 3–5 days.

Where to put that fence? Well, first estimate the available amount of feed in the entire field; then estimate the amount of feed needed by the livestock per day. A rule of thumb is to use a dry matter disappearance of 4% to 5% of body weight per day. Then position the temporary fence to give the animals X days of feed, where X is the number 5 or less.

In other words, you *allocate* feed and then set the fence so your animals will harvest that amount of feed in a few days. If you estimate wrongly, you'll either run out of feed early or have too much feed remaining after five days. In either case, you will have learned about feed allocation, and you will set the fence better the next time. Not bad — a win-win situation. And eventually your forages will thank you for this — because you will have protected the regrowth.

First Published: June 2008

Author's Note: Regrowth, regrowth, regrowth. A good grazier protects it. How many different grazing scenarios have you encountered or learned about that really can be reduced to The 5-Day Rule? The rule puts a ceiling on the number of days animals can stay in a paddock. It also acknowledges that forages can be easily damaged or stressed if that ceiling is ignored. Protecting regrowth is the key, and this 5-Day Rule begins to put structure into the free-wheeling world of grazing.

Principled Grazing

Last month, I described one of the bedrock principles of good grazing management — never leave animals in a paddock for more than five days. But my 5-Day Rule is not the only principle of good grazing. This month, I'll discuss three more. (I'll begin with Principle #2, because the 5-Day Rule is *Principle #1*.)

Principle #2: Stay in Phase II. Hmmm . . . what am I talking about? Does "phase" mean something celestial, as in "phase of the moon"? Do I mean that perhaps graziers should only graze when the moon is full? (Don't laugh. I've seen equivalent statements seriously espoused on the internet.) No, I'm talking about forage growth and how we describe and manage it.

Forage growth follows a predictable S-shaped curve, and the three parts of that curve are called *Phase I*, *Phase II*, and *Phase III*, respectively. Think of a graph in which the Y-axis is "forage yield" and the X-axis is "time." From left to right, a forage growth curve slopes upward in a sinuous shape that loosely resembles a stretched-out "S" ("sloping upward" means that the amount of forage increases with time — hopefully, a reasonable assumption).

The section of the S-curve near the bottom left is *Phase 1* — the slowly rising part of the curve when forage growth is slow because the plants only have a few leaves to capture sunlight. The forage is probably shorter than 3 inches, and that translates to less than 1,000 lb dry matter (DM) per acre on many pastures. The next section of the S-curve rises steeply — the long, nearly-vertical shank of the S. This is *Phase II* — when forage growth is exploding. The pasture contains enough vegetation to capture vastly increased amounts of sunlight, and the leaves manufacture lots of carbohydrates and proteins to create additional plant tissue. Finally, the third section of the S-curve is the top part of the "S" that flattens out. This is *Phase III.* During this period, many of the bottom leaves in the sward stop functioning and only the top leaves are effectively capturing sunlight. Although the forage is still adding more vegetation mass each day, the amount of new forage *per day* is considerably less than during the steep part of the curve. It's a section of diminishing returns. Phase III contains the highest *total* forage yield for the field, which may be nice for putting hay in the barn, but the slower forage growth means that less and less additional DM accumulates each day.

So . . . the Principle *"Stay in Phase II"* means that animals should only graze a paddock when its forage is in Phase II. Which, in essence, defines livestock movement on the farm. Ideally, a good grazier introduces animals into a paddock when the forage mass is at the *top* of Phase II and then removes those animals when the forage mass is at the *bottom* of Phase II. While, of course, always obeying the 5-Day rule. Then the animals are moved to a different paddock that is at the top of Phase II. And this timing and sequence continues throughout the grazing season, from paddock to paddock and back again. In other words, a grazier always stays in Phase II.

Why the big deal? A couple of reasons. The first reason is because Phase II is the most efficient part of the growth curve. By harvesting Phase II growth, a grazier systematically takes advantage of the least-cost part of the growth curve, the part of the curve where the most amount of forage has accumulated in the fewest number of days. In contrast, the forage growth in Phase III is less efficient because it takes more days to accumulate forage. And Phase I growth is a *very* expensive place to graze because there is very little growth on a daily basis.

Here's a second compelling reason: the nutritional value of Phase II forage is excellent. Truly excellent. Phase II forage consists almost entirely of vegetative young leaves. The crude protein levels of Phase II forage are at least 14% and often higher than 20%. Energy levels are also superb — at least 68% TDN or higher — high enough to support excellent animal performance without grain supplementation. In today's world of expensive grain and high fuel costs, Phase II forage is a grazier's economic gold mine.

In terms of practical field measurements, the "top" of Phase II is approximately 3,000 lb DM of forage per acre, depending on the type of forage and time of year. Phase II "bottoms out" at approximately 1,000 lb DM per acre. (Your mileage may vary, depending on forage species.) Which brings us to this next principle:

Principle #3: Leave enough residual. Generally, this means moving the animals when the paddock still contains approximately 1,000 lb DM per acre — which is conveniently at the bottom of Phase II. *Residual mass* is the amount of forage remaining when the animals leave the paddock. Leaving too little residual means that the animals have grazed down into Phase I, when the plants are small and growth is slower. Grazing during Phase I means grazing during the inefficient slow-growth section of the growth curve. Grazing into

Phase I also means that the forage plants may need 7–14 *additional* days to reach the bottom of Phase II, effectively adding those days to the recovery period. Which means that, instead of cycling livestock back into a paddock in 20 days, we'll need to wait 30–35 days. Or longer if the growing conditions are not ideal.

Consider what this means to the entire grazing season. Let's say that you would like to cycle your animals through a paddock four times during a growing season. But because of insufficient residual, you lose 10 days each cycle. This means that over the course of a growing season, you will have lost 30 grazing days in that paddock because you've had to wait for the forage to grow through the inefficient Phase I. Essentially, you've lost one full grazing period in that paddock. Multiply that by the number of paddocks, and you're beginning to talk real money.

But leaving enough residual forage means you must move animals when the paddock still contains a couple of inches of lush green feed. Oh, the temptation! It takes some discipline to walk away from a green carpet of nutritious forage. And I can say from my own experience that it's not easy, at first. But trust me — it works. And it doesn't take long to see that it's truly worth it.

And finally, *Principle #4: Water and minerals move with the animals.* A good grazier designs a paddock system to maximize forage growth and then puts animals in those paddocks to harvest that growth. Minerals and drinking water are supplementary items that should follow the animals into every paddock and into every grazing cell — not the other way around.

Although this principle seems very simple, it may entail some radical changes in design and tradition. The paddocks on many farms are often designed around *existing* water supplies — convenient access to a stream, walking back to a central corral or barn, etc. The same issue occurs in paddocks containing large, stationary mineral feeders. These traditional or convenient designs encourage animals to move away from their main grazing areas and congregate in small, central locations. From a grazier's perspective, this behavior causes lots of problems: areas of deep mud or heavily pugged pasture, damaged stream banks and riparian areas, badly overgrazed and undergrazed areas in paddocks, piles of accumulated manure near a barn, loss of soil fertility from pastures, etc. Basically, allowing livestock to get their minerals and water from centralized areas means we can't properly manage forage growth across the entire paddock. In other words, we lose control of our intensive grazing system.

Good graziers design systems to supply water and minerals to *all* the grazing cells. They lay hoses and pipes under fence lines, with risers everywhere. They use small drinking tubs because animals don't have to walk far to get to them. They design portable mineral feeders that one person can easily haul or sled each time the animals move. And they may even bury their mainline water pipes to reach strategic branch points.

Three principles this month, plus one principle last month. Yes, it's clear to me that good grazing *is* a principled activity.

First Published: July 2008

Author's Note: These four principles seem straightforward, and their cumulative effect is marvelous, but they are not straightforward if your grazing system has never followed them. Nonetheless, they do work. At a grazier's discussion group meeting a few years ago, one group member — a cattleman — stopped the conversation because he wanted to announce something. He said, "These principles work! I've been following them for a couple of years, and now I have more feed longer in the year than I ever had before." That caught everyone's attention.

The Eyes Have It

When we look at a pasture, we need to make strategic judgments about the best ways our animals can graze it. We talk about feed budgets, forage growth curves, Phase I and II and III, residual mass, stocking densities, etc.

But all these concepts depend on one underlying measurement: the actual amount of forage in the pasture. How do we get this number? Grass height doesn't cut it, because height tells us nothing about plant *density*. We must describe forage amounts in terms of *weight* — that is, the amount of forage dry matter (DM) per acre. And we can't just take a guess of by-gosh-and-by-golly. We have to measure forage weight objectively. This month, let's talk about a practical way of doing this.

Actually, there are a number of methods for estimating forage mass: rising plate meters that correlate a compressed forage height with a DM amount, high-tech pasture gauges that use electronic capacitance measurements, "gumboot" methods that try to correlate forage height to its mass, and simple pasture sticks that also try to equate forage height directly to DM amount. But there's one method that's so fundamental that the other methods must use it for calibration: *the cut-dry-and-weigh method*. That's right: cut the grass, dry it, and use a scale. It's old-fashioned and tedious, and very low-tech, but it's still the gold standard that gives an accurate, unbiased value for pasture mass.

The cut-dry-and-weigh method is actually quite simple: (1) cut a small sample of the pasture forage, (2) dry it, (3) weigh it, (4) record the amount, and (5) convert that number to pounds of forage dry matter per acre (lb DM/acre). I could end the article here, I suppose, but perhaps I should add a few details . . .

First, we must assemble a few items. I prefer to use a small rectangular frame that measures 11.5″ x 12″ (= 138 square inches. I know this is an odd dimension, but trust me — there will be more about this later). I use a simple wooden frame, but many alternatives can work — even a large, flattened cardboard box with that area cut out. We also need good garden shears. You can use a large pair of scissors in a pinch, but you'll quickly discover why we use garden shears, and then you'll go out and buy some. Get good ones. I once had poor-quality shears that didn't like to cut grass easily. Frustrating was the nicest word I said about them.

Here are a few more items: a small, brown paper bag, a microwave oven, a partially filled glass of water, and a small, electronic postal scale. The paper bag is for containing the forage sample. The microwave oven is for drying the sample. The glass of water — well, it's a safety feature. Have two or three of these nearby. More about that in a moment. The postal scale is critical. It must record weights to the nearest 1 gram, not 2 grams or 5 grams. You can purchase these scales at many office-supply stores and even kitchen-supply stores, and nearly all have a switch that toggles between ounces and grams. It doesn't have to be fancy or expensive. Mine runs forever on a small, 9-volt battery.

Now we have our tools. First, we record a tare weight of the empty bag. Let's say this weight is 14 grams. Then, in the field, we select a spot to cut our sample, place the rectangular frame flat on the ground, and clip all the forage within that frame. I definitely mean *all*. We're trying to estimate the *total forage mass*, and that means everything from top to bottom (the ground). Put all the forage cuttings into the bag. Choose a representative sample area — something that looks like the rest of the pasture. Exclude any stones or soil or roots or anything the animals won't consume. You might also want to avoid spots that contain large weeds like bull thistle or poison hemlock.

Weigh the filled bag. This will give us the *wet weight* of the forage (= the total weight – 14 grams of the bag). This weight is interesting but not essential. We are really interested in the *dry weight* of this sample. Now dry the sample in the microwave. Keep the paper bag partially open to allow moisture to escape. Also, place the half-full glass of water in the microwave. We found that this water helps prevent the sample from getting too hot.

Dry the forage in a sequence of short bursts. I generally begin with a series of 2-minute drying periods, although the first period could be 3 minutes. After each drying period, weigh the bag. Also after each burst, change the glass of water for a fresh glass. These glasses get very hot, so it's best to rotate them after every drying period. That's why we keep two or three glasses on hand. After a couple of 2-minute drying periods, reduce the drying period to 1 minute. At first, you'll see the weights drop rapidly. Then the weights begin to flatten out. Finally, when the weights don't change after two or three drying periods, the sample is dry. That's your final weight. Let's say the final total weight of the bag and its forage sample is 35 grams. Subtract the tare weight of the bag (14 g), and that gives us a dry forage weight of 21 grams.

A side note: drying forage will give off a distinct odor. This odor is not unpleasant (at least not to a grazier), but it may be quite strong. You might want to warn family members and houseguests about it. Also, you'll probably want to avoid drying forage samples just before your Thanksgiving dinner. Just a thought.

Back to our sample. We've now accurately measured our sample area, and it contains 21 g DM. This is not exactly a practical number, but we're almost there. Now we must convert this number to something we can use — namely lb/acre. Recall that our wooden frame has that weird dimension of 11.5" x 12" = an area of 138 square inches. There's a reason for this. We begin our calculations with our number of 21 grams per 138 square inches. Then we use the following physical constants: 144 square inches per 1 square foot, 43,560 square feet per 1 acre, and 454 grams per 1 pound. After making the appropriate multiplications and divisions, we come up with the value of 2,102 lb/acre. Let's round this off to 2,100 lb/acre. (For homework, you can work this out on your own. Use both sides of a page if necessary.)

Notice our final value: 2,100 lb/acre. Which is equal to 21 times 100. That's the reason for our odd frame size. Because by using a frame enclosing 138 square inches, once we get our microwave number in grams, all we need to do is multiply this microwave number by 100 to arrive at lb/acre. *In other words, just add 2 zeros* (i.e., 21 becomes 2,100). Simple.

In contrast, I've noticed that many official university fact sheets and Extension bulletins suggest that you use a frame of 12" x 12" (or larger). Well, an area of 144 square inches means that the conversion factor is 95.95 rather than 100. Which is easier? Your call.

Here's another interesting tidbit. Why must the area of 138 square inches be square? The arithmetic doesn't care about the *shape* of the frame; we just want to keep the same area. What about a circle? A piece of rope is certainly more convenient to carry around than a square wooden frame. So here's another tip: a 42" length of rope (actually 41.64") looped on the ground in a circle will have the same area of 138 square inches. You're right — this is another homework problem: find the area of a circle with 42" circumference. There'll be extra credit for this one.

Here are two more tidbits, from experience:

(1) This microwave drying technique works well for the typical forage amounts in grazing situations. It does not work well for stands of mature hay containing high grass (18" or longer). Long hay in a heavy sample takes too long to dry in a microwave. It smokes and possibly begins to burn. We tried this, once.

(2) There's a convenient alternative to the microwave: a food dryer — one of those handy box units with removable wire mesh trays that folks use to dry

fruits and vegetables. I have one, and I've dried hundreds of forage samples in it. The forage amounts can be much larger, so you have to work out your own mathematical conversions. But I can dry 8 samples at the same time. No need for glasses of water or repeated weights. My dryer runs at 113-118° F, so I routinely dry samples for 72 hours. We just need two weights: weigh the wet sample going in; weigh the dry sample coming out, and voilà, you're done. In scientific articles, this type of equipment is called a "forced air oven." But it's just a food dryer. By the way, the odor of drying forages is still the same.

Finally, let's look at the bigger picture: why are we *really* doing this technique? To estimate a pasture's forage mass? Not really. If we wanted to get a scientifically accurate estimate for the entire field, we would need to take at least 10–15 samples from this field, dry each one, then calculate the average of all the samples. Tedious and time-consuming would be an understatement.

The *real* goal of using this technique is to calibrate our best tool — *our eyes*. We want to train ourselves so we can look at a pasture on the fly and make a good eyeball estimate of its forage mass. Therefore, each time we take a sample, just before we start cutting, we should look carefully at that spot. *Really* carefully. If necessary, take photos or videos. Commit the spot to memory. Go through the process of drying the sample and calculating its forage mass, then associate the memorized appearance of that spot with its forage mass. Let's refer to our earlier example: If we remember the appearance of our sampled area, we will *know* what 2,100 lb/acre looks like for that type of pasture.

Now our task is to repeat this technique with many different pastures. After a while, all this sampling and practice will train our eyes. We'll *learn* and *memorize* what different amounts of forage look like in different types of pastures. Then, when we walk across our own pasture or visit another farm, we will know how much forage each field contains. All the rest will follow.

First Published: July 2013

Author's Note: Knowing the amount of forage in a field at any given moment is so critical for all pasture decisions, like when to open the gate, when to move the animals out of a pasture, planning for future stock movements, calculating feed budgets, even when considering possible renovations. This is a skill well worth mastering.

The Wedge

Graziers talk about it in their coffee shops; magazine articles refer to it; internet discussion groups tell others to use it. What is *it*? Something called a "wedge."

Huh? Is this some type of football formation, like the legendary flying wedge of the Fighting Irish? Or a weird kind of doorstop that some farmers use for propping up gates? It's neither. It's a *grazing wedge, as in the phrase "maintaining a grazing wedge."*

A grazing wedge isn't a physical item like a piece of wood. Rather, it's a diagram of pasture yields, and it looks a lot like a wedge-shaped doorstop. A grazing wedge is really a tool for making decisions about forage growth and animal movements. I'll describe it and show how it can be used.

Think back for a moment to the grazing workshops you've attended, where the presenter draws a nice, square diagram of a farm, portraying a rotational grazing system as a neat tic-tac-toe arrangement of paddocks. Then he draws arrows from paddock to paddock in an orderly way to show how animals move sequentially across the farm from left to right. Oh, it looks so clean and simple.

But do *you* know any farm that looks like that? Or forage so uniform that paddocks are always ready to be grazed in sequence from left to right?

(Okay, you can stop laughing.) Of course no *working* farm looks like that, except on a whiteboard or possibly at a research station where the research plots are tiny and carefully manicured. A real-world grazing operation has lots of diverse paddocks that are anything but neat. Typically, these paddocks will have different levels of drainage, fertility, soil pH, and slope. They'll have different histories of usage and fertilization, and they'll usually contain multiple types of forages. During the growing season, temperature and rainfall will affect each paddock differently, and the array of influencing factors will change from month to month. And, of course, no year is "average"; there are always annual variations in rainfall, heat, sunshine, and frost-free days. All these factors affect forage growth, and no two paddocks will respond exactly alike.

And within this complexity, graziers are always striving to take advantage of Phase II forage growth. For any given paddock, graziers would like to initiate grazing when its forage is at the top of Phase II and then move animals into the next appropriate paddock before the residual mass drops into Phase I. A grazier's foremost question becomes, day after day, where is the next appropriate paddock? And where after that? And where after that? Pastures change weekly, so how can a grazier keep track of all these changes and make good decisions about forage management and animal movement?

By using a grazing wedge.

The concept is actually quite simple: measure the forage mass in every paddock, rank the paddocks from highest to lowest, and then move animals into the paddock with the most forage, unless it contains too much forage.

Here are the details: on one day each week during the growing season, the grazier walks across *every* paddock on the farm, carrying a notepad. For each paddock, he carefully records the total forage mass *on that day*. The actual measurement technique is the grazier's preference — pasture gauge, rising plate meter, calibrated eyeball — but in the end, he must have a reliable value for each paddock.

Now comes the high-tech computer part of the process. (Actually, this part can be done by hand, but a computer makes it infinitely easier and faster.) Using a computer spreadsheet, the grazier creates a table with two columns — paddock ID number and forage mass — and copies the notebook data into the spreadsheet. He then creates a bar graph (histogram) from the raw data, showing the paddock ID on the X-axis and the corresponding forage mass on the Y-axis. Initially, this graph looks like an unordered jumble of vertical bars — some high, some low — bouncing randomly up and down as you look across the graph. In this form, the graph is not very useful. But then … comes the *crucial* step.

The grazier instructs the spreadsheet to *rank* the paddocks by their forage mass, from highest to lowest. The bar graph instantly changes, and an obvious pattern emerges. The X-axis ranks all the paddocks in the order of their forage mass, from highest to lowest — the highest bars are on the left descending gradually to the lowest bars on the right — and suddenly it becomes clear where the next few grazing movements will be.

One final touch: the grazier then draws two horizontal lines on this graph — one line at the upper level of Phase II growth, usually around 2,500-3,000 lb/acre; and the second line at the lower level of Phase II growth, usually around 1,000 lb/acre. This second line identifies the target residual mass.

Now look at the graph. The pattern of vertical bars between these two horizontal lines indeed looks like a doorstop . . . a wedge. With this diagram, a grazier can clearly see the pattern of forage growth in all the paddocks across the entire farm. At a glance, he can identify which paddocks should be grazed next, which paddocks have too much forage and should be topped off or cut for hay, and which paddocks should be left alone for longer recovery. This is the grazing wedge.

The paddock on the left-hand side of the wedge, with a forage mass just under the upper horizontal line, is the next paddock to put the animals in. Paddocks outside the wedge contain either too much forage (they are on the far left side of the graph, with more forage than 3,000 lb/acre) or too little forage (they are on the far right side of the graph, with less than 1,000 lb/acre). Paddocks outside the wedge are management problems that need to be addressed.

But a grazing wedge is not a static endpoint. It's a decision-making tool, designed to be used often. *Each week* the grazier must walk the paddocks again, record new observations, and recreate the graph. And each week, he must respond to the updated forage growth with a new set of decisions.

The phrase *"maintaining a grazing wedge"* means having *all* the paddocks within the Phase II growth region of the wedge, continuously from week to week, with none too far to the left, and none too far to the right.

Easy? No, especially when a farm has many paddocks. But the grazing wedge is a tool. And anyone who does much intensive grazing in the real world appreciates the value of a good tool.

First Published: July 2003
Author's Note: The grazing wedge is a wonderful tool for graziers, particularly for operations with lots of paddocks. Later in this book, you'll find another description of it, with graphs showing the actual forage mass values in 25 paddocks, and, step-by-step, how to use a grazing wedge to make sense of it all.

Fuzzy Logic

One word can make a difference.

Recently, I attended a seminar where the speaker said, "Stocking rate, stocking density . . . whatever." As if these words mean the same thing. They don't. For intensive graziers on improved pastures, one term describes a powerful tool and the other refers to a kind of fuzzy concept that is not very useful at all.

Let's first talk about *Stocking Rate* — that venerable workhorse term found in many reports and government documents. Stocking Rate means, simply, the number of animals that graze in an area over a period of time. Notice that stocking rate includes the concept of a *time period*.

People often use this concept in questions like, "What is the stocking rate on your farm?" Meaning, how many animals do you run on the place for the year or growing season. Typical answers would be one cow per acre or 1.5 cows per acre or, in dry range country, maybe one cow per fifty acres.

Cows? What about sheep and horses and yearling steers? Since, in the United States, stocking rate is usually expressed in terms of cows, we need adjustment factors to convert sheep to cows or horses to cows (but we shouldn't tell our animals — they would get offended). There are lots of published reference lists, but typical conversion factors are that one cow equals 5 sheep or 1.7 weaned calves or 0.8 adult horses or 1.0 yearling horses or 5 deer. This standardized cow is legally called an *animal unit* and is defined as a 1,000-pound adult cow with a calf by her side. Of course, there is also the issue of really large cows like Chianinas. I suppose purists would want to convert those cows to cows, but that gets a little weird.

Without doubt, however, stocking rate is a valuable concep*t for range operations*, where ranchers have little control over vegetation or soil fertility.

One of their few tools for manipulating forage growth is to adjust the number of animals in a grazing area. In a broad sense, stocking rate relates to the amount of forage produced in an area during a growing season, and, thus, the number of animals that can harvest that forage. This concept nicely applies to range country where animals generally remain in the same area for an entire grazing season.

But *for intensively managed grazing operations,* with smaller, fenced paddocks, where forages can be improved, fertilized, irrigated, renovated, and grazed using many types of management strategies, the stocking rate concept simply falls apart. That's mainly because everything is fluid on these operations, and a good manager can manipulate many factors during the growing period.

Let's say I ask you about the stocking rate on your property. If you set-stock your animals, you would give me one number. But if you renovate and fertilize the pastures so forage yields triple, you would give me a very different number. Which number is correct?

Also, stocking rate implies that all feed comes from the forages grown on that land. What if you supplement your pastured animals with grain? Or with purchased hay? Or, taking it to the extreme: what is the stocking rate of a cattle feedyard?

Things can get even more complex. What if you buy and sell groups of animals to take advantage of the seasonal growth patterns of your forage? For example, you bring in a load of old-crop lambs to graze the spring flush of grass, or you allow a neighbor to put his steers on your land to graze a summer forage like sudangrass. The calculations for stocking rate now become very complicated indeed. If we consider feed supplementation, animal additions and movements, and seasonal confinements in barns, the stocking rate concept becomes so fuzzy that, even if we could somehow derive a number for stocking rate, what would that number really mean?

Now let's switch gears and talk about *Stocking Density.* We define stocking density as the amount of biomass grazing a given area *at a single point in time,* expressed as pounds per acre. Note that stocking density applies only to grazing animals; it does not involve hay or silage or fallow land. In effect, stocking density is a *snapshot* of a grazing situation. It is a precise number, easily calculated. For example, a stocking density of 25,000 lb means that an acre contains 25,000 lb of grazing animals — which could be twenty-five 1,000-lb cows, or one hundred 250-lb ewes, or possibly one cow weighing 25,000 lb (not likely, even with crossbreeding).

We can use stocking density on a day-to-day basis to describe the *grazing pressure* on a specific area, and also to compare grazing strategies over time and with other farms, regardless of the size of the operations, the species of livestock, or the type of grazing strategies. Stocking density automatically takes these factors into account.

Here's an example: if I set-stock 200 ewes averaging 160 lb on 15 acres, my stocking density would be 2,133 lb, which is quite low. But if I use temporary electric fence to confine those same 200 ewes on *one* acre, the stocking density on that acre becomes 32,000 lb. I could achieve the same stocking density by putting thirty-two 1,000-lb cows on that acre. (Of course, I wouldn't leave those animals on that acre for very long. When the forage was grazed down to my target residual mass, I would move them to the next grazing cell.)

But let's think for a moment: which stocking density allows animals the luxury of consuming only their favorite plants? Which stocking density forces animals to take out weeds? Which stocking density results in an even distribution of manure? Stocking density gives us no-nonsense numbers to analyze situations and make precise recommendations.

Even small operations can effectively use stocking density to manipulate forage. Periodically on my place, I graze a flock of 20 ewes, averaging 160 pounds (= a biomass of 3,200 lb). My pastures also contain patches of unpalatable tall fescue, which are clumpy, wasteful eyesores. My sheep refuse to eat tall fescue when they can graze tasty plants like white clover and perennial ryegrass. If I fence the flock on one full acre, the stocking density is only 3,200 lb, and the tall fescue remains defiantly untouched. But if I section off a clumpy area with electric netting to create a tiny paddock of 1/10 acre (66 feet *x* 66 feet), I've increased the stocking density to 32,000 lb in that small area. Which is enough to convince the sheep that tall fescue isn't so bad after all. And, of course, then I move the animals before they eat the rest of the forage into the ground.

We also routinely use the stocking density concept in pasture renovation. One unconventional but extremely practical technique for planting forage seed is the *tread-in method*, also affectionately known as the *hoof-and-tooth method*. Basically, we broadcast seed onto unprepared ground — usually at twice the standard seeding rate (or more) — and allow the animals to graze that area heavily. We hope their hooves will plant the seed. Sometimes it works; sometimes it doesn't. But one rule of thumb seems to give the best results: we should use a stocking density of at least 30,000 lb. Otherwise, there are too few hooves per square foot to drive enough seed into the ground properly.

Stocking rate, stocking density. Two terms, two meanings. It's good to know the difference.

First Published: August 2003

Author's Note: The phrase "Stocking Rate" is used universally. That's too bad, because Stocking Density is the true useful tool for non-range operations and pastures. Even when expressed in metric units (pounds/acre is approximately the same as kilograms/hectare), these numbers can apply anywhere in the world. Which allows us to compare grazing notes intelligently with graziers in New Zealand, Argentina, or France.

Calculating Density

Now that this year's pasture season is winding down, it might be a good time to reflect about one of the most useful tools in our grazier's toolbox: *Stocking Density*. As we discuss various aspects of it, you might think back to your own operation, relating how these concepts played out this year on your place and how they might apply in the future.

What is this term *Stocking Density* (SD)? Actually, it's really quite simple: SD is the number of pounds of animal biomass per acre. That's it. Just add up the pounds of animals in the herd/flock/pod/whatever — regardless of species — and divide by the number of acres in the paddock. Here's an example: if I have 23 adult cows and their calves on 4 acres (at one calf per cow), and the cows and calves average 1,200 and 400 lb, respectively, then my SD is 9,200 lb/acre (= 1,200 x 23 plus 400 x 23 all divided by 4).

Because SD is just a weight of grazing animals per area, independent of species, we can generate 9,200 lb/acre on our four acres in many other ways: 460 lambs, each weighing 80 lb. Or 28 horses that average 1,314 lb. Or 283 goats that average 130 lb. Or, for that matter, 4 African elephants that average 9,200 lb. Numerically, these are all the same.

In essence, SD is really an arithmetic snapshot of how much animal mass is on a pasture at a specific point in time. I can increase SD by simply confining the animals in a smaller area — by moving the electric fence. Let's take the animals from the previous paragraph: confining those animals in two acres results in a SD of 18,400 lb/acre. Confining them in one acre increases the SD to 36,800 lb/acre. (We'll ignore the practical problems of trying to confine 4 elephants in one acre.)

I must mention an important distinction: Stocking Density is not the same as *Stocking Rate*. Stocking *Rate* means the number of animals per acre *over a period of time*, based on a standard animal unit of a 1,000-lb cow with a calf by her side. Stocking Rate is *not* a snapshot; it's more like a broad description of the number of animals the land can support *over time*. We should think of these two concepts separately: stocking density as grazing pressure; stocking rate as carrying capacity.

In practice, stocking rate is primarily a tool in dry range country, where the number of stock in an area is one of the few things that ranchers can manipulate to manage their forage. But improved pastures are a very different universe than range country. Graziers managing improved pastures can easily manipulate a vast array of things to alter the amount of feed in those pastures — like reseeding the forages or adding fertilizer and lime. Stocking Density is a precise and flexible number, ideal for understanding and managing improved pastures.

So, how can we use this SD concept? The most obvious way is to calculate the numerical grazing pressure on fields of different sizes. Let's say that the four fields on my farm are 5, 12, 19, and 32 acres, and my flock consists of 500 ewes averaging 150 lb, which gives a total biomass of 75,000 lb. Grazing this flock on the 5-acre field generates a SD of 15,000 lb/acre ($= 75,000 \div 5$). When I move this flock to the other three fields, I reduce the SD values to 6,250, 3,947, and 2,344 lb/acre, respectively.

Let's study these numbers. It's clear that the grazing pressure on the 5-acre field is more than *six times* the grazing pressure on the 32-acre field. In your opinion, which field would have more problems with weed encroachment? Which field would have a more homogenous distribution of manure? Which field would show a more uniform amount of residual forage?

The SD concept works just as well with small flocks and herds. For example, if I own a flock of 25 ewes averaging 150 lb, my total biomass is 3,750 lb. That doesn't sound like much, and fencing these ewes on one acre results in a SD of only 3,750 lb/acre. But when I move the electric netting to confine the ewes in only a 0.5-acre, then I've doubled the SD to 7,500. And if I halve that acreage again to 0.25-acre (a square of 104 feet on each side), my SD then becomes 15,000 lb/acre, and that has exactly the same effect on forages as 500 of these ewes on 5 acres. (With small operations, it's also useful to remember that one acre equals 43,560 square feet.)

But will animals get enough to eat at a high SD? Of course they will . . . *if* we move them off the pasture at an appropriate time. Let's figure this out. If our pre-graze pasture contains a *total mass* of 3,300 lb/acre, and we target a *residual mass* after grazing of 1,000 lb, then each acre contains 2,300 lb of feed (also called *available mass*). Let's say we aim for a SD of 30,000 lb/acre. If we assume that the feed intake of these ewes averages 5% of body weight, including trampling loss, then the daily intake of 30,000 lb of animals will be 1,500 lb ($= 30,000 \times 0.05$). Therefore, these animals can stay on that field for 1.5 days. If we leave them for an extra 12 hours, they'll eat more feed and reduce our residual. And if we leave them for a week, we'll end up with hungry animals and a pasture that looks like a putting green. On the other hand, if our goal is to control weeds or prepare that field for reseeding, then a SD of 30,000 lb/acre for three days would definitely help us attain those goals. And notice — these calculations can be done *before* we put a single animal onto that field.

Stocking Density has other practical applications:

It can help us solve problems with palatability and preferential intake. We know that animals always select the most palatable plants first and also avoid the less palatable plants. But a high SD forces animals to eat everything or starve, especially once they are trained to it. A good example is tall fescue, which is a valuable forage species that many graziers dislike because animals notoriously avoid it. Well, at a SD of 1,500 lb/acre, this is certainly true. But what about 10,000 lb/acre? Or 20,000 lb/acre? I've personally observed that sheep on my place will consume tall fescue quite nicely at a SD of 18,000 lb/acre.

Speaking of forage species, we can use the SD concept to manage some specialized forages, particularly those that require a high SD for good management. Two examples are alfalfa and reed canarygrass. Although alfalfa is most easily managed as a hay crop — cut all at once with a low residual and then allow a long rest period — we can graze it the same way *if* we use a high SD. The animals first graze off the forage quickly and evenly. Then we can remove the animals to allow proper regrowth. In this case, we are essentially using the animals as a substitute for hay-making machinery.

Reed canarygrass (RCG) is an entirely different type of forage. Animals definitely avoid RCG when they have alternative selections, but RCG can be one of our most productive forages if we manage it right. We need to fence off the areas of RCG as specialized paddocks and then use a high SD to force proper grazing. We can use trial and error. Will 20,000 lb/acre do the trick? If not, then try 30,000 lb/acre. Or 40,000. The SD is easy to change — just move the electric fence closer to reduce the acreage for that herd.

Have you ever tried to renovate a field using the *tread-in method* of seeding (also called the *hoof-and-tooth method*)? The rule of thumb for this technique is that we need a SD of at least 30,000 lb/acre to push the seed into the soil effectively. In perspective, that's equal to 25 cows per acre at 1,200 lb per cow.

We can also use SD as a training tool. Novice graziers are usually quite cautious when they first begin intensive grazing. They are reluctant to graze too tightly for fear of running out of feed, so they set their cross-fences far apart, creating a SD of only 4,000 lb/acre or so. While this is better than set-stocking, it's still very conservative management. But as graziers improve their skills at judging forage mass and intake levels, they move their electric fences tighter and tighter. Soon, they are routinely grazing with SD at 7,000 lb/acre, then 10,000 lb/acre, then 20,000 lb/acre. The higher SD reflects their growing confidence and skill. Manure distribution becomes more uniform, the amount of residual forage is controlled better, and their pastures become denser and more productive.

I know a local dairy farmer who uses intensive grazing brilliantly. We've done SD calculations on those fields and found that his SD values are routinely higher than 70,000 lb/acre. He moves his animals every 12 hours — this is a dairy farm, after all — but what do you think his pastures look like? Very dense forage, extremely homogenous, green, and productive, with no manure spots and few weeds.

Yes, intensive grazing is an art. But it's also a science. And with a calculator, we can plan and monitor and manage. And then see the difference.

—————

First Published: September 2007
Author's Note: This technique really works. I've done hundreds of pasture walks and field analyses where SD calculations helped describe the situations precisely and allowed me to develop practical options for grazing and pasture issues.

Cookie-Cutter Grazing

For years, we've heard recommendations about the grazing system called *Rotational Grazing*. These recommendations are repeated at workshop after workshop, almost like a mantra: break up your large fields into smaller paddocks, move animals every *X* days, give the plants lots of rest, and step back to watch more forage grow. It's too bad, however, that this system usually violates some basic principles of forage growth. There is a good alternative, but it's not called rotational grazing.

First, a definition: *Rotational Grazing* is a management system in which a producer subdivides large fields into many smaller paddocks, usually with permanent cross-fencing. The animals are then moved sequentially through these paddocks, like clockwork. I'm sure that you can visualize a typical rotational grazing diagram on a whiteboard or in a PowerPoint presentation: the farm is divided into neat square fields, with arrows linking the squares from left to right.

A rotational grazing system can be succinctly described by its number of paddocks and the length of time that animals remain in each paddock. For example, we can describe a rotational grazing system as "10-paddocks every 3 days," which means that livestock would rotate through the entire system in 30 days. These numbers also define the rest period of the forage. In this case, a single paddock will see animals for only 3 days in a 30-day period, which means a rest period of 27 days (90% of the time). Pretty impressive. And the design is neat and sharply defined, like a cookie cutter.

Researchers like these rotational grazing systems for a couple of reasons. The first is that these systems can be described easily and cleanly. There is no ambiguity to the description of "a 30-day rotation with 10 paddocks." At research conferences, scientists can discuss the pros and cons of 27-day rotations or 30 days or 36 days, etc., and argue about the advantages and disadvantages of using 9 paddocks or 15 paddocks or whatever. The combinations are endless. The second reason revolves around getting experimental results published. When scientists want to publish their research, the editors of technical journals can appreciate and understand these precise descriptions — which easily allow their readers (who are other scientists) to replicate or revise these systems at their own research institutions.

But let's think for a moment. Rotational grazing systems are, ultimately, management strategies for harvesting forages, and because forages grow throughout a growing season, a rotational grazing system means that the same X-day rotational pattern is used *throughout the entire growing season*. And therein lies a serious problem.

This classic rotational grazing system implies some crucial assumptions: (1) that all paddocks in the system are uniform in species composition, soil type, drainage, and fertility; (2) that the forages in all these paddocks will grow steadily and uniformly across all the months of the grazing season; and (3) that the weather and growing conditions will remain constant from month to month throughout the growing season. Uh, huh.

If any of these assumptions are broken, a few unnerving things will happen. For example, if forage in one paddock grows slowly and if livestock are moved onto that paddock before it contains enough available forage for the requisite number of days, the animals will graze the residual forage down too far, which means that the paddock will grow even *slower* during the next cycle. Or, if a fast-growing paddock is not grazed when it's ready for grazing, the forage in that paddock will become too tall and mature, which affects clover persistence, subsequent forage regrowth rate, and nutrient intake by the animals. Or, if the weather turns bad during the growing season (lack of rain, weather too hot or too cold, etc.), the forage in many paddocks will not grow fast enough to support the rotational cycle, which means that those paddocks will be over-grazed which will stress the plants and reduce persistence of the best species.

And here's a basic issue: will a 30-day growth period in June provide the same amount of forage as 30 days in August? Of course not. If forage growth rates are different, then the amount of forage in a paddock will be different, which means that the effects of grazing will be different.

So . . . presented with all these uncontrolled variables, how can a rigid rotational grazing system produce the ideal expected results diagrammed so neatly on the whiteboard? Simple. It can't. Especially not year after year.

Basically, a strict cookie-cutter rotational system is *not* a robust grazing system. It's really a system that teeters on the edge of being out-of-control. Graziers often find, after trying this system for a year or two, that many of their paddocks show poorer growth or increased weeds — symptoms of plant stress — and that forage yields are not as high as expected, especially when considering the extra costs of fencing and labor. Then those graziers generally adapt to something else, not exactly set-stocking, but a loosely followed hybrid grazing pattern with some cross-fencing and the periodic shifting of animals.

Does this mean that all rotational grazing is bad? Or that these systems won't provide better yields and improved pastures? Not at all. The problem lies with *rotational grazing systems that require strict adherence to a rigid formula of time and area.* In theory, these systems may seem attractive, but in practice, they ignore the reality of inconsistent field conditions, unpredictable weather, and variable forage growth.

But there is a better way: *Management-Intensive Grazing.*

Management-Intensive Grazing (MIG) is a system of harvesting forages by allocating feed to grazing animals. The producer decides how much feed the animals will consume per day and how many days he wants them in a paddock, and then he sets the fence around an appropriate area of forage. Although the perimeter fence around the entire field may be permanent, most of the internal fencing is temporary electric fence, allowing utmost flexibility and speed. This system is automatically self-adjusting because the electric fence is always placed around an area appropriate for the number of animals and the amount of forage *at the time of grazing.* Animals enter an area when it contains a target amount of forage and then leave the area when the residual amount of forage is reached.

Let's come back to the scenario I described in the third paragraph: a grazing system that uses 3-day stock movements. Now let's apply the principles of MIG to this field to determine the size of the grazing cell. If a flock of 200 ewes was going to graze 1,200 lb of dry matter per day (= 200 ewes @ 150 lb average body weight @ a dry matter intake of 4% of body weight), and the grazier wanted to keep the animals in an area for three days, then those sheep would need 3,600 lb of feed for those three days. If the target residual forage mass was 1,000 lb per acre, and the field initially contained a total mass of 2,800 lb forage per acre, the available feed in that field would be 1,800 lb per acre (= 2,800 − 1,000). Therefore, to provide feed for those three days, the grazier should set a temporary fence at 2 acres.

If, on the other hand, the field had just experienced a period of slow regrowth, and the total amount of forage was only 1,800 lb per acre, then each acre could offer only 600 lb of available forage. Then the grazier would set his fence for 6 acres (you can do the calculations). In both cases, the forages are treated properly and consistently, and the nutritional level to the livestock remains constant.

Of course, in a MIG system, land and time are *not* constant. Nothing is standardized; nothing is easily replicable. Grazing areas are adjusted on the fly, and they will probably change from month to month. A system with this many variables may make some researchers and journal editors nervous, but it makes graziers comfortable because that's the way nature works.

So, the next time you hear someone at a workshop recommend "rotational grazing," you might consider exactly what that means and how that system will accommodate the real conditions of biology and weather that will inevitably occur on the farm.

———

First Published: August 2004
Author's Note: This is the real thing. MIG is like playing a basketball game: you study the rules, learn the basic drills, and then walk onto the court. But once the whistle blows and the actual game begins, you play the game that develops, not the diagrams on the blackboard. And the next game will assuredly be different. You play the game as it develops. And that's part of the excitement of MIG. If you do it right, you win.

Mobs and Other Types of Grazing

A lot of phrases get thrown around these days about grazing: intensive grazing, managed grazing, rotational grazing, mob grazing . . . the list goes on and on. Does anyone know what these actually mean, aside from some vague notions that involve small pastures, cross-fencing, and moving animals? Well, they do have specific meanings. And when we use these phrases properly, we can make much better decisions about our grazing management.

First, I want to cover an important term that does not describe a grazing system directly, but rather is a tool that graziers use to evaluate grazing: *Stocking Density (SD)*. Very simply, SD is the number of pounds of livestock on an acre at a moment in time, expressed as lb/acre. We generally use SD in relation to standard four-legged livestock species (but not chickens, even though some folks raise these on pastures).

Here are a couple of examples: if we graze 25 ewes averaging 160 lb on a one-acre field, the SD for this field is 4,000 lb/acre (= 25 x 160). If we cut that acre in half with a temporary electric fence, the SD rises to 8,000 lb. If we cut that half-acre in half again, those ewes would be grazing on 0.25-acre, so the SD would be 16,000 lb. Another example: if we graze a 5-acre field with 30 beef cows averaging 1,200 lb, our SD would be 7,200 lb/acre (= 30 x 1,200 ÷ 5). If we move the electric fence to confine these cows on one acre, the SD would increase to 36,000 lb/acre (= 30 x 1,200). Of course, those cattle wouldn't stay on that one acre for as long as on 5 acres. They would be moved off when they had grazed down to a target amount of residual forage. Basically, SD is another way of saying *grazing pressure*, but SD sounds better and can be expressed precisely with numbers.

49

Let's also be clear about a related term that's found in many official documents: *Stocking Rate (SR)*. This is definitely *not* the same as Stocking Density. The phrase Stocking Rate is the number of *Animal Units (AU)* that a piece of land can carry for the year (or grazing season, depending on the region), where an Animal Unit is generally defined as a 1,000-lb cow with or without a calf on her side. There are reference tables that equate one AU to different livestock species and ages, as in 5 adult sheep equals one AU, or 2 weaned calves equal one AU, etc. Government agencies such as the U.S. Forest Service and Bureau of Land Management routinely use SR numbers as the basis for assessing grazing fees on public lands.

Although there are some controversies about the details of this definition, there is no controversy about the basic meaning. We can think of SR as the carrying capacity of a piece of land *over time*. In contrast, SD is a grazing pressure photograph of the land *at a single moment in time*.

Now for some of those grazing system definitions. The term *managed grazing* is tossed around a lot, generally in relation to some form of moving animals, but it's not my favorite term. What exactly do we mean by "managed"? Every field is *managed*, no matter how intensively or how lightly. Even if we put animals onto a field and come back six months later — we are still managing that field, albeit poorly. So let's jettison this term because it's imprecise and conveys nothing meaningful.

But the phrase *Rotational Grazing* has real meaning. Rotational Grazing is a management strategy where animals are rotated through a series of paddocks. The paddocks may be large or small; the rotation may be a tightly defined sequence or it may be loosely applied. By tightly defined, I mean that the rotation could be described as something like "8 paddocks every 4 days" which effectively equates to a 32-day cycle through an 8-paddock system. Or conversely, the rotation may be loose, in a practical sort of way, where the grazier moves animals hither and yon around the farm to wherever the forage is tallest.

In practice, tightly defined rotational grazing systems are difficult to run effectively over time, because while animal movement is easily defined in a uniform pattern, forage growth is not. For example, in much of North America, forage grows much faster in May than in August. This disconnect is made worse and more variable when there is a variety of forage species in the pastures.

The bottom line is that a tightly defined system of rotational grazing requires animals to enter paddocks by the calendar rather than by the amount of forage growth. This translates to different amounts of initial forage mass throughout the growing season. A tight rotation schedule may also cause animals to enter some paddocks too early and remain in some paddocks too long, so they are forced to graze to a small residual mass and thus damage the plants. Over time, this is very frustrating to a forage manager. We've found that graziers who follow tightly defined rotational systems eventually turn away from them and just move animals around the property in some form of loose rotation. Actually, this relaxed, hands-off approach is very adaptable, but the forage management is still not efficient or precise. In rotational grazing, tight or loose, stocking densities can range all over the map, although they are generally lower than 10,000 lb/acre.

In contrast, *Management-Intensive Grazing (MIG)* is quite different than simple rotational grazing. MIG may be considered a pinnacle of good grazing management. While many folks associate MIG with lots of small paddocks where animals graze intensively and move quickly, this is not entirely true. In MIG, the emphasis is not on *intensive grazing* but on *intensive management*. MIG is a thinking person's strategy. Animals are not automatically moved into fixed paddock areas by a calendar schedule, but, instead, the animals are allocated feed. Which means the grazier calculates the amount of forage needed for a specific period of time, usually under 5 days, and then sets the electric fence to outline the acreage needed to supply that feed. Once the animals graze to a target residual mass, they are moved to the next field where the forage is at its most-efficient stage of growth.

MIG is designed to follow the principles of good forage management. MIG is also a bit hard to pin down, as it weaves and bobs through the growing season, putting animals in various paddocks to take advantage of the forage's most-efficient and nutritious periods. Every year is different and every paddock is different, depending on forage species, soil fertility, soil drainage, heat units, month of the year, etc. MIG alters paddock size and animal movement in response to all these variables. Ideally, MIG never violates the basic physiology of good forage growth, so the pastures steadily improve and become denser while the animals continue to produce at high levels (average daily gain, milk production, etc.).

MIG might be a challenge, especially for novice graziers, but it's exquisitely adaptable to managing improved forages. Stocking densities can range all over the map, depending on the skill of the manager. I've seen SD values ranging from less than 3,000 lb/acre to more than 120,000 lb/acre. It takes confidence, experience, and good grazing skills to manage higher SD values. As you can imagine, higher SDs are better for controlling forage growth and creating a more uniform distribution of manure.

Let's build on the stocking density concept and go to our third phrase: *Mob Grazing.* There's really no official definition of it because this management system is still relatively new. But the general sense is that a grazier practices mob grazing when the SD is greater than 200,000 lb/acre. That's a lot of animals.

Of course, with such a high SD, animals are moved quickly. At least once each day, sometimes more often.

A SD of 200,000 lb/acre looks like this: one acre containing 286 steers averaging 700 lb. Or one acre containing 1,250 ewes averaging 160 lb. Surprisingly (and I've seen this a few times), at 200,000 lb/acre, the animals are not shoulder-to-shoulder. But some popular magazine articles have described operations that practice mob grazing with a SD at nearly 1,000,000 lb/acre. *That's* nearly shoulder-to-shoulder.

What if you have a flock of 50 ewes? No problem. Your paddocks will be *really* small. You can achieve a SD of 200,000 lb/acre by fencing these ewes in a paddock of 41.7 feet *x* 41.7 feet. (With your trusty calculator, you can work out the arithmetic on your own.) Depending on the initial forage amount, those ewes should be in that area for no longer than, uh, 14 minutes.

But seriously, why are some graziers trying mob grazing? History, prairies, and bison. The concept is to duplicate, more or less, the behavior and ecology of the huge bison herds that once migrated across the American prairies and helped create the great and fertile grasslands of that region. Large numbers of these massive animals (i.e., high SD) moved quickly over the land and did not return to the same place for a long time. A modern grazing operation would roughly duplicate this by using very high stocking densities and very long rotations. This management may or may not be combined with some grain supplementation on pasture, which effectively imports soil fertility onto the field.

The jury is still out on this one. Science has not yet caught up with this system. We have questions about soil compaction, accumulation of organic matter, plant response, forage persistence, changes in soil structure — especially with possible long-term effects. There is still a world of research that must be directed at this type of management. But some very experienced graziers around the country are using variations of mob grazing and seeing some interesting results. I would, however, feel more comfortable if there was more science behind it.

But as I write this article, I have a rather unnerving vision about mob grazing: a vast herd of pastured chickens, a mile long, 200,000 lb/acre, wingtip to wingtip, moving slowly across the prairie. *That* would be an intensive mob.

First Published: October 2016

Author's Note: We're building on our knowledge. Fifteen years ago, MIG was new and exciting. It's still exciting, but now Mob Grazing is the new thing. You can find dozens of glowing testimonials on the internet from ranchers who do it, but as a scientist, I am cautious. Something is happening on those farms and ranches, but we don't know exactly what. Testimonials don't replace good data, but testimonials can lead to research that will produce good data. All we need is a few billion dollars.

Breakthrough! A Grazing Shorthand

The Merriam-Webster online dictionary defines *breakthrough* as "a sudden advance especially in knowledge or technique." Here's one that just happened in the world of grazing: RG,2,45K. Let's talk.

Early this year at a forage conference, I attended a session on something called "Mob Grazing." Large, high-stocking-density groups of cattle or sheep moving from grazing cell to grazing cell; it's all the rage in grazing circles these days. Intense, short-period grazing sessions followed by long rest periods, reminiscent of the vast herds of bison moving majestically across the Great Plains. Some popular magazines are filled with lots of excited claims and glowing testimonials about mob grazing, but there is little real science.

The speaker at this forage conference was Dennis Hancock, the Extension Forage Specialist for Georgia. Dennis is no-nonsense about science, and he was doing a commendable job of reviewing these claims and comparing them to other systems like Management-Intensive Grazing (MIG).

Then Dennis put something on the screen that stopped me cold. It was just a couple of numbers — "RG,2" — but those numbers spoke worlds and broke through the tangle of confusing terms and concepts. As he explained, "RG,2" simply meant a "rotational grazing system where the animals were moved every 2 days." A simple code, but it concisely summarized a management system that would normally require a wordy description of three or four sentences. As Dennis continued his presentation, I scrawled a few notes on my yellow pad. I thought his coding system was superb, but I also thought something was missing. There was still a lot of ambiguity in that coding. Something more was needed, something precise and on-farm practical.

55

Then I got it. *Stocking density.*

Afterward, in the hallway, the two of us talked about this code and possible improvements. In addition to the speed of animal movement, we needed something to describe how much pressure the animals put on the pasture. Basically, this shorthand code should answer two questions: (1) how often were the animals moved; and (2) how did their grazing affect the forage? So I added my suggestion: include the stocking density as part of the code. Bingo!

So now we have it complete: *"RG,2,45K"*—a shorthand that describes the basic framework of a grazing system. (Notice that there are *no* spaces after the commas. This keeps the shorthand exquisitely short.) Our example RG,2,45K describes a rotational grazing system (RG) in which livestock are moved every two days (2) with a stocking density of 45,000 lb/acre (45K). There is no need to add lots of zeros after 45 because stocking density is generally rounded to thousands. Also, in today's computer/internet world, most folks readily understand that "K" means thousands (and in this case, *not* potassium).

Stocking density? A hugely important concept. And this terminology is now becoming quite common in the grazing world, although folks sometimes refer to it as *grazing pressure.* Either way, it can be strictly defined. Stocking density (SD) is the number of pounds of livestock per acre at any given point in time. Essentially, it's a snapshot of a field grazed at a single instant. SD is not limited to any single species of livestock or how long they remain in that field. It's just a snapshot of the weight of livestock in a field, on a per-acre basis. The pounds of livestock could be *any* grazing species: beef cattle, sheep, goats, dairy cattle, bison, horses, elk, impala, or wildebeests. One strength of SD is that it permits easy comparisons between operations that raise different species of livestock. It also allows easy comparisons from month-to-month or year-to-year on the same property as the management and pasture conditions change.

Stocking density is easy to calculate. Just add up all the animal weights and divide by the number of acres. Here's an example: a herd of 24 feeder steers grazing a 2-acre field. If the steers average 600 lb, the total herd weight is 14,400 lb. Divide by the number of acres (2), and we calculate a stocking density of 7,200 lb/acre. If we confine all the animals in one acre, the SD increases to 14,400 lb/acre. If the cattle are fenced into only a 0.5-acre, the SD becomes 28,800 lb/acre. You get the picture. We can obtain the same SD of 28,800, of course, with other combinations of animals and acres. For example, 180 ewes each weighing 160-lb on one acre. (You can do the math.) Or . . . 18 elephants each weighing 6,400 lb on 4 acres. But let's not go there.

Let's also not confuse Stocking Density with *Stocking Rate,* which is the number of *Animal Units* that an acreage can carry for a growing season. (An Animal Unit is usually defined as a 1,000-lb cow with a calf by her side, although there are some variations of this.) Government agencies such as the Forest Service and the Bureau of Land Management use Stocking Rate to manage grazing allotments on public land. They charge a standard monthly fee per Animal Unit to ranchers who graze their livestock on those lands. Stocking Rate relates to the *carrying capacity* of a property. Although Stocking Rate is an essential concept in range and mountain country for public land management, it's a concept that kind of falls apart with improved pastures because on these pastures we can change things easily: apply fertilizer, plant high-yielding forages, feed supplemental grain or hay, change livestock numbers frequently by buying and selling, etc.

Back to our grazing shorthand, which is something we can definitely use with improved pastures. In the opening paragraph, I used the example of "RG,2,45K." How has this shorthand been received in the field? Well, here in Oregon, I facilitate three rancher Forage Study Groups. In our monthly meetings, I routinely share post-conference information with them. During two Forage Group meetings last month, I described this grazing shorthand in some detail and wrote the codes on a whiteboard. Whoa! The ensuing discussions became electric.

Immediately, the ranchers began describing their own operations: RG,1,10K and RG,5,2K and RG,7,5K, etc. With this shorthand code, finally, they could describe their operations quickly and accurately. An example: one rancher explained that he ran 1,000 ewes on some acreage and moved them every day. We asked: how many acres? Oh, approximately 12 acres in each grazing cell. This was a typical long description, so we broke it down: 1,000 ewes at 175 lb each equals 175,000 lb over 12 acres equals 14,583 lb/acre. Translated into our grazing shorthand: RG,1,15K. Another example: a ranch that practices a style of mob grazing with a large flock of sheep coded its operation as RG,0.5,300K. Translation: a very large number of sheep were moved twice each day, with a stocking density of 300,000 lb/acre, which definitely qualifies for the term "mob grazing." Now everyone in the room could instantly appreciate those numbers and their relationship to other grazing operations.

Why is this grazing shorthand so important? Because it is simple, straightforward, and easily understandable. With only a few letters and numbers, we can accurately summarize the basic framework of a grazing system. The "RG" tells us that the operation follows some form of livestock rotation. The "2" tells us the number of days between animal movements. And the "45K" gives us a clear visual picture of the livestock density on the pasture, and that, in turn, provides insights into spatial concepts like forage utilization and manure distribution.

Sure, there are some things this shorthand does not cover. Things like (1) the actual species of livestock (cattle, sheep, or wildebeest), (2) the species of forage and its maturity, (3) the time of year, (4) the physical aspects of the pasture like drainage and slope, (5) the actual soil fertility of the fields, (6) the use of feed supplementation on the pasture, etc. The shorthand also does not assume anything about the availability of water and minerals in the grazing cell — i.e., are these available inside the grazing cell, or do animals walk back to the barn every day, like in a dairy operation?

But, in practice, these extra details can be described in the subsequent discussion. *Because once we write this shorthand on the board, there will be subsequent discussion.* The difference from previous discussions is that now we have a clear starting point.

Too many times, when farmers and ranchers meet, grazing discussions quickly get bogged down in extensive descriptions of their operations and the controversies about the definitions of various terms. Jargon gets in the way, long descriptions get in the way, and discussions veer off into verbal tangents.

This grazing shorthand is a true breakthrough. It eliminates verbose descriptions and cuts through the jargon. Terms like intensive grazing, rotational grazing, mob grazing, trash grazing, forward grazing, whatever grazing — they all basically boil down to the act of moving animals from field to field. The grazing shorthand code immediately tells us the critical aspects of stock movement. And graziers are very familiar with stocking density. They can easily visualize differences between stocking densities of 2,000 lb and 20,000 lb and 90,000 lb (2K, 20K, 90K, respectively).

Because everyone can understand the grazing framework and visualize the pasture, the conversation can then build on these numbers and quickly move into important details and meaningful comparisons. At that point, the real sharing and understanding begins.

First Published: April 2017

Author's Note: I'm not kidding — this simple shorthand is a real breakthrough. It distills the essence of a grazing system into a few keystrokes. Not only does it help launch meaningful discussions among graziers and other forage workers, but it makes it easy and straightforward to write about grazing systems, compare grazing trials, and describe systems that you visit or read about. As Thoreau once noted, "Our life is frittered away by detail . . . simplify, simplify."

How Many Sheep Does It Take . . .?

You've seen the acronym "AUM." Do you know what it *really* means? Let's guess: Abandoned Uranium Mine? Air-to-Underwater Missile? All Ungulates Meditate? Okay, I'll be serious. *AUM* stands for *Animal Unit Month* — a standard baseline value in the United States for stocking rates, grazing fees, reference books, and all sorts of calculations involving grazing and land use. AUM comes from the term *Animal Unit (AU)*, which is the standard livestock reference value that allows us to equate different livestock species and weights.

But there's a slight problem with Animal Unit: its universal reference definition is not exactly universal. As we're now in the middle of the grazing season, grazing calculations are on our minds, so let's look under the hood.

There's an old joke about "How many Xs does it take to do Y?" Well, our grazing version is "How many sheep does it take to equal a cow?" Reference books and government agencies routinely use the conversion rate of five ewes to one cow. This formula has been in place since the early part of the twentieth century, when the federal government first designated vast swaths of public land as forest reserves and needed some way of establishing grazing fees and stocking rates. By 1907, federal grazing inspectors had started using the 5:1 formula, and it has been in place ever since.

But the 5:1 ratio is not based on body weight. Even in 1900, long before anyone ever heard of computers or Google, scientists and ranchers were still excellent observers of livestock. They knew that five ewes weighed considerably less than one cow. At that time, beef cows in the West were generally Herefords or Hereford-crosses, and these cows tended to weigh around 1,000 lb. Commercial ewes back then generally weighed 130–170 lb. If we accept an

59

average ewe weight of 150 lb, it's clear that 5 x 150 equals 750, not 1,000. But in 1900, those folks were also good stockmen. Their real goals were to estimate carrying capacity and to allocate the forage on public lands. Sheep are much lighter than cattle, but pound for pound, they eat more than cattle. Ewes typically consume feed (dry matter intake, DMI) at 2.5%–3.5% of their body weight (or more), while cows generally consume feed at around 2.0% body weight. You can do the same calculations that those folks did. Federal land managers judged that five ewes ate as much forage as one cow, and that conversion rate is still being used today.

This is interesting background, but underlying these calculations is one crucial question: "What exactly constitutes a cow?" This is where things get a bit muddy.

If we search current reference books and scientific papers, we can find a surprising amount of variation in this definition. Most results, however, fall into three camps:

Camp #1: The big AU. An important 2011 monograph by Vivien Allen and her colleagues with the academic title "An International Terminology for Grazing Lands and Grazing Animals" gives a very precise definition. It defines AU as a mature, non-lactating 500-kg cow in the middle third of gestation fed at maintenance with zero body weight gain. Whew! Don't let the metric system throw you. 500 kg equals 1,100 lb. The nonmetric translation of this definition is a 1,100-lb pregnant cow fed at maintenance. We'll come back to some of these details later.

Other major reference books similarly define AU as a 1,100-lb cow. Two of these include the classic textbook *Forages,* used in many university courses, and Jim Gerrish's 2004 book *Management-Intensive Grazing,* a practical guide widely read in the industry.

Camp #2: The small AU. One alternative AU definition is also very common. In a formal 2005 Glossary that it presented to Congress, The Congressional Research Service defined AU as a 1,000-lb beef cow that ate 26 lb feed per day. I found the same definition echoed in documents from such diverse places as Illinois, Utah, Delaware, the NRCS, Alberta Agriculture, and even that ultimate source of internet information, Wikipedia. This Congressional document also formally defines a sheep as 0.2 AU — which simply describes the 5:1 conversion ratio in a different way.

An interesting variation of this AU definition comes from the Society For Range Management. This is a professional organization of scientists and others who specialize in topics related to grazing on public rangelands, primarily in the West. In a 1989 document, the SRM defined AU as a mature cow of 1,000 lb, *with or without* a calf by her side. Apparently, these folks didn't want to commit, so they left their options open.

Camp #3: Everything else. Other folks simply don't conform. Like the Environmental Protection Agency (EPA). For many years, the EPA used AU in its regulations about emissions and pollutants from Confined Animal Feeding Operations (CAFOs), but it has now dropped AU in favor of . . . well, counting animals. Current CAFO regulations are based on the actual number of animals, listed in various categories, and not their feed intakes. Actually, this makes sense, kind of, because the AU system really describes what goes into the front end of an animal, whereas the EPA is more interested in what comes out of the rear of the animal (although rumen gases notoriously leave ruminants from front-end mouths, but we won't quibble).

Let's return to that first definition of an AU as a mature, non-lactating 1,100-kg cow in the middle third of gestation fed at maintenance with zero body weight gain. Consider this for a moment: cows have a gestation length of nearly 9.5 months. Weaning routinely occurs at 7 months. A major goal of most cow-calf operations is to have their cows give birth every 12 months. If we do the math, we see something quite intriguing. If a mature beef cow has a calf every 12 months, that means that the middle third of her gestation must occur *during* the last part of her lactation (just before the previous calf is weaned). In practice, cows should be *gaining weight* during mid-gestation, not eating at a maintenance level of intake. Putting all this together means that the first AU definition is for a cow that really doesn't exist. To follow that logic, what is the correct ratio of sheep-to-cattle if the cattle don't exist?

One additional point: the folks who designed this same AU definition also listed the forage intake of their imaginary cow at 8.8 kg/day (19.4 lb); which equates to 1.8% body weight (19.4 ÷ 1,100 as a %). They gave a formal name to this specific amount of feed: *Forage Intake Unit* (FIU). Actually, this logic makes good sense in terms of grazing. A land-use system based on the amount of forage intake dovetails nicely with good forage management because all the calculations directly focus on the amount of forage available or consumed.

If we use FIUs, livestock conversions become less arbitrary and more accurate. All it takes is some ratio arithmetic incorporating the actual intakes of the animals. For example, a 1,000-lb Angus cow that eats 19.4 lb of forage would be exactly 1.0 FIU. A 1500-lb Simmental cow that eats 30 lb of forage (2% body weight) would be 1.55 FIU. A 150-lb ewe that eats 5 lb of forage (3.3% body weight) would be 0.26 FIU. A 100-lb lamb that eats 3 lb of forage (3% body weight) would be 0.15 FIU. And a ravenous 80-lb lamb that eats 3 lb forage (3.75% body weight) would still be 0.15 FIU, because 3 lb of forage is still 3 lb of forage, no matter who or what is grazing it.

We've come full circle. We began by trying to determine how many animals can graze on an acreage, and we ended by equating their intake to the amount of forage. It always comes back to the amount of forage.

This article contains a lot of acronyms, so let me summarize. If the DMI of an AU is an FIU, and the EPA defines CAFOs differently than the NRCS and SRM, and after translating kg to lb, some AUs are 1,100 lb and others are 1,000 lb, how many sheep does it take to make a cow? I know it's an old joke, but someone had to say it . . .

First Published: June 2012

Author's Note: You would think that developing a good definition of a cow would be easy. But because this definition carries a lot of weight and has extensive ramifications in the livestock industry and in land-use regulations, a cow must really be a cow. And these decisions are never influenced by politics. Never.

It May Not Seem Like Much . . .

I recently attended a meeting where the presenter spoke glowingly about a new miracle product from his company. His PowerPoint slides dutifully showed fancy tables and graphs, but as I looked around the room, I noticed that the audience was beginning to nod off. We've all been there before: the speaker claimed that his product would increase forage yield by 20% during the slow periods of spring and fall when the forages were hardly growing. Only 20%? But then I started to think about this number and suddenly sat up very straight. It may not seem like much . . . but his numbers actually indicated that the *effective* yield boost was much, much larger than it first appeared.

Let's do the calculations on two scenarios where this comes into play. For consistency, I'll express all numbers on a *dry matter (DM) basis.*

First scenario: *a grazing situation*: It's early spring, and in a field of 2.4 acres, our grass pasture is just coming out of dormancy. We want to graze animals on that field, but we also want to follow good grazing practices and maintain a residual forage mass of 1,000 lb/acre. That means that we should remove the animals from the field when they graze the forage down to 1,000 lb/acre. But it's only early spring. The grass is growing slowly, and the field contains a total forage mass of only 1,500 lb/acre. Because I want to protect a residual of 1,000 lb/acre, that leaves only 500 lb/acre of forage available for grazing. This *available forage* is an important number because it's the actual amount of feed we can graze. Therefore, the entire field of 2.4 acres contains 1,200 lb of available feed (= 500 $\times$ 2.4).

My flock consists of 65 ewes in early lactation weighing 154 lb (70 kg). If I assume a DM intake of 4% body weight, the entire flock needs a total of 400 lb of feed DM each day. Thus, the 1,200 lb of available forage in my field will provide feed for three days (= 1200 ÷ 400).

Still with me? Good, because now let's apply the miracle product to the field and recalculate. Let's assume this product indeed stimulates a 20% boost in forage yield. But 20% of 1,500 lb/acre is only 300 lb/acre, and that may not seem like much, so let's examine it further. The 20% boost means that the total yield increases from 1,500 lb/acre to 1,800 lb/acre. From this new amount, we'll now subtract the 1,000 lb/acre of residual forage we want to protect. The leftover forage — the *available* forage — increases from 500 lb/acre to 800 lb/acre (= 1,800 − 1,000). That means that the available feed supply for my entire field of 2.4 acres jumps from 1,200 lb to 1,920 lb — *an increase of 60%*.

Since my sheep consume 400 lb per day, that miracle product increased grazing time on that field from 3 days to nearly 5 days. Not bad.

What happened? Well, although the product increased yield of the *entire field* by only 20%, we are reserving a baseline residual amount of forage that we can't touch — the field's *maintenance requirement*, if you will — so *all the additional yield* was allocated to the forage destined for consumption. Thus, a relatively modest 20% increase in the *total* forage quickly translated into a whopping 60% increase in the forage available for production. *That's* something to ruminate about.

Speaking of ruminating and maintenance, let's look at the second scenario: *the nutrition of lactating ewes grazing high-quality grass during the early part of the growing season*. Here, the issue is the low DM percentage in the early grass. Let's alter that value by 20% and see what happens.

Some background: in the very early spring, the young growing grass is vegetative and highly nutritious, but it also contains a low DM percentage, often as low as 13%. Here in the Pacific Northwest, we call this forage "washy" because it doesn't support good production even though animals graze it voraciously. Basically, the high percentage of water in this grass so dilutes the nutrients that animals can't consume enough energy and protein to support good lactation or fast growth.

Take a deep breath — lots of numbers ahead. Also, bear with me as I am going to switch to metric values because all the reference tables are in metric and the numbers would become quite cumbersome if they were in pounds and ounces. However, the principles are exactly the same, especially the conclusion.

Let's look at the energy needs of a 70-kg (154-lb) mature ewe raising twins in early lactation. Basic nutritional principles tell us that our lactating ewe requires calories for two things: maintenance and production. In this case, production means lactation. The highest priority for nutrients is maintenance, and any calories this ewe consumes must first satisfy those maintenance needs. Any leftover calories are used to synthesize milk. We can estimate the ewe's maintenance requirement by looking at a reference table in the *2007 Small Ruminant NRC,* which lists that a 70-kg ewe in maintenance requires 0.62 kg of TDN. That's our baseline.

Here are two additional items from the scientific literature: (1) an adult ewe will take approximately 30,000 bites per day on pasture, and (2) her average bite contains 70 mg of DM (for comparison, a penny weighs 2,000 mg = 2 grams). Yes, 30,000 bites — researchers have actually spent time counting them. But really, what else does our ewe have to do except eat, sleep, and chew cud? But I digress.

If our ewe takes 30,000 bites that each contain 70 mg DM, her daily DM intake is 2,100,000 mg (= 2.1 kg), which equates to 3% of her body weight (= 2.1 ÷ 70 expressed as a percent). This intake level falls within the expected range for a lactating ewe. If the high-quality grass contains 70% TDN, her TDN intake is 1.47 kg (= 70% of 2.1 kg). Subtracting her maintenance requirement of 0.62 kg leaves 0.85 kg of TDN that she can use for lactation.

Here is where we apply a change of 20%. Let's change our grazing management slightly to allow the grass to grow a little longer and increase its DM percentage by 20% — say from 13% to 15.6%. We can accomplish this by simply waiting. Rather than putting sheep out when the grass first turns green, we wait until the grass grows to 8–10 inches. Grass this tall will have a higher DM percentage than the short plants that first come up in the field, although its nutritional quality will be the same.

Now let's recalculate. The 20% increase in DM may not seem like much . . .

Our ewe will take the same number of bites — 30,000 — but now each bite contains 20% more DM, which is 84 mg rather than 70 mg. This gives our ewe a daily DM intake of 2.52 kg. Since the forage still contains 70% TDN, our ewe's TDN intake is 1.76 kg (= 70% of 2.52 kg). Now we subtract her maintenance requirement of 0.62 kg. This leaves 1.14 kg of TDN that she can use for lactation — *a 34% increase in energy available for milk production* over the 0.85 kg TDN in the shorter forage.

Let's review. By delaying grazing slightly so the early spring grass grows taller and increases its DM percentage by a modest 20%, we boost the amount of energy available for lactation by 34%. That translates to considerably more milk for those twins, faster growth, earlier marketing, and perhaps better body condition in the ewes.

When I hear a salesperson claim that such-and-such a miracle product will double or triple my yield, I tend to be a wee bit skeptical. We've all been down that road before. But if someone states honestly that a product or technique can increase yield by 20%, then I listen very carefully indeed.

First Published: August 2010

Author's Note: Numbers . . . lots of people tend to shy away from them. But sometimes, if we do some basic calculations on these numbers using straightforward arithmetic, we can see the real meaning of a situation. And sometimes, like in this article, numbers can tell a real eye-opening story.

Let's Take a Walk

Come . . . join me for a pasture walk.

I know that you've already walked through lots of pastures, many times, but a formal *pasture walk* is different. We won't just cross fields to watch animals or chase them; instead, we'll walk slowly, focusing on the forages, not the livestock. We'll look at the pasture from a grazier's perspective.

We'll consider that our *real* crop is sunlight, that our forages are the photosynthetic machinery that harvests the sunlight, and that our animals are the sunlight products we sell in the market. You won't be bored. If you've never done a real pasture walk, there's quite a lot to see. And it won't take long; I'll get you back in time for the next page. Oh yes, grab yourself a pair of rubber boots; it's wet out there.

Let's start with this grazed field behind the barn. It's about ten acres with a border of trees and a stream at the far end. Notice that there are no cross-fences. The owner told me that he pulled his animals off 14 days ago, so we are looking at two weeks of regrowth. Hmm. Not very much, even though we've had good weather lately with some rain. Let's come back to this item in a few minutes.

Look at the color of the grass. It's a bright, light green. Looks nice, eh? To some folks that would be beautiful, but not to me. What does that color really tell us? As you look around the field, you'll see lots of patches of darker green with taller growth. Look carefully at those patches — their forage is deep green and very dense. It's obvious that each square inch in these patches contains far more leaf area than the surrounding ground. Leaf area means more sunlight captured and more feed for our animals. Well, those deep green patches are manure or urine patches, and they tell me that the field is low in nitrogen and/or phosphorus. Manure contains nitrogen and phosphorus; urine contains nitrogen in the form of urea. Those taller plants are getting enough nutrients to support a fast regrowth, while the surrounding plants are not. In practical terms, a slow regrowth translates to a longer waiting period before stock can go back into the field.

Before we started, the farmer told me that he has spread manure on this field for years, and that last fall he had also applied 60 pounds of urea fertilizer. That's 60 pounds *of fertilizer* per acre. Urea is only 46% nitrogen (the label on the bag lists "46-0-0-0"). Therefore, those 60 pounds of fertilizer really equate to only 28 pounds of *nitrogen* per acre. Frankly, that's not very much nitrogen. Also, urea is quite soluble, and in this region, this form of nitrogen is only effective for approximately 60 days. That's why the grass was light green — in spite of the manure applications, it is still starved for nitrogen.

Here's a story: last year on a different farm, as we stood in a field that looked just like this one, light green with very little growth, I noticed a large, deep-green area about thirty yards away. It really stood out; its grass was at least six inches higher than the surrounding area. But the patch was a full six feet across, much too wide for a manure patch. I joked with the farmer, "did a ewe die there?" He didn't know, so we all walked over and examined the forage. And found bones. Yes, I suppose this *does* add a new dimension to the term "fertile ewe," but I wouldn't recommend it as a routine fertilizer practice.

Let's come back to our paddock. Notice that the total pasture mass is quite low. I'd say that it's only around 1,000 pounds (of dry matter) per acre. This is after 14 days of recovery. There is a problem here. Normally, I would remove animals from a pasture *before* they grazed the residual down to 1,000 pounds. This pasture is telling me that the animals had been left in too long during the last grazing period. They had probably grazed it down to 700 pounds or even less. That's well down into Phase I growth. Plants in this part of their growth curve require a long recovery period until they have enough leaf area to capture enough sunlight for higher rates of growth. And this is early summer — we should be seeing an incredible surge of growth at this time — yet this forage is hardly growing. Fourteen days of regrowth has resulted in only 300 pounds of dry matter, a growth rate of only 21 lb/day. I would expect that forage like this, if it was in Phase II growth, at this time of year with good weather and fertility, could grow at a rate of *more than 100 lb/day*. This field, however, is being forced to struggle back from Phase I without good fertility. Think of all of the sunlight *not* captured.

There are, however, more efficient alternatives. During periods of high growth rates, some good graziers routinely expect to rotate animals through their paddocks *every 17-21 days*. But those graziers maintain high soil fertility, and they leave a lot more residual forage in their paddocks, which gives plants a running start for their next growth cycle. Those graziers can't afford the long lag period from Phase I plants. Look at this field here — after 14 days, it's just *beginning* to add enough leaf area to support good growth. It will be *another*

20 days before this farmer can properly put stock back on it. So instead of coming back to this field in 21 days, animals won't return here for at least 34 days.

One last thing — look over there, near the stream. See those large areas of tall grass that resemble bamboo? That's reed canarygrass (*Phalaris arundinacea*). It likes to grow in wet areas. Reed canarygrass may be an invasive volunteer species that farmers hate, but it's clearly growing in its niche on this farm. Since no one planted it, it must be one of the older, less palatable varieties. Those plants are tall because the animals didn't want to graze them. That tells me that the stocking density was too low in this paddock, or at least in that area of the paddock. The animals refused the reed canarygrass because they had the luxury of alternative feeds. There was no cross-fencing, so the stock could avoid these reed canarygrass areas even as they contentedly overgrazed other parts of the field. I know that most folks curse reed canarygrass, but look at that growth! Maybe the reed canarygrass is telling us something. Maybe that area should not be treated like the rest of the field. If this were my place, I would probably fence that area as a separate small field so that my animals would have no choice of feeds, and I'd move stock in and out as often as necessary to keep the plants low and nutritious. Otherwise, all that incredible growth of reed canarygrass simply means that a lot of photosynthesis is going to waste.

Well, it's time to go. Please close the gate on your way out. Let's do this again soon — we'll walk through a different paddock. And next time, I'll make sure that the electric fence is off.

First Published: July 1999
Author's Note: It all comes down to good and careful observations. Combine these with knowledge and practical techniques, and a walk through a pasture becomes a journey through a multilayered narrative. Pastures tell stories. We should be good listeners. A good pasture walk can be a fascinating and delicious experience.

Fields of Dreams

So, you came back! A pasture walk is a fine way to spend an article. Well, put on your boots and come along. There are two more fields that I'd like to show you. Just watch this gate — someday I'll get a good latch for it.

Today's first field is really interesting. Look out across it. Although it's been heavily grazed by sheep, you can still see 6-8 inch tall tufts of grass everywhere. And over on the far side of the field, in that wetter area, there are some fairly extensive patches of this tall grass. What's going on here?

First we need to identify the plants in this pasture. Crawl around and pull some up. Yeah, I know that they're short, but they still have their unique characteristics. Let's see . . . we have some perennial ryegrass and some annual ryegrass. That scarlet color at the base of the plants is distinctive for the ryegrasses. That other grass, the one with a conspicuous crease along the entire length of the blade and also a prominent, translucent ligule, that's orchardgrass. Notice how its young shoot is folded as it emerges from the joint area. The clover looks like white clover. See its stolons? Also, note that its leaves and stems are completely smooth; they have no hair or fuzz. That plant over there, of course, is a bull thistle. Try not to be too closefisted with it. But look carefully at this grass here — the tall one. The top surface of the blade is distinctly ribbed, and when you run your finger from the tip of the blade toward the base, the blade feels quite rough. Also, notice the prominent auricles and how the new shoot is rolled as it emerges from the joint. This is tall fescue. This is the tall grass we see in this paddock.

Of course, it's not exactly news that animals refuse tall fescue if they have anything else to eat. But this pasture is a good example of what can happen when animals graze a mixed sward that contains tall fescue, especially if they are managed with a low stocking density. Mixed forage species, variation in palatability, and allowing the animals to choose is a bad combination for a

71

grazing situation. Tall fescue, with its poor palatability, is like a vicious circle: as the plants grow taller, they become even *less* palatable relative to the other species in the field. Over time, these plants successfully go to seed and produce *more* tall fescue. The result: those patches grow larger and produce even *more* fescue. That's a positive feedback cycle we *don't* want.

If I were using this field for grazing, I would go over it *right now* with a cutter bar to top off the tall plants. Then, for my next rotation, I would increase the stocking density to *force* animals to consume the fescue. I could either add more animals into the field or make the field smaller with electric fencing. And for those larger patches of tall fescue: I would fence them as separate units and use my animals as a tool to graze them hard.

In the long-term, however, I would wonder why seed mixtures designed for grazing include unpalatable varieties of tall fescue. Plants with low palatability are really hard to manage in pastures that contain other forage species. On the other hand, under the right conditions, tall fescue can be a wonderful plant. It thrives in places where other grasses have a hard time, like wet areas or heavily trafficked lanes. It can be highly nutritious and a great forage for hay or silage. Therefore, in fields designated for grazing, I would only use tall fescue in relatively pure stands in areas that are suited for it. But tall fescue genetics has really advanced in the last few years, especially in New Zealand and Holland. If I were going to renovate a pasture with tall fescue, I would only plant some of the newer varieties that are actually quite palatable, like *Fuego* or *Advance*. That would open up options for both haying *and* grazing.

Let's cross the fence to another pasture. Here the rancher runs stocker cattle. Notice this creek as we cross it (at least I *hope* that you notice it). Also notice the willows and other trees along the banks and the few isolated trees in the middle of the field. And notice that there is no cross-fencing. Cattle usually graze this field continuously for two or three weeks at a time. They were just pulled off it two weeks ago.

As we look across this paddock, I would guess that the *average* pasture mass is 1,600 lb of dry matter per acre. *But notice the variability of forage growth.* Near the creek and around the trees, the forage is dense and lush and deep green — maybe 2,000 lb per acre. But in the main open areas of this field, the grass appears sparse and lighter green — maybe only 1,100 lb per acre.

Sure, some of this variability is due to shade. Around the trees, the soil doesn't heat up as much or lose as much moisture to evaporation as the open areas, and perhaps there is more ground moisture near the creek.

But think of something else . . . think manure. Livestock are really walking manure spreaders. They consume forage with all its nutrients, process it into manure, and then deposit that manure and its nutrients back onto the ground. Ideally, we'd like an even distribution of manure across the whole paddock.

Intensive grazing systems favor this because livestock are enclosed in small areas for short periods of time. But an open, set-stocking system for pasture management allows livestock to walk anywhere they want. And trees are like magnets. Animals love to loaf and bed down under trees. But — and this is crucial — what happens when they stand up? They poop and walk away. All those nutrients get dropped under the trees. Over time, livestock can transfer large amounts of soil fertility from the open areas to the trees.

How much? Let's do some numbers. A 700-pound stocker steer produces approximately 32.6 lb of wet manure each day (it's interesting that reference tables often list their approximations in decimal places). One ton of beef cattle manure, as you see it on the ground, contains 14.6 lb of nitrogen, 4.2 lb of phosphate (P_2O_5), and 9.2 lb of potash (K_2O). (Yes, these values *have* been measured, but we won't go there.) If 20 steers spend a total of 45 days in this paddock during a grazing season and dump their manure mostly around the trees, they would effectively transfer 214 lb of nitrogen, 62 lb of phosphate, and 135 lb of potash from the open areas to the shade. (You can do the calculations yourself. For example, 4.2 lb of phosphate per ton of manure = 0.0021 lb P_2O_5 per lb of manure. Twenty steers @ 32.6 lb manure/day @ 0.0021 lb P_2O_5 for 45 days = 62 lb P_2O_5.)

It's as if those cattle had systematically stripped soil nutrients from the productive areas of the field and moved those nutrients to under the trees. If we want a good forage crop year after year, we must replace those nutrients. That means fertilizer, and that costs money. For years, farmers and scientists have debated the use of shade in pastures. This is not a simple question because there are other issues like heat stress, water quality, and riparian area management. But one thing is clear: in this set-stocking system, there is less grass in the open areas.

Well, it's time to get back to the truck. I hear the next article calling. See you next season.

⟞⟝

First Published: September 1999
Author's Note: When I wrote this article, I mentioned the new cultivars of tall fescue that were still quite new. But now they are ancient history, Today we have dozens of newer, better tall fescue cultivars on the market, including a few with novel endophytes. And our ability to manage tall fescue depends greatly on the stocking density that we employ. But those are topics for another time.

Out onto the Grass

Finally, you've come back to join me on another pasture walk! It's been a long time. A couple of growing seasons have passed. But I'm delighted for your company.

This farm has quite a few interesting fields, and the owner gave us a field map and some soil tests. So finish putting on your rubber boots, walk through the disinfectant tray for biosecurity, and grab a copy of those soil test reports. I'll meet you by the gate.

Let's first head down to the bench pasture above the river. The farmer tells us that this field sometimes floods in the spring when the river comes up, but the soil is pretty well-drained so it still dries out nicely. Well, let's walk out there.

Oh my, look at that green! The entire field is a beautiful, vibrant green, and nearly all of it is grass. Nothing is over 5 inches tall. I estimate that this field contains around 1,400 lb of forage per acre (dry matter basis). What species is this grass? Let's get down on our hands and knees. Nearly all the plants look the same: thin blades (leaves), folded shoot, no auricle, very tiny ligule. That reddish color at the base is fairly diagnostic. It's perennial ryegrass. Gosh, this field is nearly a pure stand of perennial ryegrass. Very impressive. We can also see some occasional spots of grasses with flatter, wider blades. For these plants, the underside of the blade is quite shiny, the young shoot is rolled rather than folded, and the auricle is rather prominent. The base of the tillers also shows that same reddish color. Aha — this is annual ryegrass, although I can't tell if it's a true Westerwold annual ryegrass or one of the Italian ryegrass cultivars.

Let's note some other aspects of this field. The forage cover is very dense with almost no spots of bare ground. Kind of like a nice lawn, except this lawn is 25 acres, and the forage color across the entire field is a solid, homogenous, dark green. There are no spots of deeper green, indicating that this field probably has had sufficient nitrogen even though we don't see any clovers or other legumes. The soil test shows a pH of 6.4, with an organic matter of 7.2%. Those are excellent soil characteristics. I suspect that the soil microbes are very happy, and their activity is releasing a steady stream of nitrogen into the soil from the organic matter.

The owner of this farm took it over only a couple of years ago. She worked this field once with a light harrow and sprayed for broadleaf weeds. That would help explain the absence of clovers. She asked me if she needed to do some additional renovation. But as I look at this field, I see a nearly pure stand of a great forage species. If this were my field, unless I had a compelling reason to do otherwise, I would *not* spend money for additional renovation, except to add any necessary fertilizer and maybe hand-broadcast some white clover seed and red clover seed at a convenient time. Instead, I would focus on improving the grazing management, use some temporary electric cross-fencing, increase the stocking density, leave more residual forage at the end of each grazing period, and practice these techniques for a couple of years. This forage will thicken and grow well. With good management, this field has the potential of being a great, high-quality finishing pasture for lambs and stocker cattle.

I see that you brought along a grass identification book — one of those botanical reference books that show the seed heads of mature grasses. Those are indeed beautiful graphics, but I'm afraid they aren't much use here; those are pictures of mature plants *after* they've gone to seed. That's great for the botany crowd, but here in these pastures, we're looking at grasses *in their vegetative state* — all green leaves — *before* they send out those reproductive tillers. While mature grasses may be easier to identify, they have low nutritional value — not exactly our goal for growing animals. We want highly nutritious forages in this pasture, and we need to identify them when they are in their leafy state. You can probably find a couple of university bulletins that identify grasses in their vegetative state, but in today's world, you can also go to the internet for photos and Google images of vegetative characteristics.

Meanwhile, let's move on to the next field. Uh-oh, this field has some problems. The soil test for this field lists the pH at only 5.3. The soil also contains very low levels of phosphorus and potassium, so there are some serious deficiencies. Look out across the field. Can you see that the color of this grass is decidedly light green except for some distinct spots of darker green? Those dark green spots are urine spots — a sure sign that the rest of the field is low in nitrogen. Also, the farmer allowed her stock to graze here throughout last winter and into the early spring. The animals kind of mucked it up — "pugged" as we say in the grazing world. You wouldn't want to ride a four-wheeler across it very fast. Watch your ankles as we walk; I'd rather not carry you back.

Notice the forages in this field, especially their lack of density. The taller bunch grasses are tall fescue, and they are quite clumpy with some open ground between the plants. I also see lots of broadleaf weeds. Also, notice the tiny grass between the tall fescue plants. This is a bentgrass. There are a couple of different species of bentgrass. They all spread through rhizomes or stolons, but they are all small and low-yielding. The bentgrasses may provide great cover for tennis courts and putting greens, but they are not exactly suited for high-yielding pastures. They take up space from the more-productive species and outcompete them for nutrients.

What can we do with this field? There are two parts to this answer: (1) change the soil fertility, and (2) change the management. For the soil fertility, the first step would be to increase the pH by applying limestone ("lime"). The amount of lime would depend on the soil's buffer index (sometimes called "SMP Buffer"), which is listed in the soil test report. This is a lookup number that we compare to published reference tables. These tables tell us how much limestone to apply to reach a target pH. Increasing the pH would also increase the availability of soil phosphorus and improve the microbial activity in the soil. In addition to the lime, I would also apply a well-rounded fertilizer, like 16-16-16 or something similar.

Then, to change the management, I would find a way of keeping the animals off this field during the winter. I know it's expensive to feed hay in a barnyard throughout the winter, but the ultimate gain in productivity in this field will outweigh those costs. The owner could also consider identifying a different field as a *sacrifice area* for next season. And to change the plant composition in this field, I might try broadcasting annual ryegrass seed at the high seeding rate of 40–50 lb/acre. Annual ryegrass seed is relatively cheap, and this strategy could provide lush forage without the expensive commitment to a perennial species. In fact, I could do this annually for a couple of years until I developed a good long-term plan for this field.

Let's walk back to one more field, the one near the barn. Look at the difference across the fence. Our side of the fence is deep, lush green, with a thick stand of grass and clover. The other side is, well, quite different: lighter green, not very dense, and clearly not as lush. What's going on here? One word: compost. For the past two years, the farmer has made compost from the barn bedding and meticulously hauled it onto this field, maybe 1–2 tons per acre per year. This may not be a scientific experiment to win a Nobel Prize, but that fence line comparison tells a compelling story. Ironic that after sixty years of near-universal use of commercial fertilizer, we are now rediscovering the value of the age-old technique of using compost.

As we walk back toward the house, let's look at the plants growing alongside the farm lane. Wow — we can see a veritable cornucopia of forages here: grasses like orchardgrass, tall fescue, velvet grass, some unidentifiable (by me) annual bromes, and lots of annual bluegrass. We can see legumes like white clover, sub clover (subterranean clover), common vetch, the tiny black medic, and a few larger plants of birdsfoot trefoil. Also lots of plantain, although this is just the common buckhorn plantain weed and not the improved forage variety of narrowleaf plantain like 'tonic'. Isn't it fun to identify forages and know what we are looking at?

Before you get into your pickup, let's review things for a bit. What did we see? We saw one surprising field with a great potential for explosive high-quality forage growth, one field that needs some work on a couple of levels, one field that clearly shows the striking results of applying compost, and an impressive array of forage species that we can identify. Not bad.

Well, I guess it's time to get going. Thanks for coming!

First Published: June 2016

Author's Note: This chapter is the third of the series of pasture walk articles in this book. Some real specifics here. I've also used a number of technical terms that are common among graziers. Pastures are complex and technical environments. We can understand them and manage them better if we know what to look for.

Setting Things Up

When I teach square-dancing, I sometimes joke, "If you don't know where you're going, go there quickly!" But if you are trying to set up a grazing system with a real-world livestock operation, that is most assuredly *not* how to do things.

I can think of many situations where you need to set up a grazing system from scratch: you may have just bought a new farm or taken a plum job as a farm manager or signed a long-term lease on some acreage. Lots of possibilities and stories here. But regardless of its past history, the land is now yours to manage, and you've decided to manage it for grazing. So how do you begin? How do you go about designing a sustainable grazing system? This month and next, we'll lay out the principles (about grazing systems, not square-dancing).

Here are some things you *don't* do: you don't start plowing fields willy-nilly. You don't run out and buy a standard pasture seed mix because all the neighbors use that mix. You don't build lots of permanent cross-fencing based on a hazy concept of rotational grazing. Not unless, of course, you just won the lottery, and when that money runs out, you expect to win it again.

The first thing you really need to do is take an inventory of current production — for every field on the property, field by field. You'll want these production numbers expressed as pounds of forage per acre. If your only records are numbers of bales, then pull out your trusty calculator and convert bales to pounds. If you are lucky enough to have historical records over multiple years, take the average. Then, using your judgment, maybe reduce that number by 10-15% because whose memory is exactly perfect anyway?

If a field had only been used for grazing, you'll need to determine how many animals were on that field and for how long. Estimate their average body weight. Calculate a daily dry matter intake at 4% body weight (which includes a cushion amount for trampling and manure), and come up with a reasonable number for the forage production in each field. Work in dry matter (DM) amounts. That's easy for grazed fields because you calculated yield as a DM intake, but for stored forage which always contains some water, you can convert total amounts by assuming 90% DM for the hay, 50% DM for the hay-crop silage (balage, wrapped wet bales, Ag-bags, etc.), and 30% DM for corn silage. Don't worry about decimal places — you're simply trying to get a roundhouse figure for each field's historical yields.

Once you have these numbers, you should try to plot out the *distribution* of these yields throughout the growing season. For example, was 75% of the hay always harvested in the first cutting? Did *anything* grow before April 15th, and if so, in which field? How bad was the notorious "summer slump" that everyone talks about? Distribution of forage growth, of course, depends a lot on geography and fertility and plant species, but right now you are simply trying to get a picture of the high parts and low parts of this farm's growing season.

Then — here's a big step — take a no-nonsense look at the operation's livestock management calendar. We could do this for cattle, sheep, or goats, but because this is a sheep magazine, I'll be prudent and do it for sheep.

For sheep, the main question is very simple: *When do you lamb?* Because once you select your lambing date, *you have essentially locked in all the nutritional periods of the year.* (Accelerated systems are slightly more complex, but the same principles still apply.) The highest nutritional requirements occur in early lactation; the second-highest requirements occur in late gestation. For both periods, you *must* supply high-quality feed, especially forage. And, of course, the weaned lambs also require exceptionally high-quality forage. The bottom line is that your lambing date determines everything. (And a beef cattle operation would have a corresponding calculation once it determines its calving date.)

You can estimate *total* forage needs of the operation relatively easily. A 160-lb ewe will roughly consume 1,500 pounds of forage DM during the year (hay, silage, grazing, whatever). Adjust for your breed's weight. Then multiply by the number of ewes to get a rough total.

Next, a crucial preliminary step: you need to identify the *holes* in your current forage system. Holes are periods during the year when forage or feed supplies are tight or expensive, like during the periods when the pastures don't supply much usable forage. Before you begin changing a system, before you start going anywhere, *you must first understand where you are.* You might want to reread that first paragraph.

Take a sheet of graph paper and carefully outline a yearly calendar that, for every month, shows your flock's nutritional needs (in pounds of feed) and also the pounds of feed produced by the land. Compare these two values for each month. When are the surpluses? And very importantly, when are the shortages? *Basically, the questions are: what do you have and when do you need it?*

Now you have a reasonable framework — a roadmap of where you should direct your resources for intensifying or renovating any field. Now you can begin to go there, quickly or otherwise . . .

Here's an example: let's say that you run an upper Midwest sheep farm with lambing in early March. Your ewes, therefore, have their high nutritional requirements for late-gestation in February and even higher nutritional requirements for early lactation during March and April. The late-gestation period is a bit of a problem because pastures in the upper Midwest are notoriously white during February, which means that you'll need to buy or store good forage for that period.

Because the early-lactation requirements occur during late winter and early spring, you will have, at best, only a few weeks of grass growth during the latter part of this period. But you'll need high quality forages during the *entire* period, which means that you'll first use purchased or stored legume hay and then shift to very early pasture growth, if you have any. This is all very expensive. If you want to maximize grazing and reduce forage costs, you might want to evaluate whether you really need to lamb in early March.

But, in any case, look at your pastures. Recall that legumes tend to come up later in the spring than cool-season grasses because legumes require higher soil temperatures. Therefore, you're going to need grass. Do any fields contain grasses that specialize in very early spring growth like winter wheat or triticale or crested wheatgrass?

If your soil fertility is high, you'll probably have plenty of good-quality forage during late lactation. Most forages in the Midwest grow best during late spring and early summer. But the weaned lambs will still need to go somewhere (you do wean at 60–80 days, don't you?). You could drylot them, of course, but aren't you trying to set up a *grazing system*? Does the farm have any fields that grow lots of forage during late June and July? This is not easy because most cool-season grasses either mature at that time or seriously slow down during hot weather. And you are not just looking for total tonnage. Good lamb growth needs high-quality *vegetative* forages — like legumes or forage brassicas or very young actively growing grass.

But now let's step back, look at the big picture, and try to refine our plans — specifically, how *each field* fits into the needs of the *entire* operation. Your annual forage plan may need some fields for big hay tonnage, specialized fields for summer growth, fields for growth in the very early spring, fields for finishing lambs, fields for stockpiling forage for the winter, etc. Every field plays an integral part in the system, every field has a purpose, and every field is different.

That's the big picture. Next month, we'll look at some specific management choices.

First Published: June 2006
Author's Note: Go there quickly? Where are we going? We need to identify the where in there. Then we need to see which there is already here. Then we can compare the big picture of the operation with the calendar. This is really kitchen table stuff (with the help of a spreadsheet) that we should do before we climb onto our large tractors or buy lots of fencing supplies. Before we start changing things, we really need to think out the details about the here and there.

The Next Steps

So what's next? Last month we covered the first steps for setting up a grazing system — broad brushstrokes showing the big picture and its current deficiencies, with clues about where we should direct our resources for plugging the holes. Now we need to flesh out the details.

Folks often ask me about soil types. You know, those soil survey maps in every county office of the Natural Resources Conservation Service (and now available online). Soils with names like "Oakland silt loam," or "Kalapa silty clay." These are listed in books with extensive reference tables for each one. Interesting information, yes, but in practice, have you ever *looked carefully* at a soil survey map? Examine any area, and you'll see a confusing jigsaw puzzle of soil types, usually unrelated to any field pattern on your farm. Soil types zigzag crazily across fence lines, field boundaries, and farm lanes.

These reference tables meticulously list the detailed characteristics of each soil type. One particular value in these tables intrigues me: *stocking rate*. The reference tables show that one soil type will carry X animals per acre, while a different soil type will only carry Y animals per acre. Really? Are these stocking rate numbers as constant as a soil's drainage characteristics or its proportion of clay? Hasn't anyone heard of fertilizer? Or intensive grazing? Or supplementary feed? I can always increase the number of animals by adding fertilizer or feeding extra grain. Let's carry this logic to its extreme: What is the stocking rate in a feedyard?

Basically, soil classifications give us interesting background information, but they are only peripheral to setting up a grazing operation. We need something more useful. We need detailed *soil tests* of each field.

A soil test gives us a reasonably accurate picture of a field's fertility. A grazier trying to apply fertilizer or lime without having soil fertility numbers is like a doctor recommending drugs without looking at the chart of a patient's vital signs.

So, as part of our baseline information, we need a soil test from every field. We should treat each field as a single unit, unless a field is not uniform. Then we should use common sense and take a composite sample from each logical biological area. For example, if a field contains a flat area and also a hill, we should take at least two different samples: one from the flat area and one from the hill. (Remember that each submitted sample is a composite of soil cores from 15–20 holes in the ground, properly mixed.)

Soil tests aren't expensive — many labs charge less than $25 for a test that will give the basic fertility characteristics. Compared to the costs of renovation, the cost of soil testing is almost trivial. If we are going to spend thousands of dollars on seed, fertilizer, and lime, not knowing if we *really* need those fertilizers or if a particular seed will grow well in that soil — well, *not* having a soil test can be very expensive indeed.

Now, duly armed with soil test reports, should we go out, buy seed, and start plowing? (I'm defining *renovation* as some form of major reseeding, either by plowing or disking or no-till drilling. These operations can all radically change the forage species. Breaking the soil also changes the soil structure. In contrast, frost-seeding is not a full renovation because it just adds a bit of seed at an opportunistic time without disturbing anything else.)

Not yet, not yet. For each field, we should first decide if we *really* need to renovate or if we should first try to make major changes in the management. Sometimes, changing management will encourage the growth of plants that otherwise couldn't compete, especially if the field already has good seed in the ground. Sometimes, this alone will give astonishing results at a fraction of the cost of a full renovation (although it can take much longer). I'm talking about management changes like increasing fertility, changing the soil pH, grazing properly with high stocking densities, leaving sufficient residual pasture mass, killing weeds, and perhaps broadcasting extra seed onto the open areas of a pasture.

What about the prospect of a full renovation of old fields? We can't go into many details here, but here's a thought: if we fully renovate a field — go the whole nine yards with a disk or plow, apply fertilizer, lime, and new seed — but then we don't change the management of that field, what do you think will happen in a few years? The first year, of course, will probably look very good, especially if our seed mix includes fast-emerging forages like annual ryegrass or red clover. But then, after a couple of years, the pasture will probably drift back to the same poor-performance field that we started with. *Because that's what did best under the old management.* Changing management is critical. Our only real question is this: do we change management first and see what happens, or do we renovate first and then change management?

Speaking of renovation . . . if we choose to do it, what seed should we plant? Be careful here — this is not a simple question. For a permanent pasture, we will have to live with this choice for a long time. So, therefore, we shouldn't just drive down to the local seed store and buy the common "pasture mix." We should spend lots of time scanning seed catalogs, yield reports, and online comparisons, and also talking to folks who truly know about forages and grazing. The new forage species and improved forage varieties can be light-years ahead of the old genetics, and renovation is a clean opportunity to improve things.

But here is a temporary alternative: if we want a year's grace period before planting that permanent pasture, we can broadcast lots of annual ryegrass seed onto the field, fertilize it properly, and spend the year learning our grazing and fencing skills with a huge yield of highly nutritious forage. Hey, annual ryegrass is an annual. It can give us a year's grace period to learn and read, so that next season we can select our permanent forage species with more knowledge.

Next, we need to evaluate our fencing. Of course, the perimeter fencing is critical, especially against predators. That's a given. Let's move beyond that. To control grazing, we need internal cross-fencing. If we choose to use electric fence, we must deliver electricity to every field with transmission lines, such as wires on step-in posts or on offset brackets. Once these are in place, we can attach electric cross-fencing anywhere and thus move animals anywhere, as well as adjust the size of any grazing cell.

One question I often hear: should our cross-fencing be electric or permanent? If we are just starting out, then, by all means, use electric fencing: it's flexible and effective. Fencing manufacturers now sell all sorts of clever doodads to make electric fencing do almost anything except make coffee or calculate our taxes. We can use electric netting or step-in posts to move animals daily. We can even use those items as semipermanent fencing. My basic rule is that we shouldn't plant wooden fence posts or build permanent cross-fencing until we know *exactly* where we really need that fence. Remember that our pastures will change and our management will (hopefully) improve. After a couple of years, when we see how things are going, we'll have all that perspective and knowledge, and we can set permanent fence posts with confidence. Maybe fencing is *your* favorite activity, but it's not mine, and I would rather do it only once and then live happily with the results.

Oh yes, lest we forget . . . all grazing systems contain animals that need water and minerals every day. But centralized water troughs and mineral feeders *don't work* in intensive grazing systems. We need to deliver water and minerals to the animals in every grazing area, not the other way around. This implies an effective water-distribution system to each grazing cell, maybe with some trenching or at least some mainline pipes. Initially, we can temporarily lay pipes on top of the ground under fence lines until we see the best place to bury them. Plastic hoses are your friends. We might need lots of portable mineral feeders and water hoses and couplers and risers, but that's part of setting up a new grazing system.

Well, there we have it. Of course there's more, but not here. Enough of the "we." From here on, it's "you." The details on *your* place will be *yours*.

A grazing system — fun to work out, deeply rewarding in many ways, and as unique as the person setting it up.

First Published: July 2006
Author's Note: We've just tapped the surface. But it's a start. Every farm and ranch is different, and the final arrangements for each one — well, those are among the most fascinating and rewarding aspects of setting things up.

At the Gate

It's early spring, and you're excited. You are standing next to a pasture gate looking at a field with anticipation and also with a question. The spring sun is warm, the grass is just beginning to green up, and you're going to make some changes. This is the year, you've promised yourself, that you will finally begin to improve your pasture management with a strategy of managed grazing. *Management-Intensive Grazing* (MIG) — you've heard about MIG for years. You have studied the books and attended the workshops. Now you're ready to begin with the first steps, almost . . . because you have a very practical question: what *exactly* are the first steps?

You have done your homework, of course; you've taken soil tests from all your fields and obtained soil maps showing all the soil types in those fields and their characteristics. You have compiled extensive field records for the past ten years, so you know the average forage yields for each field and the periods of high and low growth throughout the growing season. And you've outlined an animal production calendar that charts the monthly nutritional needs of your livestock. Using these tools, you have developed a feed budget that identifies the feed surpluses and feed holes in the calendar and the amounts of forage you will need to fill those holes.

In addition, you've conscientiously studied the major principles of good grazing management. Such as "The 5-Day Rule" that says that you should never leave animals on a field for more than five consecutive days to avoid grazing the regrowth. And the principles of always grazing the forage during its Phase II growth, and leaving enough residual forage to maintain good plant health and shorten the cycle time to graze the fields again. Also a fourth principle: to supply water and minerals to the livestock wherever they graze, not the other way around, so the animals have everything they need in a pasture and don't need to walk to a barn or drink out of a creek.

But now, when you're actually standing at the gate ready to start — now what? Exactly *what* should you do, aside from opening that gate and letting your animals into that beautiful green grass?

Well, here's something that you should *not* do: *don't try to change things in every field during this first year.* It's nice to be optimistic, but trying to implement everything at once is a recipe for a nightmare. These first years of MIG are learning years. I might, ahem, speak from experience — not everything works perfectly or goes smoothly 100% of the time. Things happen. And if you attempt to initiate MIG in lots of fields at once, well . . . many fields mean many potential issues, sometimes arising very quickly. The days will not contain enough time to resolve all these issues, and your fields will soon have forage that is either too short or too long. You'll be running from field to field juggling tasks and trying to solve problems. Within a year or two, there's a good chance you'll reconsider this MIG system, tear down the extra fences, buy some hay, and return to that comfortable set-stocking management system that certainly seemed less stressful.

But we can avoid that scenario. Here's a better idea for this first year: just try to implement MIG *in only one or two fields.* Nowhere is it written in stone that all fields must be treated alike. You *don't* have to manage all your fields in the same way. During the first year, you can learn your MIG skills in one or two fields while the other pastures continue to produce forage as they did before. I can guarantee that those other fields will still be on your farm next year, and as your management skills improve . . . well, you can cross that bridge whenever it's convenient. As some baseball fans like to proclaim, wait until next year.

Okay, let's say that you've decided to concentrate this year's MIG efforts on *one* field. The main management issues that you should now address are that field's soil fertility, physical facilities, forage (including species, varieties, plant density, and forage yield), and finally, your day-to-day grazing management of the livestock. Let's also say that you have sheep.

First, soil fertility. Those soil tests you took are invaluable. Use them to guide your fertilizer decisions. Lots of local sources can give recommendations about soil fertility and fertilizer: the Extension Service, NRCS, soil-testing laboratories, feed and fertilizer stores, etc. Make sure your field has enough nutrients by spreading the appropriate amounts of phosphorus and potassium (*potash* in fertilizer lingo) and sulfur. You may have already started these applications in the previous autumn, but certainly make fertilizer applications as early in the spring as is practical. And don't forget limestone or dolomitic limestone if you need to raise the pH. In fact, sometimes spending money on limestone can be the best investment you can make in a field.

Also, you'll need to apply nitrogen — probably more than you've done in the past, and you'll need to apply it in a couple of split applications rather than in a classic single springtime application designed to support first-cut hay production. There are typically two major methods of splitting the annual nitrogen allocation — either by the calendar (every 60 days, etc.) or immediately after each grazing. The total annual amount of nitrogen may be in the range of 100–200 *units* of nitrogen per acre. (One unit of nitrogen = one pound of actual nitrogen. That's the unambiguous way of saying 100–200 pounds of *actual nitrogen per acre* without confusing the terminology of pounds of the material in the fertilizer bag versus pounds of actual nitrogen.)

Next, let's consider the forages. What is already growing in that field? Can you identify grasses when they are still young and vegetative? Orchardgrass, tall fescue, timothy, Kentucky bluegrass, smooth brome — they all have unique characteristics. Unfortunately, formal botany books are not much use to graziers because they inevitably show pictures of *mature* grass plants with seed heads, which is exactly what you *don't* want to see in your fields. Besides, it's still early spring, and all you can see are the young green blades. You'll also want to identify any legumes in the field, like the true clovers, alfalfa, sweetclover, lespedeza, or the vetches. And some broadleaf weeds may be valuable, like chicory or plantain, or they may be just weeds. You need to identify the different species of forages so you can treat them properly and see which ones respond to your new management. If you don't know what is already growing in your field, find someone who can help.

Sometimes, just by strategically adding the correct fertilizer and good grazing management, you can obtain an excellent forage response — denser, thicker stands of high-quality grasses and legumes. This assumes that those high-quality plants are already in your pasture, but if those plants are not in your pasture, then what? Expensive renovation? Maybe not, at least not yet. You might not want to spend money on a full renovation before you know where you are going with that field and how you can best manage it.

So here's a shortcut tip — a temporary one, to be sure, but very practical for this first year: *plant annual ryegrass (ARG) in that field.* Particularly an Italian type that will stay vegetative throughout the summer. ARG is an easy, dependable grass. It's a very aggressive seed that you can broadcast onto bare ground, although drilling or disking will usually result in a better stand. ARG emerges quickly, grows spectacularly well in response to fertilizer, and provides extremely high-quality feed. And its seed is usually one of the least expensive on the market. Get a certified variety, plant it heavily, fertilize it well, and step back and watch it grow. Then spend the summer learning your MIG skills with a productive ARG sward: setting fence, gauging forage growth, mastering the art of feed allocation and residual mass, keeping records, etc. And at the end of the growing season, ARG has one more advantage — it's an annual. ARG is like a master reset button that allows that field to begin the next season with a clean slate. You'll still need to make decisions about future forages and possible renovation, but next year you'll have an extra year's knowledge and experience under your belt.

The other two things you have to address this first year: the field's physical facilities and your day-to-day grazing management. We'll take them up next month. Meanwhile, you might want to walk through your field and identify the plants. See you next month.

———✂———

First Published: July 2011
Author's Note: This startup procedure may sound a bit hard or convoluted, but it's really not. I'm just laying out the process step-by-step. The good thing about the process is that it works. It really, definitely works.

The Electric Field

I'm glad you're back. It seems that you really *are* interested in trying that newfangled grazing strategy called *MIG (Management-Intensive Grazing)*. Last month, we discussed two main starting points for MIG — forages and soil fertility — and also a practical tip for planting a low-risk forage for the first year. Now let's focus on another must-have for any MIG system: the physical setup of the field.

Because we are planning to concentrate our efforts this year in one field, we need to review that field's attributes — specifically: fences, water, and minerals — good things to think about *before* putting animals onto that grass.

What's the condition of the fences? You'll need a perimeter fence around the field and also maybe some cross-fencing. The perimeter fence is really a no-brainer: it needs to be good, period. The perimeter fence is your barrier against the outside world. It must keep animals in, and it must also keep animals out. You don't want your sheep to cross the road — it's a litigious world out there — and you certainly don't want all the neighborhood dogs and coyotes to visit for dinner. Maybe you are fortunate and your perimeter fence is in great shape: well-constructed, high-tensile wire fence, or a new, tight field fence. But even if it is not so good, an old fence can still do the job for a year or two if you install offsets that will support an electrified wire along the inside of the fence. One or two strands at the right height(s) will keep your animals from pushing against the fence or squeezing through those tantalizing holes. And that wire can also serve as a convenient transmission line, as we'll discuss below.

Cross-fencing is absolutely essential for a MIG system — how else can you allocate feed and control stock density? But here's a crucial point: your cross-fencing should not be permanent, at least not initially. Toss away those steel T-posts and fence-pullers for the cross-fencing, or use them in a different field.

Since you are learning how to implement MIG, your cross-fencing should be as flexible as possible, so you can change and adapt and react as needed throughout this growing season. Use electric netting or step-in posts with electrified polywire. These are simple, temporary systems that are quick to erect, quick to pull down, and completely flexible for changing locations around the field.

Temporary cross-fencing is also a good strategy for future decisions because, over the years, you can expect your pasture to change in forage composition, growth patterns, and yield. Temporary electric fence will give you the flexibility to adjust the sizes of grazing cells in response to these forage improvements. You can always build permanent fence later, once you gain lots of experience and become confident of your positions, but right now, temporary fence keeps your options wide open.

There are five zillion ways to set up electric cross-fencing. Here are two that I've used quite effectively:

1) Across the middle of the field, you can construct a simple electrified line using smooth wire or polywire on step-in posts. Your grazing cells will extend to the right and left of this line, and the central wire will act as a convenient electricity source — a transmission line — to hook your cross-fencing or netting.

2) Another option is to install offsets on the perimeter fence, as I described above. This electric line not only protects the perimeter fence but also becomes an electricity source where you can easily hook your cross-fence polywire or netting.

Oh yes, here is another useful strategy, a universal one: find someone local who is a successful grazier, someone who's had lots of serious experience with MIG and electric fence. Learn from her. It will be time well spent.

Electric fence has one obvious and inviolate rule: it needs electricity. An electric fence without electricity is . . . well, not exactly useful. A few years ago on some rented pastures, I used electric netting to subdivide the field and control my sheep. The neighbors were amused. They took one look at this zigzag netting, which admittedly did look kind of loose and droopy in places, and they said that it would never hold animals. Well, they missed the point — electric fence works by fear, not strength. Electric fence doesn't have to be strong; it doesn't "hold" animals in the classic barrier sense like barbed wire or taut high-tensile wire. Animals don't push against an electric fence, at least not more than once. After they get hammered by 5,000 volts, animals are usually very good at keeping their learning curve very short.

Which means, of course, that you should get a good charger, properly grounded. Also purchase a *good* fence tester. These little hand-held devices will tell you if the fence is carrying a proper charge. Buy one with a digital readout that can tell you precisely whether the fence is carrying 8,000 volts or just 1,000 volts. And some newer units also have a little arrow in their screen that indicates *the direction* of a voltage drop. The first time you need it, you'll see how incredibly useful this is. Instead of spending hours searching for that hidden spot in the bushes where an old metal post is leaning up against your fence, the smart arrows will help you locate the site within minutes. Wow.

Now for two non-fence attributes of our field: water and minerals.

To control forage growth, you must have the flexibility to move livestock to wherever they are needed and set up grazing cells on-the-fly. Each grazing cell should be self-contained. If livestock are forced to walk back to a barn or creek for water, you effectively lose control of your forage management. The animals will inevitably graze your vegetative regrowth, and they'll probably loiter near the water source, especially if there is shade nearby (trees, barn, etc.). The bottom line is that you really need to supply fresh drinking water to every grazing cell in the field. Your water system doesn't have to be fancy — hoses are your friends. Even a long black polypipe laid on top of the ground under the central transmission line fence will do the trick. Just install some couplings to run hoses off this line. I've seen graziers work wonders with long hoses, valves, and drinking tubs.

Finally, your minerals. The same principle applies as with water, namely, that every grazing cell should be self-contained. Your mineral mix must be conveniently available to the livestock wherever they graze. Every time you move animals; you move minerals. Design or buy a mineral box that can be moved by hand or dragged behind an ATV. Own a couple of these boxes so you don't have to move the same one every time. Again, the mineral setup doesn't have to be fancy or expensive. There are some good commercial products on the market, but for MIG, you'll want to avoid the large stationary mineral feeders that are built as if the entire farm revolved around them. Remember, flexibility and time-savings are paramount.

So . . . we've covered forages, soils, fencing, water, and minerals. Now just one more thing about starting MIG: actually moving the animals. We'll open those gates next month.

<hr />

First Published: August 2011
Author's Note: Fencing isn't everyone's favorite activity, especially setting posts and stretching wires. But setting up and moving electric fence for MIG systems can be exceptionally rewarding because you can quickly see the results in the forage. One good thing to remember, however, is that before you move the electric netting, turn off the electricity.

Ready, Set, Graze . . .

Finally, you're ready to move sheep into that first field — the start of your *Management-Intensive Grazing* (MIG). All your background work is done. Perimeter fences – check. Places to connect electric cross-fencing – check. Soil tests – check. Fertilizer and lime – check. Properly seeded forage – check. Vegetative growth a few inches deep – check. Water – check. Minerals – check. And to top it all off, it's a beautiful, warm, sunny spring day. The grass is so green; it's glistening. It's almost calling you into that field.

You plan to introduce your flock into a small grazing area (a *gazing cell*), but exactly how small? Well, now you must make two very basic decisions that will govern your grazing management: (1) how many days should your animals remain in a grazing cell? And (2) how much residual forage should be left when the animals move to the next grazing cell? Recall that the *5-Day Rule* spells out the maximum number of days animals can remain in a paddock before they start grazing the regrowth. But that's only a maximum, not necessarily the most convenient for *your* farm.

Well, for this article, let's make these choices forthwith: let's say that you want to move animals every *three days*, and that you would like to leave *1,000 lb of residual forage*. (That's 1,000 lb of dry matter per acre, in case you were wondering.) There's nothing magical about three days, it's just a convenient length of time that fits your schedule.

So . . . now you look at the field and make a crucial determination: how much forage is actually out there? You can estimate this in various ways: you could take small samples in 1-foot square frames, dry them in a microwave, carefully measure the amounts of dry matter (DM), and use these numbers to calculate the total forage mass in an acre (lb DM/acre). Or you could use equipment like a rising plate meter or a falling plate meter or a specialized pasture measuring stick, which is popular in some areas of the country. Or, a

95

perennial favorite, you could make a wild guess (not exactly a recommended technique). Actually, with practice and experience, your eye will become a very good measuring device, and it won't be long before you can make reasonable estimates by simply looking at the pasture. But whichever method you choose, you will need to be fairly confident about the results. Let's say that you made some measurements and conclude that this first pasture contains a total forage mass of 2,400 lb DM/acre.

Because we want to leave a residual forage of 1,000 lb DM, then the *available forage* in this field is 1,400 lb DM/acre (= 2,400 − 1,000). This is the amount of forage we want our sheep to graze.

Managed grazing is really about allocating feed. Therefore, you need to estimate your flock's forage consumption, so you can calculate how much acreage to allocate for three days of grazing. Let's say that your flock consists of 60 crossbred ewes in early lactation. (Extra details: the ewes dropped a 175% lamb crop, but the lambs are still quite young and dependent on milk, so their impact on forage consumption is negligible. Also, you might have noticed that I neatly ducked the issue of "breed" by classifying the ewes as "crossbred." Clever, eh?) The ewes average 160 lb. Here's a useful rule of thumb: let's assume these animals will consume forage DM at 5% of their body weight. Therefore, 60 ewes each weighing 160 lb equals a total flock weight of 9,600 lb. A 5% DM intake means that your flock needs 480 lb DM each day (= 5% of 9,600). Therefore, if you want to keep the ewes in a grazing cell for three days, your flock will need 1,440 lb of available DM. Which means that one acre of this field will supply enough feed for three days. That's the size of your grazing cell for this field at this time of year, and that's where you should set your first cross-fence.

Background note: some folks might consider 5% a high value. Well, considering that this forage is young spring growth with relatively low fiber levels, and that the ewes are in early lactation which is their period of highest nutritional requirements, and that the animals will trample a bit of this forage into the ground, a 5% disappearance rate is a reasonable estimate.

However, what if you are wrong? What if you did not estimate the forage mass accurately? (An easy miscalculation if your estimation technique involves a wild guess.) If you overestimate the forage, you'll run out of feed too early. If you underestimate it, you'll still have some leftovers after three days. In the first case, three days of grazing will reduce the residual too much and put the forage into Phase I Growth — too short — and thus add more days to its regrowth period. The good news is that for the *next* grazing cell, you'll readjust your fence to allocate a little more than one acre, or you'll graze the sheep for only two days before moving them, instead of three days. If, on the other hand, you overestimated the forage so that too much forage remained after three days, you can simply add another day or two to the grazing period. And for the *next* grazing cell, you'll recalculate and set your fence closer than 1 acre.

Notice that I wrote ". . . for the next grazing cell." In managed grazing there is always a *next* time. One of the beauties of MIG is that after three days, you get another chance to set the fence and allocate feed. Each grazing cell gives you useful experience. You see the results, learn from this feedback, adjust the size of the new grazing cell, and watch what happens. And you'll do it again for the grazing cell after that, etc., etc. Of course pasture conditions change as plants grow, but throughout the growing season you get chance after chance to readjust your cell sizes. Each time you readjust is a learning experience. It doesn't take long before your eye can accurately read the forage. And as you gain confidence, you'll get better and better at setting the next fence.

The sheep, of course, learn *their* role very quickly. They watch you open the fence every few days to give them a new break of delicious, young forage. At first they may hang back, alert, timid about coming near you. But after a few times of moving to a new grazing cell . . . well . . . suddenly, when you walk into the field to move fence, the sheep rush over and become your best friends. They'll avoid the electric fence, but they will stand nearby and wait for you to magically open it. And as soon as you create the opening, they'll run past you and flow beautifully into the next grazing cell. No shouting or pushing or driving animals — you just watch them move themselves, smoothly and quietly. Not bad.

Let's round out this discussion with two more points. With all these decisions and activity, don't forget to move the water and minerals. Each grazing cell must be self-contained for water and minerals. Also, as you shift animals from grazing cell to grazing cell, you'll need to remember to set a back-fence, so the sheep can't wander back into an earlier cell and graze the regrowth.

You'll discover that, after three or four moves, things will begin to fall into place, into a routine. And as you get better at estimating forage amounts, your confidence will grow, and the forage and sheep will respond.

In a way, managed grazing is like a sporting event. Months of preparation and training have led to this point, this field. You've planned a lot, worried a lot, calculated a lot. Now the whistle blows. The game starts. You're off and running!

―✕―

First Published: September 2011

Author's Note: Management-Intensive Grazing means intensive management, not intensive grazing. Livestock always graze intensively, but managing that grazing takes a lot of discipline and thought. MIG is essentially a thinking person's approach to forage management. It's challenging, exciting, and rewarding. It's a synthesis of principles, mathematics, physiology, practical skills, and art. There's nothing quite like it. These last few articles may help open the door to this art.

Section 3

Soils, Soil Fertility, Fertilization

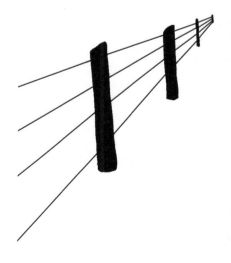

Cash and Carry

Each summer, most farmers spend weeks making hay or silage, and then, during the rest of the year, feed that forage to animals or sell it to willing buyers. On the other hand, we all know of farms that have worn-out hay fields of low fertility, fields that need renovation with lots of fertilizer and seed to return to good production. Making hay, renovating the fields — this is a relationship that needs adjusting. Let's talk.

To make hay, we cut the forage, dry it enough to prevent mold growth, package it into convenient bales, and then haul it to a barn or a buyer. From the perspective of soil fertility, silage is just like hay, only wetter, and because the fertility principles are exactly the same, we'll keep things simple in this article by focusing only on hay.

We should ask ourselves a simple question: *how much fertility is removed from the field when we make hay?* Yes, of course, we've all been exposed to those popular rules of thumb — helpful adages like "one ton of hay equals 4.2 light-years of proteinaceous megajoules" or something equivalent. But I can never remember these rules either, so let's compute the numbers ourselves. Then you can do it for your own place.

Let's assume that we have a field where we make a grass-legume hay of average quality that contains (on a dry matter basis) 14% crude protein, 0.30% phosphorus, 2.3% potassium, 0.22% sulfur, 0.45% calcium, and 0.21% magnesium. The standard chemical abbreviations are P, K, S, Ca, and Mg. And because we are interested in soil fertility, which is related to the amount of nitrogen, we must convert the crude protein value back to nitrogen (N). Since crude protein is defined as N x 6.25, the N content of our hay is 2.24% (= 14 ÷ 6.25). We also must recognize that our hay is not completely dry, despite our best efforts. Let's say that our hay contains 10% moisture, which equates to 90% dry matter. Therefore, one ton of our hay (2,000 lb) contains 1,800 lb of dry matter, and this dry matter contains (rounding off for ease of reading) 40 lb N, 5 lb P, 41 lb K, 4 lb S, 8 lb Ca, and 4 lb Mg. (Recall that we add two decimal places when converting a percentage to a multiplier. For example, 0.30% P means that we must multiply by 0.0030.)

Our field, of course, will produce more than one ton of hay per acre. I know that university agronomy trials often publish results showing hay yields of 8 tons or more, but let's be more conservative with our field. Let's estimate that with three cuttings in a season, we will harvest a total of 4 tons of hay per acre (= 160 bales at 50 lb per bale). Multiplying these 4 tons by the amounts of each nutrient per ton, we calculate that our total harvest contains 160 lb N (= 4 x 40), 20 lb P, 164 lb K, 16 lb S, 32 lb Ca, and 16 lb Mg. This is the fertility removed from each acre of our field when we haul the 4 tons of hay back to the barn.

160 lb of N! Wow! Where is all this N going to come from? Well, legumes can "fix" N from the atmosphere, and if the paddock contains a high percentage of well-nodulated legumes, those plants may provide 50–100 lb of N. Also, under proper conditions, the soil's organic matter will release some N into the soil. But the rest . . . the rest must come from an external source like fertilizer, manure, or compost. If all 160 lb of N are derived from a fertilizer like urea, we would need to apply 348 lb of urea to each acre (urea is labeled as "46-0-0-0," meaning that it contains 46% N). If we used a blended fertilizer like 16-16-16-6 (commonly called "Triple-16") that contains only 16% N, we would need to use *1,000 lb* of this fertilizer to deliver those 160 lb of N.

It gets worse. Let's focus on P, K, and S, because these are the major mineral constituents of soil fertility. No atmospheric "fixing" here; these nutrients must all come from the soil or from fertilizer. Some soil particles do indeed break down and release minerals, but not very quickly. Supplying these nutrients with Triple-16 (16-16-16-6) may be a bit daunting.

We should also realize that the nutrient levels listed on fertilizer bags aren't always what they seem. People often automatically think that those numbers represent direct percentages of those elements, but that's not completely true. Although the tag values for N and S do represent their percentages in a fertilizer, the tag values for P and K do *not* represent the percentages of P and K. Why? Because, by law, these tag values actually represent the percentages of P_2O_5 (*phosphorus pentoxide*) and K_2O (*potash*), which contain 44% P and 83% K respectively. Therefore, in terms of real nutrients, 16-16-16-6 should properly be labeled at 16-7-13-6, a revision that would not be overwhelmingly popular with fertilizer companies.

If we want to use Triple-16 as our fertilizer, we would need to apply 286 lb per acre to supply 20 lb P and — hang on to your hats — 1,262 lb to supply 164 lb K. (The details for K: we need 164 lb of K using a fertilizer containing only 13% K. Therefore, 164 ÷ 0.13 = 1,262.) And supplying 16 lb of sulfur would require 267 lb of Triple-16. Hmmm. Maybe we should all buy stock in fertilizer companies.

Alternatively, we could select fertilizers with higher levels of K, such as muriate of potash at 0-0-60-0, which could supply our needed K with *only* 329 lb of fertilizer.

But here's something to consider: *these fertilizer amounts do not actually improve the fertility of the soil, they just maintain it.* They only *replace* the nutrients removed by our hay crop. They don't correct any preexisting nutrient deficiencies. If we want to *improve* soil fertility above previous levels, *we would have to apply even more fertilizer.*

Fertilizer is not free. You can apply your own prices to these fertilizers, but for grins, let's say that Triple-16 costs $17.00 for a 50-lb bag (a current local price), which means that 300 lb of this fertilizer would cost $102. Amortized over our 4-ton yield, that fertilizer would add $25.50 to the cost of producing each ton of hay. But this amount of fertilizer doesn't even supply all the N and K we need, and we've also not included the costs for labor and machinery.

Fertility replacement is part of the true cost of making hay. If we harvest our hay and we try to save money by not replacing this fertility, we are actually mining the soil. Over time, our fields will "wear out" and our forage yields will decline. Sound familiar?

So, this summer, before we climb on our tractors and crank up the haying equipment, we might want to consider the *true* costs of this activity. We do have some alternatives. If we make hay, we can use that field as a winter-feeding area for that hay, and thus in a crude way recycle some of the fertility. Or we can protect that field by using it *only* for grazing, where the animals just recycle the nutrients and charmingly deposit manure, which ultimately will help improve the soil's organic matter.

And if we need to feed hay, we can buy it — *importing the soil fertility from that other farm* — which we can then spread across *our* fields during the winter-feeding period. And we'll probably buy that hay for less than what it really costs that farmer to make.

First Published: June 2002
Author's Note: These numbers are real. When I give workshops on soil fertility and show these calculations in front of the room, the attendees become very quiet. Whatever numbers we choose for the quality and yield of the hay, the results are inescapable. Although fertilizer and hay prices will change over time, the fertility numbers don't. They certainly make one think.

The Real Cost of Hay

We have never been here before. Diesel costs have doubled. Fertilizer prices have tripled or even quadrupled. And the price of grain, particularly corn — the nutritional replacement we rely on when hay prices are high — has doubled. How can we cope? Should we make hay or buy hay or avoid hay completely or rent more grazing land or get rid of animals or . . .?

This is serious business. We must make choices. For starters, we need to know how much it actually costs us to make our own hay. Then we can compare alternatives and make decisions.

For this article, I'll use the current prices from my local area in southwestern Oregon. You can substitute your own local values. Your mileage may differ, but the basic cost framework is solid.

I'll focus on the two main categories of haymaking costs: (1) the direct costs of harvesting that include: diesel, depreciation, insurance, repairs, and your time, and (2) the costs of replacing the soil fertility removed in the hay.

What about other costs? Like depreciation of the barns and fences, amortization of the pasture renovation, 401(k) retirement plans for the teenagers bucking hay, etc. Okay, I agree; my analysis may not be quite accounting perfect, but I'll leave those refinements to the accountants. Right now, I will just do the main back-of-the-envelope calculations, a little bit of cowboy logic — straightforward costs and common sense. It may not be academically perfect, but it will get us fairly close.

Back to the direct costs of harvesting hay: diesel, depreciation, insurance, repairs, and time. I think that trying to estimate each individual component would be extremely tedious; it would be enough to make our eyes glaze over. But there's an easier answer — find someone else who has already done it, like a custom operator. My guess is that anyone who makes a living by custom haying has already calculated those numbers.

I asked around and discovered that local custom operators charge around $60 per ton of hay to cut, rake, and bale. That gives us hay bales lying in the field. We could subtract 10% for profit, but then we should add it back as the cost of hauling those bales into the barn. That leaves us with the direct costs of harvesting at $60 per ton.

Now we must estimate the costs of replacing the soil nutrients contained in those bales that we hauled off the field. Here's where we have to face the skyrocketing fertilizer costs. We'll focus on the four nutrients removed in the largest amounts: nitrogen, phosphorus, potassium, and sulfur.

The first step is to estimate the amount of these nutrients in the hay. I don't have a convenient forage laboratory in my basement, but over the years I've studied hundreds of local hay reports. To corroborate my experience, I also checked the website of the Dairy One Forage Lab (Ithaca, NY), where I found its useful Feed Composition Library that summarizes thousands of analyses. Interestingly, ahem, my values and the library's values were very close.

Let's say that our hay is a fair-quality grass-clover hay cut early enough to contain 11% crude protein. This hay also contains 0.25% phosphorus, 2.15% potassium, and 0.18% sulfur.

We must translate these numbers into *pounds per ton*. One ton of hay is 2,000 lb. At 90% dry matter (DM), that ton contains 1,800 lb of DM. To calculate the amount of nitrogen in that DM, we must convert the crude protein to nitrogen. The handy-dandy conversion value is 6.25 (this is the same number we use to multiply nitrogen to obtain crude protein, except that now we are going the other way. So we divide by 6.25). Therefore, our 11% crude protein equates to 1.76% nitrogen. Which means that our 1,800 lb hay DM contains 32 lb of nitrogen. For brevity, I'll generally round off amounts to the nearest whole number.

The other three nutrients are straightforward multiplications (you can do the math at home). We calculate that our 1,800 lb DM contains 5 lb phosphorus, 39 lb potassium, and 3 lb sulfur.

Therefore, we must replace 32 lb N, 5 lb P, 39 lb K, and 3 lb S at current astronomical fertilizer prices. I'll use local bulk fertilizer prices from August 2008 (this month). For arithmetic simplicity, let's assume that we'll use commercial fertilizer to replace *all* the nitrogen rather than relying on legumes. We can always adjust later. Anyway, two common fertilizer products that are available locally are "Triple-16" (16-16-16-6) at $848 per ton (= 42.4¢ per pound) and potash (0-0-60-0) at $732/ton (= 36.6¢ per pound).

Now pull out your calculator.

Remember that the *second* number on a fertilizer bag is P_2O_5 not P, so to convert to straight phosphorus, we must multiply the 16 by 44%, which gives us 7. Similarly, the *third* number on a fertilizer bag is K_2O, not K, and, therefore, we must multiply that 16 by 83%, which gives us 13.3; and similarly, the 60 in potash by 83%, which gives us 50. The fourth number is the percentage of sulfur, with thankfully no adjustments needed. That means that in straight nutrient percentages (true N-P-K-S), our Triple-16 should be properly labeled 16-7-13.3-6, and our potash should be labeled 0-0-50-0. Frankly, I don't think the fertilizer companies would approve, but it's arithmetically more appropriate for our purposes. In any case, applying 200 lb of Triple-16 to an acre would supply 32 lb N, 14 lb P, 27 lb K, and 12 lb S. This gives us enough nitrogen and more than enough phosphorus and sulfur, but we are still 12 lb short on K. We can make up this difference by applying 24 lb of potash.

The costs? Well, 200 lb of Triple-16 at 42.4¢ equals $84.80, and 24 lb of potash at 36.6¢ equals $8.78. These numbers give us a fertilizer replacement cost of $93.58.

Now for a total haymaking cost. We add our direct costs ($60) plus our fertilizer replacement costs ($93.58) to get a final total cost of making a ton of hay at $153.58. We'll round it to $154.

But what happens if we can successfully use legumes to supply nitrogen? Well, if we can supply half our nitrogen through the wonder of nitrogen fixation, then we would only need to apply 100 lb of Triple-16, and that would cost $42.40. This amount of Triple-16 would provide enough N, P, and S, but it would only supply 13 lb of K. We would still need to make up the 26-lb deficit of K with 52 lb of potash costing $19.03. Therefore, relying on legumes for half our nitrogen leaves us with a fertilizer replacement cost of $61.43, a nice savings of 34% on the fertilizer bill. Adding this reduced fertilizer cost to the direct costs, our total haymaking costs are now $121.43 per ton. We'll round this to $121.

These calculations show that it costs me $154 to make a ton of fair-quality grass-clover hay, or $121 if I can obtain half the nitrogen from legumes. Either way, these numbers are probably higher than you expected.

I still must make choices. If I can sell this hay at $200/ton, I am happy. If the local market is only $90/ton, with buyers tending to complain loudly if the price rises above $100, then I would be losing money to sell the hay. But if I could buy *someone else's hay* for $100/ton, that's a good deal because I would be purchasing soil nutrients at a discount rate. (I suppose the weed seeds are thrown in for free.)

More choices: if a soil test showed that my field was high in phosphorus and potassium, I could choose to *mine* the soil without replacing those nutrients, at least for a few years; and if I were raising a pure legume stand of alfalfa or red clover, I wouldn't need to buy nitrogen either. If, if, if. But here in southwestern Oregon, where alfalfa is hard to grow, the finances of making hay are very sobering indeed.

Which means that, in practice, we should seriously look for ways of *not* needing hay — like extending the grazing season with stockpiled forages or using specialty forages. We should increase the period when our animals can harvest their forage by actually grazing it. And let someone else worry about the hay.

First Published: August 2008
Author's Note: This was written during a period when grain and fertilizer prices shot through the roof. Ironically, it was also written just before the stock market prices plummeted through the floor. Further evidence that life is a roller-coaster journey and that being as self-sufficient as possible with grazed forages is a prudent business strategy.

Nutrients Lost: Hay Versus Lamb

Here's a question I hear a lot: how much soil fertility does grazing remove from pastures compared to hay? To state this another way: if I graze a flock of sheep on the field and then sell the lambs, do those lambs and ewes remove as many soil nutrients as when I make hay or balage from that field? Hmmm. Lots of things go into that equation, so let's work on some answers.

In fact, let's describe a hypothetical field and work out the exact amounts of nutrients removed by haying and by grazing, step-by-step. Since this is a magazine article and our field is hypothetical, we can include some attractive features. We'll select a reasonably fertile area of 5 acres. Our field is flat, well-drained, and of course, tightly fenced. (We'll use five acres rather than one acre because real fields are usually more than one acre and the stocking rate calculations will seem more realistic.) Under our good management, this field has produced reasonable forage yields in the past. We will assume that the forages are growing nicely by May 1 and that forage growth ends in mid-October. Our forage mixture is a nutritious combination of grass and clover. We'll also assume that our forages grow evenly in a vegetative state throughout the growing season, with no peaks or valleys, and that the plant nutritive value remains consistent and high. Remember, this is a hypothetical field, so we can dream, can't we? Actually, none of these ideal characteristics alter the underlying principles or calculations; they just make the calculations easier and cleaner.

What is our annual forage yield? Let's say that, over the entire growing season, our field produces a respectable 2.5 tons of hay per acre. At 90% dry matter (DM), this equals 2.25 tons DM/acre. Therefore, our 5-acre field yields a total of 11.25 tons DM (= 5 x 2.25), which equals 22,500 lb DM. This is an important number.

Now let's calculate the nutrients lost in hay. We will assume that our hay is hauled to a barn or sales arena, which means that the nutrients are trucked away from the field. For this exercise, we are interested in the primary plant nutrients of nitrogen (N), phosphorus (P), and potassium (K). (Note for experienced graziers: we are interested in the *elements* N, P, and K, and not the fertilizer bag levels of P_2O_5 and K_2O.) Our hay is vegetative forage, so let's also assume that it analyzes at 14% crude protein, 0.25% P, and 2.0% K. These are reasonable values for this type of forage.

The hay calculations are relatively straightforward — we'll just apply those percentages against the total DM yield of 22,500 lb. But there is one quirky exception: the crude protein value must first be converted back to nitrogen because we are interested in the nitrogen as a plant nutrient. The standard conversion factor is 6.25. You may recall that crude protein is actually a calculated number: we first test for nitrogen and then multiply that value by 6.25 to get crude protein. For the purposes of this article, we must go back the other way. Therefore, 14% crude protein in the hay equals 2.24% N (= 14 ÷ 6.25). So, by applying the percentages of 2.24% N, 0.25% P, and 2.0% K against 22,500 lb yield, the soil nutrients removed in the hay from these 5 acres are: 504 lb N, 56 lb P, and 450 lb K.

Now for the comparison. We must calculate the amount of nutrients that leave the field when we graze sheep. Unfortunately, this is *not* a straightforward calculation, so bear with me. First, we need to describe the flock management — which will tell us how many sheep leave the field at the end of the season and their weights. Then we must identify the percentages of nutrients in those animals. But these calculations include an important proviso: we are only interested in the *net loss* of nutrients from the field, not the entire weight of animals that walk off the field.

Net loss? Net loss means the amount of soil nutrients contained in the *additional* weight that animals gain while they are in the field — above the amount that entered the field when we first opened the gate in the spring. To be specific, grazing sheep that only maintain their weight through the summer represent *zero* net loss of nutrients from the field. During the summer, soil nutrients simply recycle through those sheep while they graze, going into one end as grass and coming out the other end as pellets. For example, if I graze 20 dry ewes in a field for four months, and every ewe weighed 160 lb when it entered the field and still weighed 160 lb when it left the field four months later, the net nutrient loss from that field is zero. But, you ask, what about gut fill? Well, sure, animals leave the field with a full rumen, but they also enter the field with a full rumen. Full equals full, so we consider that amount a wash.

Back to our calculations. First, we'll calculate the number of sheep that can graze that field for the season and how much they will gain. Then, as we did with the hay, we'll identify the percentages of nutrients in the animals and apply those percentages to the additional weight gain. Still with me? Here goes . . .

Our 5-acre field produces 22,500 lb DM for the growing season. Let's assume that our ewes each weigh 160 lb. They drop a 200% lamb crop in April, lose no lambs at lambing, and enter the field on May 1 each raising two 20-lb lambs. How many of these ewes can we graze for the season? Normally we would assume a DM intake of 3% body weight for the ewes, but because these ewes are rearing twin lambs that are growing, and we don't want to use complex simultaneous equations or daily iterations of feed intake in our calculations, let's include an extra intake cushion to account for the feed consumed by the lambs. We'll simply increase the DM intake of the ewes to 6% body weight, which means that a 160-lb ewe would eat 9.6 lb DM per day. Our grazing period is May 1 until Oct. 7, which is 160 days. (160 days is a very convenient number, as you'll see. Remember, with our theoretical field, we can create all sorts of adjustments to make our calculations easier.)

So, 22,500 lb of DM at 9.6 lb per day gives us 2,343.8 ewe-days. Dividing this by 160 days gives us 14.6 ewes for the entire period. Let's round this off to 15 ewes.

Fifteen ewes with a 200% lamb crop means 30 lambs. Let's say that no lambs die, coyotes never find them, the lambs have no worms, and on October 7, all the lambs weigh exactly 100 lb. (I'm beginning to like our theoretical field.) When the flock leaves the field on Oct. 7, the ewes all still weigh 160 lb, so *their* net nutrient loss to the field is zero. The lambs have each gained 80 lb ($= 100 - 20$), representing a respectable daily gain of 0.5 lb ($= 80 \div 160$). Therefore, the total net live weight gain of the lambs is 2,400 lb ($= 80 \ x \ 30$). *This* is the additional weight gain of the entire flock in that field during the grazing season.

Now the big step: we need to calculate the *net loss* due to these lambs. How much soil fertility is in that additional weight gain? Well, body composition numbers are not exactly found on feed tags, so I searched the scientific literature, including some older physiology textbooks like the legendary *Duke's Physiology of Domestic Animals* (1977) as well as many recent research articles. I finally came up with some solid numbers: on a live-weight basis — i.e., as they walk across the scale — 100-lb lambs contain approximately 16% crude protein and 5% ash. Using the same conversion factor of 6.25 to convert crude protein back to nitrogen, their nitrogen content is 2.56% ($= 16 \div 6.25$). The ash is nearly all bone, and bone contains 27% calcium and 13% phosphorus. For the purposes of soil fertility, we're really interested in the phosphorus. Therefore, 13% of the 5% ash equals 0.65%. The potassium value

I found in a 1968 book on body composition. No calculations here, just a lookup number. The potassium content of lambs at that weight is 0.17%.

Now we have our three percentages of soil nutrients: 2.56% N, 0.65% P, and 0.17% K. When we apply these percentages against the 2,400 lb of additional body gain, we get the following *net nutrient loss* from grazing 15 ewes and their 30 lambs for the season: 61 lb N, 16 lb P, and only 4 lb K. These are the nutrients removed from the field in the sheep.

There we have it. In our example, grazing sheep and selling the lambs removes *88% less nitrogen, 71% less phosphorus, and 99% less potassium* compared to making hay from the same field.

It's interesting that grazing removes so little potassium. Potassium is usually the nutrient most depleted in a long-term hay field, primarily because it constitutes a significant percentage in forage and many tons of hay are hauled off year after year. But in animals, although potassium is critically important metabolically, the actual amount in the body is relatively small when compared to phosphorus which is a major component of bone.

We made lots of assumptions for our theoretical field, so these numbers are hardly exact. The hay numbers are pretty good, but the sheep numbers? Well, even if we had overestimated feed intake and could increase the flock size by 50%, or had a lambing percentage better than 200%, or allowed the ewes to gain body condition through the season (and there are other possible variations as well) — all these changes would have indeed increased the net loss of nutrients through grazing. *But not by much.* The difference between removing nutrients in hay is so much greater than by grazing that these refinements really don't change the relative patterns of the numbers.

Finally, we can also express the nutrient losses on a "per acre basis" by simply dividing by 5. On a per acre basis, hay removed 101 lb N, 11 lb P, and 90 lb K. Grazing removed 12 lb N, 3 lb P, and 1lb K (that's *one* pound of K). And when we put real costs on these numbers — namely, the fertilizer needed to replace lost nutrients — the financial differences are stunning. So, from a no-nonsense business perspective, how much is it worth to find ways of increasing the grazing and reducing the need to make hay? *That* may be something to ruminate on.

First Published: August 2013

Author's Note: I wrote this article in response to a simple, direct question from a rancher. These numbers and calculations are important. In essence, they can determine the long-term sustainability and profitability of a ruminant livestock operation. Which underscores the importance of the big decisions.

Sticker Shock

If you get a chance this week, drive over to your local feed and seed store and price some fertilizer. Whoa! Sticker shock! After a quick double take, you might begin to wonder if you are trying to buy fertilizer or a Lexus.

In western Oregon last autumn, we all thought that fertilizer prices were already sky high: urea (46-0-0-0) was at $446/ton; sixteen-twenty (16-20-0-14) was at $344/ton; and 11-52-0-0 was at $490/ton. But that was last October, and things have changed since then. Last week, our local prices for those same fertilizers climbed to $624, $460, and a whopping $722 — increases of 40%, 34%, and 47%, respectively. In just four months! To add insult to injury, I recently found a 2004 price list where those same fertilizers were priced at $294, $207, and $276, respectively.

Aside from wringing our hands and making unnerving numerical comparisons, what can we do about this situation? I know, I know — oil prices are above $90/barrel, the value of the U.S. dollar is plummeting, and the ethanol boom is driving corn prices into the stratosphere. Which means that we shouldn't hold our collective breaths in the hope that fertilizer prices will drop anytime soon. To repeat, what are some options?

Option #1: Hunker down and wait. We could simply refuse to buy any more fertilizer. Period. Close our wallets, tighten our belts, and buy nothing. In most cases, however, this wouldn't be a very good option, at least not by itself. The reason? Without soil fertility, plants don't grow. Our animals will still need feed, and growing feed is usually cheaper than buying it. Skimping on feed can cause all sorts of short-term and long-term livestock problems. Oh yes, our fields might "get by" for a year or two, with some fields showing reduced yields and others showing *very* reduced yields, but I think that we have a better chance of making a profit if we approach this problem in a more proactive way.

Option #2: The numerical approach. We can figure out how much forage we need and then compare that to our potential production. It's useful to know that in a 12-month period, a 150-lb ewe will consume approximately 1,500 lb of forage, and a 1,100-lb beef cow will consume approximately 9,000 lb (4.5 tons) of forage. (All numbers are on a dry matter (DM) basis. For the purposes of this article, we'll ignore grain, minerals, and water.) Therefore, a flock of 250 ewes would need approximately 375,000 lb of forage (187.5 tons), and a herd of 40 beef cows would need 360,000 lb of forage (180 tons). These numbers represent *all* the forage for the year — grazed pastures, hay, winter silage, the works. Now we compare these amounts to our forage production. If we have 80 acres that typically yield 2.5 tons of forage/acre, our farm produces 200 tons of forage. If we save money by not applying fertilizer and thus allowing soil fertility to decline, our average yield may drop to, say, 2.1 tons/acre, resulting in only 168 tons of total production. If the average yield fell to 1.8 tons per acre, we would have only 144 tons of forage. Now we have some numbers to guide our decisions.

Option #3: Reduce the number of animals. Now that we have a handle on how much forage we need or can get away with, this year may be a great opportunity to cull the bottom percentage of the flock or herd. We all know the animals that should be sold. We can finally get rid of those "favorite" animals that really haven't produced profitably in 30 years but are still around eating feed and looking good (they look good because they haven't produced). Fewer animals means less feed. This is good.

Option #4: Use someone else's fields for grazing or hay. Substitute forage from our place with forage from a different place. This relieves some pressure on our fields. But rentals may not be easy to find. Especially in corn country, where in these days of the ethanol boom, the nearest available rental acreage may be in Alaska.

Option #5: Identify the annual forage holes and try to fill them. This is an important concept, even during good times. We should ask ourselves a crucial question: when do our fields produce feed? Actually, we're really interested in the inverse: when *don't* those fields produce feed? Specifically, where are the feed holes in the yearly calendar? The answer, of course, depends on the region and on the forage skills of the producer. For most of the country, one major hole is obviously during the frozen winter months when nothing grows. Another hole usually occurs during midsummer when many perennial forages suffer a summer slump. In western Oregon, our classic holes are during midwinter when our grass, while growing, slows down, and then during the bone-dry summer season, unless we have irrigation. If we can use our expensive fertilizer to plug those holes with strategic forage growth and nutritious grazing, we will reduce our need for hay, and thus reduce our expenses, despite higher fertilizer costs. Which is a very good thing.

Let's think outside the box for a moment. We can try winter stockpiling: reserve the un-grazed autumn growth of tall fescue to create standing forage into the winter. Or plant turnips, rape, or kale for post-frost grazing. Or, in the Pacific Northwest, we can use summer stockpiling, which is the same stockpiling principle at a different time of year, by spring-planting forage brassicas or Italian ryegrass. Or we can overcome the summer slump by planting summer-active forages like chicory, plantain, crabgrass, gala grazing brome, clovers, or even alfalfa. Or planting a warm-season annual grass like sorghum-sudangrass or teff or some of the millets. And in regions with mild winters, we can fall-plant fields with winter-active forages like annual ryegrass or winter wheat or even plantain. These are just a few options, some rather creative, but this might be a good year to think about them.

Option #6: Take soil tests from every field. This is critical. Knowing each field's fertility allows us to make rational economic decisions about where to use fertilizer, or not use it, and what type of fertilizer is best. For example, we shouldn't apply phosphorus onto fields that are already high in phosphorus. Same for potassium (potash). For some fields with low pH, the best use of our funds might be to increase the soil pH with limestone and thus increase nutrient availability to the plant roots, in effect replacing expensive fertilizer with cheaper limestone. And in the fields with the highest yield potential, we should also test for micronutrients like boron and molybdenum. Sometimes adding those micronutrients to a fertilizer mix will make a huge difference in yield response.

Option #7: Treat each field differently. Practice triage. We shouldn't spread our expensive resources evenly across all the fields just because we've always done it that way. We can decide which fields have the potential of giving the biggest bang for our fertilizer bucks, and then concentrate our fertilizer applications on those fields. Based on their soil tests, of course.

Option #8: What about mining? For fields that are fortunate enough to contain very high levels of phosphorus and potassium, maybe we can mine those soils for a couple of years, at least until fertilizer prices go back down. Take our cuttings of hay without replenishing these nutrients. We'll still need to add sulfur, of course, and also nitrogen if these fields don't contain legumes. But in some situations, this option may be a good one.

Option #9: Extract nitrogen from the air. We should become enthusiastic about our local legumes and maybe even some exotic legumes. If managed properly, legumes will "fix" nitrogen from the atmosphere. Add legumes to existing pastures. (Remember to add inoculant to the seed first.) Drill white clover or lespedeza into grass pastures and then manage those fields to maximize legume growth. In some situations this may be challenging, but the high cost of nitrogen fertilizer is a compelling motivation. Or plant some short-term fields with red clover — an aggressive, high-yielding hay and grazing crop that lasts 2–3 years and fixes lots of nitrogen. Or include peas or vetch or other annual legumes in seed mixtures to take advantage of their nitrogen-fixing nodules. But we should also learn something about bloat, just in case everything doesn't go perfectly every time we put animals onto those fields. It's good to recall, however, that legumes represent a technique that was developed long before we had the luxury of cheap commercial nitrogen fertilizer.

Let's look at the good side: these high fertilizer prices *do* focus our thinking. And a fertile mind can dream up lots of options.

First Published: March 2008

Author's Note: I wrote this article in the spring of 2008 when international market conditions and variable exchange rates made for an exciting time in the fertilizer industry. Prices have indeed moderated and steadied since then, and farmers and ranchers are breathing easier, but these fertilizer options are still viable. Especially for long-term business decisions about raising livestock in forage-based operations.

Efficient Nitrogen

Recently, I went to my local farm store and priced urea fertilizer at $466/ton. Two years ago, urea was selling at $700 because worldwide demand, oil speculation, and international protectionism had driven the price up 50%. I've been thinking: what if this happens again? Actually, the proper question is *when*, not *if*, because all those factors are still in place. They are just being masked by the current recession, and they will emerge again once the world economies recover.

But what about us? We need nitrogen to raise forage. Without nitrogen, we're in trouble. So here, at the beginning of another growing season, I'd like to list some ideas about using nitrogen in our fields, things to help us use it efficiently, things to think about as we raise and harvest our forages. I'll list these ideas as bullet points because, well, bullet points are easy to read.

- Let's begin with a field of new-mown hay. Smells good — like freshly mown hay. Let's say that our first cutting is 2.5 tons (all values are on a per acre basis), and that we have just hauled this hay down the road for sale to a neighbor. How much nitrogen just left our field? Well, 2.5 tons of hay equals 5,000 lb. Assuming 10% moisture (90% dry matter), we calculate that 4,500 lb of dry matter was hauled off the field. If the hay contains 12.5% protein, using the standard conversion factor of 6.25 to convert from protein to nitrogen, we calculate that our hay contains 2.0% nitrogen ($12.5 \div 6.25$). Therefore, 2% of 4,500 lb means that 90 lb of nitrogen left our field. Just to replace that nitrogen (urea contains 46% nitrogen), pound for pound, without considering any losses or inefficiencies, we would need to apply 196 lb of urea, and that would cost $45.67 at today's prices and $68.60 at the prices of two years ago.

119

- If our field produces two additional cuttings of hay this year, its total annual yield may reach, say, 5 tons. If I sell all that hay to someone else, I've moved 180 lb of nitrogen off the field, which must be replaced by 391 lb of urea. At today's prices, that would cost $91.10 and 50% more if prices return to previous higher levels. (For a homework assignment, you can do the math.)

- Moving hay off a field incurs nitrogen replacement costs. Some folks, however, use their fields as hay-feeding areas. Feeding hay on pasture can indeed add nutrients back to the pasture, including nitrogen. But if the hay comes from a different field or someone else's farm, it can also add weed seeds. Kind of the yin and yang of using hay as a source of soil nutrients.

- The amount of nitrogen in a pasture is not permanent; nitrogen moves out of the system naturally. Nitrogen losses occur in a couple of flavors. The first is *leaching*. Soil nitrogen is converted to soluble compounds like nitrates that dissolve in the soil moisture. When this moisture becomes too much to cling to the soil particles, like from excessive irrigation or high amounts of rainfall, this moisture moves downward in the soil and carries the nitrogen with it. Once the nitrogen leaches below root depth, it's lost to the plants.

- Plants that have taproots like alfalfa, birdsfoot trefoil, chicory, plantain, and red clover can still capture that nitrogen, at least for a while, but eventually some nitrogen leaches below those taproots.

- Another way that nitrogen leaves the system is into the atmosphere, either by *volatilization* or *denitrification*. In the volatilization process, soil nitrogen is converted into ammonia, a gas. Maybe it's not enough ammonia to make a pasture smell like a sink cleanser, but because volatilization happens 24/7, molecule by molecule, the amount lost over an acre can still add up to quite a bit. The second process, denitrification, occurs more commonly in wet or saturated soils that are low in oxygen. Microbes use nitrates as a source of oxygen. They strip the oxygen from the molecule, leaving only nitrogen gas that then escapes into the air.

- Haying is not grazing. Haying *removes* nutrients from a field; grazing does not, at least not in significant amounts. Yes, some nutrients are contained in the body mass *gained* while on pasture, but that amount is minuscule compared to the *pounds* of nitrogen and other nutrients contained in *tons* of hay. Lactating dairy cows remove more nutrients than growing stock, but again, this loss is still tiny compared to the losses in hay or silage.

- Grazing, even intensive grazing, *does not add nutrients* to the soil. Grazing essentially recycles nutrients through the animal from the front end to the back end, with a small amount taken out in the middle to support animal growth or lactation. It's true that when animals enter a field, their digestive tracts contain nutrients that are ultimately deposited onto that field. But correspondingly, when those animals leave the field, their digestive tracts also contain nutrients. Kind of a wash, unless animals routinely leave the field starving, which is definitely *not* a recommended management practice.

- Manure from grazing animals is just a form of recycling; it doesn't add nutrients to the field. Of course, compared to commercial fertilizers, manure is a package of organic nutrients in a slow-release form. Manure also helps increase the soil organic matter and improve soil tilth, which are good things. So, while grazing doesn't necessarily add nutrients to a field, it can improve the form and composition of the soil environment.

- Manure distribution can be managed. A low *stocking density* (pounds of animal per acre) allows lots of space between manure pats. High stocking densities promote a uniform grazing pattern and also an even distribution of manure. The higher the stocking density, the better the manure distribution.

- Trees are manure magnets. Animals like to loaf around trees and lie down in the shade. But have you ever watched cattle or sheep get up after lying down? What happens when they first stand up? So, year after year, season after season, animals deposit urine and manure around the trees. This adds a lot of nutrients in the shaded areas, where the ground is compacted and not much forage grows. But more importantly, the animals have systematically moved soil nutrients from the fertile center of a field to areas under the trees.

- Cool, shady areas near ponds and creeks are also pleasant loafing areas. As animals gather there and cheerfully deposit their manure and urine, not only do they remove nutrients from the other areas of the field, but they also put those nutrients near water where they can be flushed downstream — a total loss of nitrogen to the field. Allowing animals near creeks and ponds is a good way of losing control of soil fertility.

- Grazing techniques make a difference. Leaving a high *residual* (forage mass) at the end of a grazing session immensely improves forage regrowth and plant health. High residuals also keep the topsoil cooler and reduce nitrogen losses from volatilization.

- Have you ever looked at a field and seen tufts of dark green forage amid a sea of light green grass? Those tufts are taller forage growing on urine or manure patches. A urine patch can contain the equivalent of 200–1,000 lb N/acre in that tiny area. If you see deep-green patches of forage, you are seeing a symptom that the field needs nitrogen.

- Legumes are good, at least the species that animals eat. (The legume family also includes scotch broom, gorse, and toxic lupins, so I don't want to refer to legumes with an unqualified "good.") The *Rhizobium* bacteria in legume root nodules capture ("fix") atmospheric nitrogen and create a net *increase* of nitrogen in a field. University plot trials show that some legumes can fix more than 150 lb N/acre annually, but that is under small, carefully run plot trials with monoculture plantings. Pastures are more complex ecosystems that rarely contain 100% legumes. Under practical conditions for mixed pastures, we can hope that the legumes will add 80–100 lb N/acre with good management.

- Legumes only fix nitrogen if they have functioning root nodules. Periodically check legume roots and look for lots of nodules. Without nodules, legume plants may still flourish if there is enough nitrogen in the soil. But without nodules, legumes are just another group of plants that require soil nitrogen; they are not adding nitrogen to the system, even though we may assume so.

- Of course, we can always add nitrogen to the system as commercial fertilizer. But if the price of commercial nitrogen rises 50%, we will come back to the original point in my opening paragraphs — that on-farm nitrogen efficiency is critical because with commercial fertilizers, it's not *if* those nitrogen prices will rise, but *when*.

First Published: May 2010

Author's Note: Fertilizer prices go up and down — it's a fact of nature (and markets and currencies and also sunspots and maybe the win-loss record of your favorite baseball team). We usually have no control over fertilizer prices. But we can control fertility losses and nitrogen efficiencies. That way, we can "fix" some issues with nitrogen.

Fertilizing by the Numbers

When I heard about a new rule for applying fertilizer on winter pastures in the Pacific Northwest, my first thought was that someone was pulling my leg. What do you mean — just add up the daily temperatures? Are you also trying to sell me the Brooklyn Bridge?" But the joke was on me. *This* rule works.

It's called *T-Sum 200*— a guideline for applying nitrogen fertilizer to grass pastures in preparation for early spring growth. The rule is this: starting on January 1, calculate the average of the maximum and minimum air temperatures, in Celsius (°C). Do this each day and keep a running total and when that total reaches 200, apply your fertilizer. This will maximize grass growth for the next 60 days.

For example, if New Year's Day is a balmy 48° F and then at night drops to 32° F, the average temperature is 40° F, which equals 4° C. If January 2 has maximum and minimum temperatures of 36° F and 32° F, respectively, the average is only 34° F (= 1° C). Therefore, our running total on January 2 is 5 (= 4 + 1). The interior valleys of southwestern Oregon generally reach 200 during the first two weeks of February. Last year, my place reached 200 on January 31. Warmer years will be slightly earlier; colder years will be later.

The value of 200 is not sorcery; it's the peak of a fertilizer response curve. Research has shown that nitrogen applied at that time, for these types of pastures, will cause more grass growth than if applied three weeks earlier or later.

Like any rule, this one has a couple of quirks:

(1) Any temperature below freezing is assigned the value of zero (= 0° C. This is because temperatures *below* 0° C have the same zero effect on grass growth as 0° C).

(2) This rule only applies to nitrogen fertilizer, not phosphorus or potassium.

(3) This rule was originally calibrated on pastures of perennial ryegrass (*Lolium perenne*), but it works for other forages that start growing early and can respond to higher fertility, like orchardgrass, annual ryegrass, and tall fescue.

A disclaimer: this rule works in places like western Oregon, England, and New Zealand — regions with cool, wet winters perfect for perennial ryegrass. It is not designed for, say, Minnesota or Maine, where winter temperatures are much cooler than cool. Not to mention the frozen ground. Perhaps someone, somewhere, will work out T-Sums for other regions. Meanwhile, this is a good start . . .

The T-Sum 200 rule really just monitors the cumulative amount of heat units available to grass plants. You may ask: why not simply use a soil probe and measure the soil temperature directly? We've tried that; it doesn't work. Try using a soil probe across a pasture yourself and you'll see enormous variation, with numbers ranging plus or minus 10 degrees or more. Many factors influence soil readings besides air temperature: the amount of moisture and grass cover at each spot, the type of soil, the proximity of shade trees, the northerly or southerly direction a slope faces, etc. Although plant roots are not directly exposed to air temperature like they are to soil temperature, measuring air temperature gives a better average — and that is really what we want. We're trying to see the entire forest, not just the trees. Air temperature smooths out all the soil variation and gives us a guideline for applying fertilizer to an *entire* field, not just to a single spot.

But why perennial ryegrass? Because the rule was developed in regions where perennial ryegrass is the main late winter/early spring forage for high-producing pastures. Perennial ryegrass comes up quickly during the fall, grows slowly during the winter, and then explodes in growth in the spring. Traditionally, ranchers here apply fertilizer in March or early April to boost growth for grazing and hay. This schedule is fine for late spring growth, but it does nothing for earlier growth. Some improved ryegrass varieties will start growing quickly by late winter, especially when they have enough heat units and also enough groceries (soil nutrients). The T-Sum 200 rule keeps track of the heat units, and the timely application of nitrogen fertilizer provides the groceries.

Many grass pastures also contain clovers, but this nitrogen application won't affect them unless the extra growth is not consumed. Remember, we are talking about *very* early in the season. Soil temperatures will be high enough to support grass growth but are still too low for clover. Anyway, young grass blades are already very high in nutritional value, so clover is not nutritionally important at that time. When the clovers begin to wake up in late March or so, that first growth of grass — your first crop — will have already been eaten, thus allowing sunlight to reach the young clovers.

T-Sum 200 may be specific for a region, but its premise is universal and is more fundamental than simply choosing a date for nitrogen fertilization. T-Sum 200 supports a system for producing feed to match your animals' needs. Fertilizer is cheaper than hay. The T-Sum 200 Rule helps maximize forage production when other sources of feed (hay and silage) are expensive or scarce (unfertilized grass). It's during this early spring period when lactating ewes may reach peak lactation and their requirements for feed are highest, or when cows enter their third trimester of pregnancy.

But the inverse of this principle is equally true: T-Sum 200 also tells you when *not* to add fertilizer. Namely, if you don't need the extra feed, then don't add fertilizer to produce it. A poorly timed fertilizer application doesn't just waste money; it can also hurt a pasture. If you produce lots of grass in the late winter and then *do not* use it, that tall grass will still be there as competition when the clovers begin to grow in mid-spring. Sunlight won't reach those young clovers. Those clover plants will be under stress, and many will die. Therefore, by using nitrogen in an untimely fashion, you could actually *reduce* the overall value of the pasture by eliminating the clovers.

Speaking of rules, T-Sum 200 is not the only formula of interest. In a musty agricultural report from the early 1930s, on the bottom of the last page, in small print, I found a formula for happiness. It was really quite simple: just multiply the number of animals on your ranch by the square root of your birthday, expressed in kilometers. Gosh . . . and here I sit without any metric tools.

First Published: January 1997

Author's Note: T-Sum 200 is a powerful tool. Time and again in this area, we've seen good responses to early nitrogen fertilizer applied at this time. Of course, there are the usual caveats about wet ground, runoff, etc., but those are practical cautions that would apply to any fieldwork during the winter. But here's an interesting and unexpected twist: we've noticed that the T-Sum 200 date seems to coincide with the date that the local daffodils begin to flower. Isn't that interesting?

Like a Dance for Nitrogen

Let me take you on a wild ride. Every hour during the growing season, a most extraordinary phenomenon occurs in our fields: nitrogen fixation. Modest legume plants with their tiny root nodules quietly extract nitrogen gas from the air and convert this nitrogen into compounds that plants use to create proteins. Although we take this biological process for granted, it's such an essential process that human society might not exist without it. Really, there's nothing modest about it at all.

This story has two amazing parts. The first part is the general process of how plants "fix" nitrogen — which means capturing nitrogen from the atmosphere. The second part of the story is how certain bacteria infect the roots of those plants and create a highly specialized nitrogen-fixing factory in those roots.

Pulling nitrogen from the air is no trivial matter. Although nitrogen comprises 78% of our atmosphere, this nitrogen occurs as a stable N_2 molecule. The two nitrogen atoms are bound together with a *very* strong triple bond. So strong that if we want to break this bond ourselves, we must use the industrial *Haber Process*, a heavy-duty manufacturing procedure involving very high temperatures, high pressures, and metal catalysts. In fact, each year we rely on the Haber Process to produce the more than 100 million *tons* of synthetic nitrogen fertilizer that is used on farms.

In contrast, legume plants quietly fix nitrogen in their roots. No loud industrial clanging, no risk of high-pressure explosions or toxic fumes. Instead, in the tiny dark spaces of the soil, specialized gram-negative rod bacteria called *rhizobia* (there are a few related genera) infect the plant roots during early root

127

development. These bacteria combine with plant tissue to form a highly organized root mass called a *nodule*. The bacteria contain an enzyme known as *nitrogenase*, which is the actual molecular complex that uses plant energy — originally captured in the leaves during photosynthesis — to accomplish its tasks. The nitrogenase enzyme splits the N_2 triple bond and adds hydrogen atoms to convert the free N to ammonia (NH_3). The ammonia is then quickly converted to other biologically useful nitrogen compounds like amino acids and proteins. As we all learned in school, this is a classic *symbiotic* arrangement, where two independent species form a partnership in which both gain. The bacteria gain nutrients from the plant and a secure place to flourish and reproduce, while the host legume plant gains nitrogen in a useful form, giving the plant a competitive edge in a harsh world where nitrogen is often in short supply.

The nitrogenase enzyme, however, deserves closer inspection. This is the guts of the fixation machinery. Nitrogenase consists of two large metalloproteins (proteins that contain metal atoms): *dinitrogenase reductase* which contains iron, and *dinitrogenase* which contains iron and molybdenum. These metalloproteins are two of the most complex metal-protein arrangements known, and we can see why: they intimately work in tandem to fix nitrogen. These two molecules routinely do something that the industrial Haber Process only achieves with high pressures and high temperatures.

But here's a practical tip: notice that nitrogenase contains *molybdenum*. That means that legumes require molybdenum to capture nitrogen. Therefore, if they are expected to add nitrogen to the soil, fields of clover or alfalfa must have more molybdenum than fields of grass. But molybdenum is a micronutrient, so only a little is needed — perhaps only a few grams per acre. The application rate depends on specific soil characteristics. The lesson here is to be aware of the need, and then check with your local agronomist.

One peculiar characteristic of the nitrogenase enzyme is that it is irreversibly inactivated by oxygen. This poses an interesting metabolic conundrum. The plant's root cells and the *Rhizobium* bacteria all require oxygen to survive, yet oxygen will also shut down the nitrogen-fixing molecules that are their reason for existing. What's a fellow to do? Well, legumes have evolved an elegant solution: *leghemoglobin*. This molecule is designed much like the hemoglobin in our own blood, and it does much the same thing — holds oxygen and transports it. The root nodule cells synthesize leghemoglobin. When atmospheric oxygen permeates through the nodule's outside shell, the leghemoglobin captures these oxygen atoms, holds them, and keeps them away from the nitrogenase enzyme. But at the same time, it transports enough oxygen to root cells and bacteria to allow them to respire properly.

And like our own hemoglobin, leghemoglobin is red when it's loaded with oxygen. If you take a healthy nodule and carefully split it open (with a scalpel or fine tweezers), you can actually see a distinct pinkish color. That's the leghemoglobin. Which brings us to a time-honored maxim. I'm sure you've heard the old phrase, "You can't get blood from a turnip." Well, yes, that's true, but if you look closely at a legume root . . .

Now for the rest of the story — nodulation — the formation of root nodules. If anything, this is even more remarkable than the chemistry of nitrogen fixation.

The nodulation story starts with a young legume seedling just beginning to send out roots. These roots release *flavonoid* compounds into the surrounding soil. If the right species of Rhizobium is present and detects these flavonoids, the bacterial *nod* gene (probably for nodulation, get it?) goes into action and produces a species-specific *Nod factor* that then binds to surface receptors on the root epidermis cell. Then things really begin to happen.

The root epidermis cell begins to bulge outward, forming a microscopic *root hair* that extends outward and pushes into the soil. Calcium ions stream from the interior of the epidermis cell to the tip of the lengthening root hair. The rhizobia bacterium cell then attaches itself tightly to the side of the root hair. As the root hair continues to grow, something very peculiar happens: the bacterial Nod factor causes the root hair to change its direction of growth. Instead of continuing to grow outward, the tip of the root hair does a 180-degree turn and grows back on itself, forming a tight clamp that looks a little like a bobby pin — trapping the bacterium between the two parts of this clamp. Now sandwiched between two root hair cell walls, the bacterium reproduces and grows into a tiny microcolony. This bacterial colony then projects a living microtubule — called an *infection thread* — down through the center of the root hair. This infection thread extends downward, working its way into deeper layers of cells. Parts of the infection thread fuse with the cell walls of some root cells. Bacteria populate the infection thread and then move into the nodule cells.

This is the beginning of a *proto-nodule* — an intermingled blend of bacterial and legume material. The rhizobia then differentiate into *bacteroids* that lie *inside* the nodule cells, surrounded by plant cell cytoplasm. These bacteroids synthesize nitrogenase, and the plant synthesizes leghemoglobin and other molecules and also provides nutrients to the bacteroids. The proto-nodule grows larger and differentiates into a well-organized protuberance on the root. We now have liftoff — a fully functioning nodule.

Communication . . . recognition . . . attachment . . . growth . . . involvement . . . fusion . . . mutual benefit . . . nitrogen — a system for capturing atmospheric nitrogen that evolved piece-by-piece over millions of years. It's the epitome of species cooperation. The legume and the rhizobia engage in an intricate duet, move for move, increasing in complexity, almost like a dance.

On our farms, however, we hardly give it a thought. During the growing season, we go to the seed store, buy some legume seeds and inoculant, mix them together, dump the seed into our seeder, plant it, and hope for the best. Two or three months later, we may walk through the field, dig up a few plants, and look for nodules by carefully teasing the soil away from the roots. If we find nodules, we are happy. If we don't, we scratch our heads.

But if we recognize the marvelous complexity of legume nodules and the intricacies of nitrogen fixation, we might strive to do a better job. The next time we buy legume inoculant, we'll make sure that it is fresh — not more than six months on the shelves at room temperature or one year in the refrigerator. We'll also check the expiration date. And, of course, we'll be extra careful to choose the right inoculant to match our legume species. We really want that dance to go well.

First Published: April 2009

Author's Note: If there is such a thing as a miracle in evolution, this is it. This astonishing series of events and communication actions result in functional root nodules, the fixation of atmospheric nitrogen, and incorporation of that nitrogen into plant and bacterial proteins. Clover plants and alfalfa may not look as impressive as the redwood trees, but if we think carefully about what goes on in those roots, we are in awe.

Fixing Things with Nitrogen

A local rancher recently asked me an intriguing question: did I know anything about some commercial bacterial products that are supposed to replace nitrogen fertilizer? No, I was not familiar with them, but I said that I would find out. And so I began a search path that started easy enough with our familiar legume species and the bacteria in their roots, but it soon led into some dark corners of microbiology and then into a wild array of strange topics: blue-green algae blooms, tropical casuarina trees, oxygen-starved mudflats, ethanol production, the evolution of chloroplasts, and even a soft-skin mollusk that eats wooden ships. The topic: diazotrophs. New to you also? Let's explore . . .

We are all familiar with the bacteria that inhabit the roots of legumes like the clovers and alfalfa — namely, the *Rhizobium* bacteria that *fix nitrogen* and form tiny nodules on the roots. Let's hold onto this thought for a minute.

While rhizobia are well-known and important, they are just a small subgroup of a much larger category of bacteria called *diazotrophs*. Simply put, diazotrophs are bacteria that can *fix nitrogen*. That is, they capture atmospheric nitrogen and convert it into nitrogenous compounds like amino acids and proteins that they use for their own cellular metabolism. Diazotrophs are actually an extensive group of bacterial families and species. Some of these bacteria only live with other organisms, often in a symbiotic arrangement like the rhizobia and legume plants. Some species are free-living bacteria that survive quite nicely on their own.

In the big picture, however, diazotrophs are incredibly important. Why? Because life is built on proteins, and proteins are composed of amino acids that all contain nitrogen. But in many environments in nature, nitrogen is very

131

scarce. Enter the diazotrophs. Wherever these bacteria live, their nitrogen-fixing activities effectively bring more nitrogen into that system — in the roots of clover plants, in association with coral reefs, in coastal mudflats, or even in the open ocean. In fact, nearly everywhere there is life.

Pulling nitrogen from the air is not easy. Since we (humans) use a lot of nitrogen in fertilizers and other compounds, we convert atmospheric nitrogen into useful products with the Haber Process — a heavy-duty industrial procedure involving high temperatures and high pressures. But diazotrophs quietly accomplish the same thing inside their cells with the enzyme *nitrogenase*. This *enzyme complex*, which is composed of many molecular subunits, is built around the atoms of iron and molybdenum. (This is the main reason we include extra molybdenum in fertilizers designed for legumes.) The nitrogenase enzyme is so critical that its genetic code has remained remarkably stable across thousands of species of bacteria and millions of years of evolution.

One interesting quirk of the nitrogenase enzyme is that it is poisoned by oxygen. Therefore, the diazotrophs have all developed clever strategies to protect this enzyme from free-ranging oxygen atoms. Some colonizing diazotrophs have specialized thick-walled cells that prevent oxygen entry. Some diazotrophs live in places that are oxygen-free (*anaerobic*). Some diazotrophs use specialized transport molecules similar to hemoglobin to carry oxygen to the rest of the cell. That's why we see the reddish color in clover nodules — rhizobia contain *leghemoglobin*, an oxygen-transport compound that turns red when loaded with oxygen. When you have the chance, dig up a legume root and carefully split open some of the nodules. If the nodules are healthy and functioning, you will see red.

So what types of diazotrophs exist, and where do they live? Start with our familiar *Rhizobium* that colonize all the species of legumes — clovers, alfalfa, soybeans, peanuts, peas, vetches, etc. And also other legume plants like gorse, kudzu, and acacia trees. But many non-legume plants can also fix nitrogen: alders, casuarina trees (Australian pines), California lilacs, bayberry, mountain mahogany, and dozens of shrubs, weeds, and small trees. These plants are inhabited by diazotrophs of the *Frankia* genus. Like the *Rhizobium*, the *Frankia* bacteria also form root nodules, and because diazotrophs provide nitrogen, they give their host plants a competitive advantage on soils that lack nitrogen. Not surprisingly, many of these plants thrive in marginal areas of low fertility.

Then there are the *cyanobacteria* — a huge and varied category of diazotrophs. But, oh what a category! Perhaps one of the most ancient and successful forms of life on Earth, these bacteria contain the metabolic machinery for photosynthesis, and that allows them to obtain carbohydrates from sunlight. In fact, cyanobacteria may account for more than *one fifth* of all photosynthetic activity on Earth. In addition, many species also contain nitrogenase, so in essence they can capture both nitrogen *and* sunlight — a very powerful combination for survival. Cyanobacteria are found nearly everywhere, even in such hostile environments such as hot springs and salt flats. Cyanobacteria can be free-living, either as single cells or in colonies, or they can live in complex arrangements with a multitude of plants. Some of the free-living bacteria are the blue-green algae (although called algae, they are really bacteria) that can cause those notorious toxic "blooms" in the oceans and lakes. Some cyanobacteria live in conjunction with the microscopic diatoms in the ocean, others in coral reefs, sponges, and lichens. There is currently active research on diazotrophs in wetlands and ocean sediments, primarily because of their potential influence on wetland restoration and industrial contaminants.

Here are two cyanobacteria facts of striking importance: (1) researchers are working with cyanobacteria to create fuel — by growing blue-green algae in large seawater vats to produce ethanol, and (2) because of their ancient capacity for photosynthesis, there is increasing evidence that a primitive type of symbiotic cyanobacteria evolved into the chloroplasts that are now found in the leaves of all higher plants.

Diazotrophs are not just associated with the plant kingdom. At least one animal species survives because of diazotrophs. And causes a lot of damage. The *shipworm* is a small, peculiar, wormlike marine creature that is actually a mollusk — related to clams and oysters. (There are many species of shipworm. *Teredo navalis* is the most common one.) It has a soft body and no hard external shell. It does, however, have very tiny shells at one end that act like teeth. It's notorious for boring into any submerged wood: docks, piers, old wooden ships. Like termites, the shipworm body houses bacteria that help it to successfully digest cellulose. These diazotrophs live in a special gland in its gills and produce amino acids the worm lives on. So, between the low-nitrogen wood fiber and the nitrogenous amino acids produced by the diazotrophs, this is a very happy animal. Much to the chagrin of harbor-masters and wooden-boat enthusiasts everywhere.

Let's return to agriculture. Some nitrogen-fixation has been recorded in sorghum-sudangrass and sugarcane due to diazotrophs, although we don't understand the mechanism yet. And in some Asian countries, farmers deliberately use diazotrophs to increase the yields of padi rice. The water fern *Azolla,* which grows in the wet rice fields, contains the diazotroph *Anabaena azollae.* Rice farmers plant Azolla together with the rice or they incorporate it into the soil when the rice seedlings are transplanted. Either way, the extra nitrogen fixed by the diazotroph becomes an organic fertilizer to the rice.

Which brings us back to the main promise of diazotrophs and the reason for that rancher's question about commercial bacterial products that could replace nitrogen fertilizer. Diazotrophs bring nitrogen into a system. We already do this routinely with rhizobia and legumes. But wouldn't it be fantastic if we could get diazotrophs to create a successful symbiotic relationship in corn or wheat or the common grasses we use in pastures? Or if we could find ways of linking diazotrophs to high-yield biofuel plants like switchgrass or reed canarygrass or the tropical grass *Miscanthus*?

Private companies are already touting this, kind of. They are selling bacterial material that is supposed to replace nitrogen fertilizer. These would be dried diazotroph spores, of course. The idea is to apply these products to growing plants to increase the nitrogen available to those plants. Hmmm. It's one thing to add free-living diazotrophs to the soil environment, but to keep them there successfully for a significant period of time so they fix nitrogen and then transfer that nitrogen into plants — well, there are a lot of metabolic steps between moving nitrogen from the air through bacteria and then into the plant.

But it's a tantalizing dream, and we can dream, can't we?

First Published: September 2013
Author's Note: Diazotrophs represent a part of nature that most folks don't think about. But these bacteria are fascinating, and some species directly influence various aspects of our agriculture. Future research, especially on genomics, will unravel how we can better capitalize on their ability to fix nitrogen. Meanwhile, they make a good read while we sit by the fire on a cold winter night.

Flying Blind, or Not

How often have you been at a grazing workshop when a speaker asks, "How many of you have taken soil tests from your pastures?" Only a few hands go up. The speaker then sermonizes about the need for soil testing. Everyone nods yes, yes, yes, and then the discussion moves on to other topics.

Here in Oregon, I teach a course on forage management to farmers and ranchers. In the first session, I ask the ranchers the same question about taking soil tests . . . and invariably get the same response. But then we *do* something about it. Over the next few weeks of class, I walk everyone through the process of taking soil samples from their own farms, including how and where to sample. Then we fill out the laboratory's submission forms, label the bags of soil samples, box them up, and mail them to the lab. When the reports come back, we systematically review the results in class, so that by the end of the course, everyone knows what those numbers mean and how to use them.

So let's discuss soil tests for a bit. Don't worry — I won't sermonize about the need to take them. The principle is very simple — *without soil tests you're flying blind*. Without those soil test results, you could spend thousands of dollars on fertilizer that you might not need, and you might miss critical nutrient deficiencies that you could otherwise solve or avoid. So, let's assume that you've already submitted some soil samples to your favorite laboratory and have received the reports. We'll now review a few main numbers and see what they mean.

One of the first things I look at is soil pH — the measure of acidity or alkalinity. (The scholarly definition of pH is the logarithmic transformation of the molar concentration of hydrogen ions, but that's not very useful to someone on a tractor.) In the laboratory, pH values can range from 1 (pure acid) to 14 (pure base), with 7 as the neutral midpoint. Most soils, however, fall between a strongly acidic pH 4.5 and a strongly alkaline pH 8.5. Improved forages prefer pH values between 5.8 and 7.5. The main thing about soil pH is that it influences many soil attributes, including nutrient solubility and thus availability, and also the speed of organic matter breakdown. Since plant roots can only absorb nutrients when those nutrients are in solution, solubility is critical. For example, phosphorus generally becomes more available as the soil pH rises above 5.8. Therefore, increasing the pH of a very acidic soil will increase the efficiency of phosphorus fertilizers.

"Increasing the pH" — that's an interesting concept. We generally increase soil pH by applying limestone (calcium carbonate), usually by the ton. (Other substances will increase pH, like dolomite, but the principles are the same.) The question is: how much limestone should we add? Doesn't one standard amount work for all soils? Or should we just add limestone until our bank account runs dry?

Well, one size definitely doesn't fit all. Each soil is different, and a good soil test report gives us the answer — with a number called the *Buffer Index* or *Buffer pH* or *SMP Buffer* or something like that (different labs use different terminology). This number looks like a pH value, but it's actually a *lookup number* that is designed to be used with published reference tables. To use it, we go to a nifty *Lime Requirement Table* that lists Buffer Index values in the left-hand column and "Target pH" values as column headings. We then find our field's Buffer Index number in the left-hand column, run a finger across the table to the target pH column (i.e., pH 6.0, pH 6.4, etc.), and read the number. That number is the amount of limestone that we should apply to raise the current soil pH to the target pH, in tons per acre of 100-score limestone. These tables are often included in lots of university and government documents about fertilizer management, and they are compiled locally. Armed with the Buffer Index value from our soil test report, we can look up the amount of limestone needed and thus estimate the cost of improving the pH of that field. Then we can decide if it's even worth it or if our money should be spent elsewhere, like on other fields.

One important point: two soils with the same pH can have very different Buffer Indices and thus will require very different amounts of lime. These differences depend primarily on the amounts of clay and organic matter in these soils. Although soil chemistry is complex, using the Buffer Index number is not. Consider the alternatives: we can either spend lots of money on limestone, hoping that it takes less than nine tons to improve the pH, or we can look it up in the table *before* we spend the money. It's nice to know.

Another number I examine in a soil test report is the *organic matter (OM)*. I'm not talking here about roots and leaves. I'm talking about microscopic particles that are mostly composed of *humus* — the colloidal residue of decayed vegetation. Their huge surface area gives them a profound effect on soil fertility, especially if the OM level is very low or very high. Very low generally means less than 3%. Gardeners and row-crop farmers worry about this all the time because organic matter helps retain soil moisture and is also a reservoir of slow-release nutrients. One reason we give so much value to manure and compost is that these are excellent sources of organic matter. In western Oregon, we are fortunate that many valley soils have OM levels greater than 5%. But soils on the Oregon coast routinely contain more than 12% OM, which is very high. Soils with this much OM can potentially retain vast amounts of nutrients and release them under the right conditions. Such high OM levels can alter the usual recommendations for lime and fertilizer. Another nice thing to know.

In terms of the main soil nutrients — phosphorus and potassium — we can expect all soil tests to list them, either in parts per million or pounds per acre. But a good soil test will also list the levels of magnesium, calcium, and sodium, and that gives us a more complete picture of a field's fertility. What these values mean and what to do next — well, this is where you go to your local resources because agronomy is local. Numerous state and county agricultural offices, websites, and private consultants will have recommendations about the appropriate nutrient levels for your local crops and forages, and how much fertilizer to apply to achieve these levels. For pastures in our area, we like to see soil P and K levels of 15-20 ppm and 175-200 ppm, respectively. Your numbers may differ because of your local conditions.

Here's another useful soil characteristic: *Cation Exchange Capacity (CEC)*, sometimes called *Base Saturation*. The surfaces of soil particles — primarily clay and organic matter — are coated with lots of negatively charged binding sites. These sites attract and bind atoms that are, logically, positively charged (*cations*): potassium, magnesium calcium, sodium, and hydrogen. The CEC is the sum of all these binding sites.

A good soil test will list the CEC value of the soil and also the percentages of this CEC occupied by the various elements. The sum of all these percentages is 100. Here's an example from a field on my place: 3.5% potassium, 14.9% magnesium, 57.0% calcium, 1.2% sodium, and 23.4% hydrogen. Yes, these numbers do total 100%.

These percentages can tell us quite a story. Some examples: Most plants need at least 3% of the CEC as potassium. Very high percentages of magnesium (>22% of the CEC) will cause some soils to bind up and drain badly. High percentages of sodium can indicate salt intrusion or interfere with plant uptake of other nutrients. Low percentages of calcium can indicate a calcium deficiency, regardless of the soil pH. But in a practical sense, we don't need to become soil scientists to deal with these numbers. Once we have these numbers from a soil test, we can show them to people who do this for a living and get *their* advice.

And then . . . well, let's stop here. There's more, of course. There's always more. Topics like nitrogen, sulfur, micronutrients, and sampling strategies. But this article isn't a textbook. It's just a small opening in the window to let in a little light, so we can see better.

First Published: August 2006

Author's Note: This is so basic (excuse the pun) and so important. Whenever I do a pasture walk with farmers and ranchers, we always carry clipboards with the soil test reports. With those numbers, our conversations can get down to brass tacks about amounts of fertilizer, the economics of the field, and the potential options for other fields on the property. Without those numbers, well, we don't have the information we need to make good decisions.

The Dirt on Soil Tests

Some livestock producers think of soil tests for pastures the way some folks think about asparagus. We know about them, we know they are good for us, and occasionally we do them — if for no other reason than to please everyone else. Then, after we finally receive our test reports, we review the numbers and buy fertilizer based on those numbers. But here's something we might ruminate on: should we accept the numbers in those soil test reports without question? Many of us make significant economic decisions based on those numbers, maybe thousands of dollars each year, but can we really be confident that those numbers represent what we think they represent?

Here's what we submit to the laboratory: a small bag of soil. Okay, let's assume that we conscientiously followed the official recommendations. We dutifully made 20–30 small bore holes in the field, mixed those soil bores in a plastic bucket, carefully took a composite sample from that bucket, put that small amount in a bag, and then submitted it to the lab. Let's say our sample weighed one pound. The top 6 inches of soil in an acre weighs approximately 2,000,000 pounds (that's *2 million pounds*). If our composite sample was taken from a 20-acre field, we are depending on that single pound of soil sample to accurately represent *40 million pounds of topsoil*. Are we comfortable with those test report numbers yet?

Background note: I'll call the composite soil sample that we send to the lab "the sample," and the 20–30 little holes that we make in the soil I'll call "soil bores." The sample we send to the lab is a composite subsample of those many soil bores.

When I teach my Forages Course to farmers and ranchers, we cover soil testing in considerable depth. Not just how to interpret the numbers, but also — *especially* — how to take soil samples to get reliable numbers. Why emphasize procedure? Because so much depends on a taking good sample. Fact sheets from universities and commercial labs usually provide general guidelines for taking soil samples, but there are more facets to this procedure than are obvious. This month, let's cover some of those nonobvious aspects of taking good soil samples.

Here are two major questions: *when* should we take soil samples and *how deep* should we take them?

The when, of course, depends on what you are looking for and where you live. It's kind of hard to take a soil sample in Minnesota in January, and there are months during the spring in western Oregon when some fields are under water. But in practice, the timing rule is actually rather straightforward: take your samples at the same time every year, even if you sample the fields years apart.

For example, if you always sample in May, then in subsequent years, take your samples in May, plus or minus a couple of weeks. The reason is simple: during the year, soil nutrients undergo predictable annual cycles. Rain and snow can cause nutrient leaching, freezing and thawing can change nutrient availabilities, and soil organic matter breaks down during the growing season and releases nutrients.

Let's say that you sample a field at different times during the year, and you see differences in soil fertility values. Can you confidently conclude that those numbers changed because of your excellent management? Or did they change because of natural nutrient rhythms in the soil? Or both? The trouble is that you can't tell the difference. In statistics, we call that *confounding*, meaning that two or more things are changing at the same time. We avoid this problem by being reasonably consistent in our sampling time.

Next: how deep should we sample? Well, this depends on what you grow. In our typical cool-season pastures, most of the forage root mass generally lies within the top six inches of the soil. Therefore, take your samples only 6 inches deep. This is not a time for macho strength; if you use a spade or soil probe, put a piece of duct tape at the 6-inch level to help guide your digging. On the other hand, if we grow forages with major taproots, like alfalfa or red clover or chicory, or if our field is composed of warm-season grasses that usually have deeper roots than cool-season grasses, then we should sample deeper.

Which brings up a subtle point. Some standard fertilizer recommendations are based on a *plow depth* of 6–9 inches, particularly if those recommendations are designed for row-crop systems like corn or soybeans. In contrast, forages in pastures generally depend on soil nutrients in the top 6-inch horizon of the soil. The lesson? We should be careful in extrapolating some fertilizer recommendations directly to pasture situations.

Here's an interesting exercise: take *two* soil samples from a single hole — one *beneath* the other. Take the first sample from the top 6 inches, then a second sample directly below it from the next 6–12 inches. Send the two samples to the lab. The results will probably be quite different because some nutrients wash downward (leach) in the soil profile and thus end up deeper in the soil. This will demonstrate that if you make your soil bores too deep, the nutrients from the lower levels will often mask with the actual nutrient values in forage root zone and give you misleading numbers.

Now some geography. I mentioned earlier about taking 20–30 soil bores in a field. Where exactly in a field should you take these soil bores? I've seen some university and company fact sheets that recommend that you follow a "Z" pattern or an "X" pattern or some other pattern with straight lines. Don't do that. Although straight lines are easy to follow, think of this: what if one of those lines coincides with a fertility gradient in the soil or lies on top of an old cattle trail that once had lots of manure? All samples in that line would be similar. Would they represent the average of the field?

Our goal — based on using a one-pound sample to represent millions of pounds of topsoil — is to obtain the best, most unbiased estimate of the average fertility of the field. That means that we must take a good representative sample. And that means, in technical statistical terms, that the sampling errors should be randomly distributed (here, the word "error" does not indicate a mistake. In statistics, error is the unexplained deviation from the average). In statistics, this means that we should take our soil cores in a random manner, not in straight lines that can introduce a systematic bias in the results.

The best way of obtaining a random sample is to be random: wander around the field nearly aimlessly and make lots of soil cores — here, there, nearly everywhere. Randomness is our friend. But we should also use some common sense: avoid outlier spots that are clearly not representative of the average, like areas under trees (where manure collects) or along fence lines (where animals pace) or under obvious piles of manure. The bottom line is that we want to know the *average* fertility values of the field because, in the future, we will treat the entire field as a unit with the same fertilizer and the same management.

Speaking of fields, how should we sample large fields? Or even small fields that have multiple biological areas? Here's a straightforward principle: we should *sample each biological area as its own field.* Especially the first time we take soil tests on a property because we want to get a baseline report for each biological unit. Scrutinize the fields carefully. For example, if a large field contains a flat area and also an area with a slight slope, we should consider these two areas as two different fields, regardless of the existing fence. Or if the drainage in one part of a field is clearly different than the other part, we really have two different fields. Don't let fences get in your way or govern the sampling procedure. Previous owners constructed their fences for all sorts of reasons, but often not based on soil fertility. For soil testing, we should follow the basic principle of obtaining a separate soil test report for each biological area.

There is a compelling reason for this. We are trying to get accurate information that will guide our future management decisions. Short-term decisions will involve buying fertilizer and lime. But in the longer term, we will use soil test results to make decisions about grazing management, renovations, and laying out temporary and permanent fences.

Which brings us to the question of soil types — you know, the soil names that appear on all government agency soil maps; names like "Stayton silt loam" or "Klickitat gravelly clay loam," etc. How should we consider these areas when we take our soil samples?

Oh my, we are out of space. Hmmm. Well, please come back next month. We'll need to get into more depth about this one.

First Published: August 2015
Author's Note: The top 6 inches of soil in an acre weighs around two million pounds. Our sample is approximately one pound. That defines the main issue. The rest of the details of sampling technique is, really, just common sense.

Well-Grounded
Decisions

Last month, we left off when I introduced the subject of soil types — you know, those intriguing names you see on government county maps, names like "Jumpoff clay loam" or "Marcola cobbly silty clay loam." Are these names important for taking soil samples? Let's continue our discussion on soil tests.

These names, of course, are the formal names of different soils. They roughly correspond to species names for plants and animals. Each soil has a unique set of characteristics, like composition, slope, drainage, fertility, etc. Government soil maps show these soil types and also pages of technical descriptions. This information reflects a vast amount of careful and tedious work by federal soil scientists and cartographers who mapped each area and field in nearly every county in the United States. The USDA Soil Conservation Service (now NRCS) published these maps in hundreds of massive volumes with titles like "Soil Survey of XYZ County," with each volume the size of the Chicago phone book. Today, we can easily download many of them as pdf files. The pdf files are definitely lighter than those old books, but those USDA volumes were certainly impressive in a bookcase.

Our practical problem is this: how do these soil types influence our soil sampling decisions? When we overlay field maps with the NRCS soil maps, things can look very confusing. Soil types are generally inconvenient; they don't follow fence lines or ownership boundaries. While occasionally a field may contain only one soil type — lucky day — usually our field maps look like giant jigsaw puzzles, with three or more different soils interlocked in byzantine patterns across the field. Should we sample fields according to these soil types? Should we rebuild our fences to follow those jigsaw outlines?

143

For pastures, the answers are no and no. The basic principle is that we should manage each field *as its own biological unit*. A field may contain many soil types, but we still treat it as a single field. If a large field has too much obvious physical variation — if, for example, it contains a poorly drained flat area and also a better-drained slope — these represent two different biological units, even if they each contain multiple soil types. We should separate these two biological areas by building a fence and treating them as two separate fields. We build our fences as we need to. In either case, soil types are part of the picture, but they usually do not define our field boundaries.

Basically, we should focus on the big picture — the *average fertility* of a field — because that's how we will manage the field. Our decisions about fertilizer, lime, and seeds will apply to the *entire field inside the fence*, not to subunits of this field as outlined by convoluted soil maps. Therefore, even if a field contains multiple soil types, we sample the field in a random and complete way to obtain a good representative soil sample of the entire field.

Here's an interesting high-tech wrinkle. Some companies offer a service where they come onto your farm, and, using GPS-guided equipment, take dozens of soil samples in a grid pattern across each field and create detailed gradient maps of soil fertility for these fields. Then they apply fertilizer with precision equipment, so that each spot in a field receives the exact amount of nutrients it needs. These companies don't use field averages; they rely on multiple tests within a field. They apply lime and fertilizer based on the soil tests, not soil types.

Once we take our composite soil sample, we send it into our favorite laboratory. Each lab, of course, offers a package of the major soil fertility variables — phosphorus, potassium (potash), organic matter, pH, etc. But what about the minor elements known as *micronutrients*? Like copper, iron, manganese, boron, zinc, and molybdenum. Most labs also offer packages for these, but should we pay for these packages and use the numbers?

Let's step back and consider their value for pastures. The levels of most micronutrients in plant tissue will rise and fall based on soil availability. There are many published reference charts that show deficiency symptoms for these nutrients. However, there is a difference between farmed row-crop fields and the pastures.

Row crops are almost always monocultures — i.e., a single plant species like barley or soybeans or tomatoes. On any given day during the growing season, all the plants in a monoculture field are at the exact same point in their production cycle. Also, agronomists have carefully characterized the micronutrient requirements of many high-value crops for their various stages of growth. Testing these plants for the micronutrient levels in their leaves will give a clear indication of any micronutrient deficiency, and this information would apply to all the plants in the field. For these plants, soil tests can be correlated to plant tissue levels. If a deficiency exists, then applying the specific micronutrient will generally solve the problem.

Now let's think about pastures. Most pastures are definitely not monocultures. Pastures are complex communities containing multiple plant species. (There are exceptions, of course, like alfalfa hay fields or the grass seed fields in Oregon.) Most pastures contain three, four, five, or ten different forages from two or three different plant categories: grasses, legumes, and other broadleaf plants like chicory or plantain. Some forages are annuals; some are perennials. On any given day during the growing season, two or more of these species will be dominant. A month later, different species may dominate the sward. And because these forages are all growing at different rates, on any given day some will be vegetative, some will be in early bloom or late bloom or already headed out, and some will be showing young regrowth; and this sward profile changes from day-to-day during the growing season.

Also, most forage species have not been as intensely-characterized for their micronutrient requirements as row-crop plants.

What does this mean for analyzing the micronutrient levels in the soil? Well, in general, we simply don't have a good handle on the specific micronutrient requirements of a pasture because there is usually so much plant variation within a field and so many things are changing weekly. We don't have good reference numbers anyway. If we tested our pasture soils for micronutrients, what could we confidently do with those numbers? Not much.

But we do have other options: we can rely on agronomic advice from dependable local sources. Over the years, our land-grant universities have conducted lots of research on micronutrient responses, and these results represent good local data. Universities have developed some general guidelines for each area. Things like adding boron in high-rainfall regions or adding molybdenum for legumes in low pH soils. These might be broad-brush recommendations, but they are local. While we may not need to spend money for micronutrient assays in our individual fields, the plants still require these nutrients. We can use local or regional recommendations as valuable guidelines for making good management decisions.

Speaking of micronutrients, here's a question that often comes up at workshops. Someone will ask something like, "If my soil is high in copper, does that mean I should worry about copper toxicity in my livestock?" Let's rephrase the question more broadly: if the soil is high in a mineral, will the forages growing on that soil automatically be high in that mineral? (With the implied corollary that a high level could cause problems in the livestock.)

I have a two-part response to this. The first part is that if we are concerned about the mineral levels in the feedstuffs, then we should always run tests on the actual feeds that the animals eat. That tells us unequivocally what is going into their mouths.

The second part of my response deals with the cause-and-effect relationships between soil chemistry and plants. While a one-to-one relationship seems plausible, the reality is not as clean. Let's say that mineral X is high in the soil. To get to high levels in a plant requires many individual steps. Firstly, mineral X would have to be in a form that the plant can absorb through its roots. Secondly, once in the roots, that mineral must be converted into a form that can be translocated upward into the leaves and stems. This is the vegetation that animals will actually consume. Thirdly, even if the mineral is in the leaves, it must be in a form that will be absorbed across the animal's digestive tract once it is consumed or would be chemically active in the gut while it moves through the digestive tract.

There's more. The leaves may contain other minerals or compounds that can interact with mineral X and influence its absorption across the gut wall. Finally, we must ask: is the mineral a required nutrient by the plant? For example, we know that extra nitrogen in the soil will increase the nitrogen level in the leaves, but if we are talking about uranium, some plants will simply refuse to absorb extra uranium under any conditions.

These are a lot of steps, a lot of ifs. So, is there a direct relationship between the soil level of a mineral and the nutritional effects in the animal? The answer is usually no. The physiological steps are complex and variable, and each mineral is different. In the end, we can't automatically extrapolate the results of soil tests to forage tests to animal responses.

Well, those soil types are interesting, and some have intriguing names, but in reality they are not very important for our day-to-day decisions about soil fertility and fertilizer needs. Soil tests, however, are gold. They are critical for understanding our pastures and critical for our management decisions. To take the best samples possible just requires a little depth to our knowledge.

First Published: September 2015
Author's Note: These are real questions that have come up in workshops and classroom sessions. It's true that soil testing is a bit complex. But then again, once we learn about the underlying principles and interlocking relationships, so are most things.

Looking for Nitrogen Answers

It all began nearly two years ago at a monthly rancher meeting on Oregon's south coast. We were studying an interesting agronomy paper from Wisconsin, and one of the ranchers asked a simple question.

The Wisconsin study had been straightforward enough. Researchers applied different levels of nitrogen to small grass plots and then measured the amounts of nitrogen (N) in the resulting growth and the efficiency of nitrogen capture. The result provided good information about the practical economics of nitrogen fertilization . . . for those forages under Midwestern conditions.

Then one of our ranchers asked: why didn't we have this information *here* — for *our* growing seasons, using *our* levels of nitrogen fertilizer, on *our* soils, with *our* species of grasses grown under the unique conditions of the coastal Pacific Northwest? Good question, because locally derived information could really help guide our decisions about fertilizer strategies. But local information simply did not exist. Everyone looked at each other in surprise, but things didn't stop there. We wanted to do something about it. Within a month, group members held a special meeting to plan their own nitrogen-fertility project to generate this information.

This is the story of that project. About how ranchers and others from the agricultural community worked together to roll up their sleeves, design and carry out a true research project, and derive information critically important to their operations. This is no small thing.

First some background: the rancher study group on the south Oregon Coast is officially called *FANG* — the *Forage And Nutrition Group*. This is a limited-membership, private group of 10–15 ranchers who meet monthly to

147

discuss technical issues, conduct pasture walks, share experiences, and evaluate new ideas and techniques. The discussions are usually spiced with the no-nonsense financial insights of working ranches. FANG has been meeting monthly since 2000. I am the group's facilitator.

Anyway, back to the story. In addition to the ranchers, other folks pitched in — staff from the local Soil & Water Conservation District, an Extension Agent who specializes in water quality, and me. The first thing we decided was that this project would be a true scientific study, not just a classic "demonstration plot" that did not have enough replications or did not conform to an appropriate scientific experimental design. We wanted to derive good comparative information that could withstand professional scrutiny. This meant using the scientific method with multiple experimental sites on multiple farms.

So we designed an experiment to address the following question: how do different levels of nitrogen fertilization affect grass yield and the efficiency of nitrogen use in highly productive grass pastures? (We restricted the study to grass pastures because nitrogen-fixing legumes in a nitrogen trial would really muddy the numbers. This was a reasonable decision, as most pastures in the area are dominated primarily by grass, especially during the winter and early spring.)

Also, since the member ranches all contain steep slopes and are located in salmon country, we wanted to see how much fertilizer nitrogen, if any, moved into the groundwater. This point is particularly relevant because many government regulations are predicated on the assumption that nitrogen fertilizer contaminates groundwater. In reality, however, we really don't know if this is true for our pastures. We really don't know if routine applications of nitrogen fertilizer on dense, well-managed grass swards will result in nitrogen leaching into groundwater.

We addressed our question by setting up an experiment. We chose five nitrogen *treatments*— 0, 100, 200, 400, and 800 lb N per acre. The highest N-application rate in the Wisconsin trial was 300 lb/acre, but the FANG ranchers wanted to test a much wider x-axis because some members were already applying more than 300 lb N to their fields. Plot size would be the same as the Wisconsin study: 3-feet wide and 20-feet long, and we would replicate these plots on three different ranches.

From a statistical perspective, we had 5 treatments and 3 blocks. A *block* is a ranch. Because each ranch contained a complete set of all 5 treatments, and because the treatments were randomly assigned to plots within each block, this experimental design has the formal designation *Randomized Complete Block* design — which is a simple but powerful way of arranging the 15 plots to obtain valid data. We also collaborated with two agronomy faculty from

Oregon State University and the University of Wisconsin to help us with plot techniques and statistical analyses.

Here are some other practical design details: we planted a 6-foot alley between each plot to avoid border effects, and we built tall, stout fencing around each block to keep out the elk. (Yes, elk.) We located the plots on west-facing hillsides to maximize potential movement of runoff N into the groundwater. We chose to apply fertilizer in four split applications. We would harvest the grass with a lawnmower on 8 dates during the growing season, and the specific harvest dates would be governed by the amount of forage growth. And we planned to follow the good grazing practice of leaving a 2-inch residual at each collection (approximately 1,000 pounds per acre).

The members of FANG worked all this out at their monthly meetings, step-by-step. It was a learning experience for everyone. The discussions were as intense and technical as you would see in any group of graduate students at a land-grant university, except the ranchers added their very practical knowledge of soils, equipment, and economics.

You might ask, why didn't the ranchers just accept the results of the Wisconsin trial? Because the coastal Pacific Northwest environment is so different from the upper Midwest. Our growing season begins in October when the rains start, and it continues into June when the rains end and the soils become bone dry. Winters are cool and wet with few frosts. The ground never freezes. Sometimes the wind blows strong enough to push hay bales off trucks. Soil fertility is also different from most other places. Soil pH is typically below 5.5, and organic matter levels are greater than 12%, even on the hillsides. (If you're not familiar with soil chemistry, those organic matter levels are *very* high.) And our predominant forages are perennial ryegrass, annual ryegrass, orchardgrass, tall fescue, and some clovers.

We crafted an official project proposal and submitted it to a USDA agency. But here's the rub: we couldn't just sit back and wait for their decision because otherwise we'd miss an entire growing season. In this trial, our goal was to work with dense, well-established grass pastures. Unfortunately, a new seeding of perennial grass takes a full year of growth to become sufficiently dense for our purposes. Therefore, we had to begin preparing the experimental plots even before we knew if we had funds for the experiment.

So we took soil tests, obtained seed of a highly productive variety of perennial ryegrass, and constructed the three areas anyway. We planted the seed very densely, used herbicide to control all broadleaf plants, built strong fences, and applied other nutrients as required (P, K, and S). Although the USDA initially rejected our proposal, nine months later we received some alternative funding from a state government source. It wasn't everything we wanted, but it was enough to do some good. Last October, we hand-spread the first application of nitrogen, and throughout the winter and spring we have been making collections and compiling data.

Of course, our equipment has been quintessential ranch gear, supremely practical but not exactly scientific "state-of-the-art." Our harvesting unit was a trusty lawnmower with a grass catch bag. Our "laboratory workbench" was a piece of plywood on two sawhorses. We weighed samples on a postal scale. We determined forage dry matter by drying our samples for 48 hours in a "forced-air oven" — which was really an 8-tray food dehydrator. But even without a high-tech gloss, the experimental design is still sound and the data is dependable.

We're still in the middle of it. As of this writing, the ranchers have taken four yield collections and have applied nitrogen three times. To measure the amount of nitrogen leaching into the groundwater, we've dug wells at the lower end of each experimental plot and installed water collection equipment. We will soon take groundwater samples for water quality analysis. We have already amassed valuable information about winter grass growth, its nutritional value, and its response to varying levels of N. After we take our final collection in June, we'll run all these numbers through a statistical procedure called *Analysis of Variance* that will help us make sense of the data.

Because of this project, everyone gains. People working together, rolling up our collective sleeves, combining practical field knowledge with disciplined science, and deriving information to guide our ranching and business decisions. And the discussions at our monthly FANG meetings continue to explore the information, weigh options, and look at alternatives. We are all excited about this project and the data we're collecting. It will help us see the forest instead of just the trees.

First Published: May 2006

Author's Note: This is another facet of the relationship between nitrogen and forages. This chapter is the first of three that describe the nitrogen fertility trial conducted by the FANG ranchers between 2004 and 2007. It lays out the background of the trial and describes our initial activities. I originally wrote this chapter in 2006, while we still were in the middle it. The next two chapters, written years later, describe additional details of the experimental design and most importantly, the results and conclusions.

How Much Nitrogen Is Too Much?

Back in May 2006, I wrote an article called "Looking For Nitrogen Answers" in which I described a nitrogen fertilizer experiment we were beginning to conduct on three ranches on Oregon's south coast. By "we" I mean the forage study group of ranchers I facilitate known as FANG (Forage And Nutrition Group). We carefully designed an on-farm trial to answer some practical questions about the efficient use of nitrogen fertilizer and how much nitrogen could end up in the groundwater. In that article, I described the experimental design, how we arranged the plots, what questions we were trying to answer, and how the ranchers had worked together to make the trial happen. I said I'd get back to you with the results. You've been very patient.

Hmmm. It's now eight years later. I'm thinking . . . maybe this would be a good time to get back to you with the results? Especially as we are coming into the summer when you may be thinking about fertilizer. Well, here we go . . .

The basic question for the trial was this: how do different levels of nitrogen fertilization affect grass yield and the efficiency of nitrogen use in highly productive, nonirrigated grass pastures? We also wanted information on some secondary questions: (1) what are the effects of different levels of nitrogen on forage nutritional value, (2) how does nitrogen fertilization change–soil fertility, and (3) how much nitrogen will cause potential contamination of groundwater, which could ultimately end up in streams and rivers? These are all practical issues that have economic fallout, and the members of FANG worked for more than two years to conduct a disciplined scientific trial, collect data, and come up with some useful answers.

151

But first, I should review the setup. Jargon alert! The next three paragraphs contain scientificese — words dense in scientific and statistical meanings but possibly resembling obscure crossword-puzzle gobbledygook. I need to include this description, so our results don't seem to come out of thin air. (However, for this class, you are permitted to skip the next three paragraphs. But if you do read them, you'll get extra credit . . .)

Our trial was designed as a *Randomized Complete Block Design with five treatments (nitrogen levels) and three blocks (ranches)*. This means that there were 15 individual grass plots (= 5 treatment plots *x* 3 ranches). The three ranches were on the southern Oregon Coast within a couple of miles of the Pacific Ocean. All the plots were located on west-facing hillsides that had slopes of 14%–21%. Each grass plot was 3-feet wide by 20-feet long with a 6-foot buffer alley between adjacent plots. The five nitrogen treatments were 0, 100, 200, 400, and 800 lb N/acre (per year) applied as urea (46-0-0-0) split into 4 equal applications during the growing season. The zero nitrogen treatment is what people often call the "control."

Each ranch contained all five treatments, which were randomized among the five plots. The block of 5 plots on each ranch was surrounded by a tall, sturdy, elk-proof fence (yes, elk). The forage was the improved variety of perennial ryegrass 'Kingston' that had been planted one year previously to allow us to conduct our trial on a mature grass stand with good root mass. We eliminated all the clovers and broadleaf weeds in the plots with the herbicide 2,4-D because we did not want the nitrogen fixation by legumes to interfere with the data.

Our trial ran for two growing seasons: 2005-2006 and 2006-2007. In the coastal Pacific Northwest, the growing season on nonirrigated pastures is defined by the rainy season that lasts from October through June. We collected pasture samples from November through July: seven times in the first growing season and six times in the second growing season. We tried to duplicate good grazing techniques by always leaving a 2-inch residual at each cutting. During that first growing season, we also sent forage samples to a laboratory for nutritional analysis. And during the summer after the second growing season, when the ground was bone dry, we tested the subsoil beneath the root zone for the residual amount of soluble nitrates as an indication of potential excess nitrogen that could leach into the groundwater once the rains began again in the fall.

To put it bluntly, running a trial like this was a lot of work. And with all this work, we got good results that we can use.

First, I'll describe the forage yields. All the nitrogen applications increased forage yields above the control, although not in a simple additive way. The 100 and 200 N treatments gave approximately the same boost in yield, and the 400 and 800 N treatment gave a larger boost, but definitely not twice as much.

Which meant that we got a good yield improvement with 100-200 lb N, but the efficiency of additional nitrogen declined dramatically.

This reduced efficiency was confirmed when we analyzed the nitrogen usage. We calculated two variables to help us understand fertilizer efficiency. The first one, called *Apparent Nitrogen Recovery (ANR)*, is the percentage of applied nitrogen that ends up in the above-ground forage (i.e., not the roots). For simplicity, we averaged the values over both growing seasons. Applying 100, 200, 400, and 800 lb N per year gave us ANR values of 40%, 27%, 22%, and 12%, respectively. This was a clear example of diminishing returns: the percentage of nitrogen captured in the forage dropped steadily as we applied more and more nitrogen.

Our second calculated variable essentially showed the same results. The second variable, called *Nitrogen Use Efficiency (NUE)*, is the number of pounds of increased forage (dry matter) caused by each pound of nitrogen in the fertilizer. For example, let's say that we add 100 lb N/acre and boosted the forage yield by 1,210 lb over the control plot. Our NUE would be 12.1 (= 1,210 ÷ 100), meaning that each pound of nitrogen resulted in 12.1 lb of additional forage.

In our trial, the NUE values for the 100, 200, 400, and 800 N applications (averaged over the two growing seasons) were 12.1, 7.4, 5.1, and 2.5. Again, diminishing returns. At the upper extreme, we saw that adding 800 lb N per acre (in four 200-lb applications) gave us only 2.5 lb forage for each one lb of nitrogen. And when we equated these numbers to dollars, the cost of fertilizer versus the value of the resulting forage, it became strikingly apparent that more is not better economically. We concluded that the economic sweet spot for nitrogen fertilizer in our coastal grass pastures was somewhere between 100 and 200 lb N/acre/year. In practical terms, this would suggest four applications of 30–40 lb N during the growing season.

We also observed an interesting inconsistency between the calendar and the pattern of forage yields. In Year 1, peak forage yields occurred in April; in Year 2, peak yields occurred weeks later in May. This clearly underscores the importance of conducting forage trials for more than one year because there are significant year-to-year differences in rainfall, temperature, etc. Actually, this conclusion is not surprising, but how many forage presentations have *you* attended where the results reported were from only one year of data?

When we analyzed the effects of nitrogen on nutritional value of the forage, we were particularly interested in the levels of crude protein. We found that *any* nitrogen fertilizer increased protein above the baseline control. The 100 and 200 N treatments increased it only a little (1–4 percentage units) but the 400 and 800 N treatments increased protein levels by up to 10 percentage units. That's a lot. We also observed, much to our surprise, that the unfertilized perennial ryegrass maintained its crude protein levels above 16% for nearly the entire growing season — from November through May — and protein levels dipped to only 13% during the summer. Recall that these plots contained no clover or alfalfa. That grass had better protein levels than we expected.

And finally (at least for this month's article), we observed an important item about soil fertility. We know that soil organic matter contains nitrogen. In this trial, our coastal soils contained extremely high levels of organic matter — between 8 and 18% — so we expected that this organic matter would be a huge reservoir of nitrogen. The question was this: how much nitrogen was intrinsically released by the soil during the year? And our control plots gave us an answer. Those control plots received no nitrogen fertilizer, so any nitrogen in the forage had to come directly from soil release. Our calculations showed that the forage yield in the control plots contained only 40 lb of nitrogen. Not overwhelming, and certainly not enough to support high levels of forage production. Interestingly, this amount is similar to the intrinsic nitrogen release by other soils in western Oregon, where those soils contain much lower levels of organic matter.

We found more information from our trial. Some very interesting things. Let's finish next time.

First Published: April 2014

Author's Note: Reading the setup description for this trial — one can become almost breathless. A good experiment, even a straightforward one like this, takes a lot of work to design, conduct, sample, and analyze. And the fieldwork of this trial was conducted entirely by the ranchers in the FANG. That's not a small thing, not at all.

Results, Our Nitrogen Trial

Let's continue discussing the results of our nitrogen study, a disciplined, scientific trial conducted by ranchers on their own operations that resulted in practical information we can use.

This was an on-farm trial conducted by the Forage Study Group *FANG* (*Forage And Nutrition Group*) on three ranches on Oregon's south coast. We constructed fenced plots of perennial ryegrass to test different levels of nitrogen fertilizer (urea). The N treatments were 0, 100, 200, 400, and 800 lb N per acre per year, applied in four equal split applications each year. We conducted this trial for two growing seasons (which follow the Pacific Northwest rains that begin in the autumn and last until early summer). In last month's article, I described the procedural methods in greater detail and also reviewed some results, which included forage yield, nitrogen fertilizer efficiency, and an estimate of the amount of intrinsic nitrogen released into the soil each year from the organic matter. This month, more results. I'll focus on forage quality, soil pH, and the potential for groundwater contamination.

Everyone is interested in forage quality. After all, forage nutrients are what our sheep and cattle actually consume, and if our forage quality resembles the quality of dry fishing poles, high yields of it really don't do anyone any good. We measured forage quality six times during one growing season, from November through July. So, what was the nutritional value of our forage, and how did the higher levels of nitrogen affect it?

I discussed crude protein levels last month. Now let's move on to energy. (By the way, all nutritional values here are on a dry matter basis.) Classically, we describe the energy value of a feed in terms of *TDN (Total Digestible*

Nutrients). This number roughly equates to the digestibility of the feed, and it certainly reflects the amount of calories our livestock can obtain from a feedstuff. TDN values generally range from 45%–90%. Some rules-of-thumb: old straw at 45% TDN, medium-quality hay at 50%, good-quality hay at 60%, oats at 75%, and grains like corn and barley at approximately 90%. And of course, young forages in their vegetative (leafy) stage have high TDN levels that decline as those forages mature during the late spring and early summer.

What happened nutritionally with the perennial ryegrass in our plots? As we expected, the TDN levels were quite high during the autumn, winter, and mid-spring — at 64%–66% from November until mid-April. Then the TDN values dropped as the grass matured, but not too much, to only 61%–62% by July. Actually, 60% TDN is still reasonable-quality feed, especially for mature grass. We found that the different levels of N fertilizer had *no effect* on TDN levels, unlike with protein where higher levels of fertilizer N definitely increased the crude protein levels of the grass. Actually, we were not surprised by the lack of effect of the N on TDN because many other researchers have observed the same results.

The main minerals tracked were calcium and phosphorus; we wanted to evaluate the actual levels of each mineral as well as the ratio between them. Some interesting findings here: throughout most of the growing season, forage calcium levels held in a relatively steady range of between 0.30–0.40%. But from November through May, we observed that the higher levels of N fertilizer depressed the calcium levels in the forage. For example, if the 0 and 200 N treatments averaged 0.36% calcium in April, the 400 and 800 N treatments averaged only 0.33%. This difference disappeared entirely in June. And as the grass matured in July, all calcium levels rose rapidly to 0.45%.

In contrast, phosphorus levels followed a different path. Starting at 0.40% in the autumn, phosphorus levels rose to 0.50% by January and then fell steadily throughout the spring and summer until they reached 0.20% by July. N levels had no effect on phosphorus.

But when we calculated the *ratio* between forage calcium and phosphorus (the famous *Ca:P ratio*), we saw something rather unusual. If you look at standard nutritional reference books, you'll see that the dietary *requirements* for calcium and phosphorus generally result in Ca:P ratios of between 1.2–1.5. In practice, we usually recommend a Ca:P ratio of 2.0 in a total diet (i.e., twice as much calcium as phosphorus) because the higher Ca:P ratio helps avoid the problems of urinary calculi in growing males and also supports good bone formation. We noticed, however, that the Ca:P ratio in our ryegrass was only around 1.0 in the winter and early spring, and it was *below 1.0* in January. This *inverted* Ca:P ratio was made worse by the higher N treatments because they caused lower calcium levels.

We were particularly intrigued by these results because for years on these ranches we had observed hypocalcemia (milk fever) in ewes around lambing time and also spontaneous bone fractures in young lambs and calves. These distressing problems occurred during the winter and spring — at the same time we recorded low or inverted Ca:P ratios in the grass. If applying high levels of nitrogen fertilizer made this situation worse, this was information that could help us understand and manage the problems that we were seeing with calcium metabolism.

In addition to nutrition, we also obtained data on soil fertility. We took soil samples at the beginning and at the completion of the trial. One thing stood out clearly in our data: the effects of fertilizer on pH. Every university course in soils and agronomy teaches about the *acidifying effects* of commercial fertilizers, meaning that over time, many fertilizers tend to reduce soil pH. For example, reference charts list urea with an *equivalent acidity value* of 84, which means that applying 100 lb of urea requires 84 lb of limestone to counter the acidifying effect of the urea.

In our trial, we applied urea to our grass plots many times over two years, sometimes at very high levels. Did we reduce the soil pH? In a word, yes. At the beginning of the trial, the soil pH values on our three ranches were 5.0, 4.4, and 5.1 respectively. (Soils along the Oregon coast are naturally quite acidic.) We found that the lower levels of N fertilizer did not change these pH values appreciably, at least by the end of the second year, but the *higher* levels of N definitely did, especially the 800 lb N treatment. At the end of two years, the soil pH in those 800 N plots had dropped to 3.9, 3.7, and 3.9, respectively — just like the textbooks warned. We were very proud of that, in a perverse way. You might call it a textbook example of the acidifying effect.

The last thing I'll cover involves a critical question we asked in this trial: if we apply nitrogen fertilizer to dense, well-managed grass pastures, will some nitrogen leach downward through the soil into the groundwater and thus potentially contaminate streams and rivers? Agriculture is often accused of polluting waterways, but much of agriculture is based on row-crop farming where fields often contain open ground (i.e., space between plants). What about well-managed perennial pastures that have no open ground? A dense sward of grass has lots of vegetation and a thick, well-developed mass of roots. Will fertilizer nitrogen move down through this vegetation into the groundwater?

We tested this by analyzing the subsoil for residual nitrogen. At the end of the two-year trial, during the dry summer prior to the onset of the next season's rains, we took deep soil samples from each plot — more than 20-inches deep, which is below the root zone for our forages. We analyzed these samples for the amount of residual nitrogen (nitrates + nitrites). In western Oregon, the dry summer is the proper time to test for subsoil residual nitrogen because high soil levels would indicate excess nitrogen that could potentially leach downward during the autumn rains.

The results were clear. On all three ranches, nitrogen fertilizer applications of less than 400 lb N/year resulted in minimal residual nitrogen (nearly zero). Only the N applications of 400 and 800 lb N/year caused an increase in the levels of unused subsoil nitrogen. But interestingly, this effect occurred on only two of the three trial ranches. We concluded that: (1) typical levels of annual N, 200 lb N or less, do *not* result in excess nitrogen leaching into the groundwater, at least not in our dense, well-managed perennial grass pastures; and (2) there is variability in response among ranches, which means that one size does not fit all.

Yes, we did a lot of work over two years, but we learned a lot. We obtained practical results about grass yields, nitrogen fertilizer efficiency, protein and energy levels of the forage throughout the growing season, calcium and phosphorus ratios, the effects of nitrogen on soil pH, and the potential for groundwater contamination. Many dedicated people spent their time and energy working to make all this happen — ranchers in FANG, folks from the local Soil & Water Conservation District, some other agency personnel, a couple of faculty members from two universities, and me. It was definitely a team effort.

Working together to obtain good information. An experiment with useful results. Practical information, practical ranches, practical ideas; we rolled up our sleeves and got it done. Together.

First Published: May 2014

Author's Note: We learned a lot. Based on the results from this trial, many of the ranches in FANG changed their fertilizer programs, making them more efficient. And using a disciplined scientific method to obtain good information, adapting procedures from university experiment stations and using them on actual farms, ranchers and government personnel working together on a practical problem to obtain meaningful results — well, this is a model that should be duplicated everywhere.

The Money Pit

Ah . . . May. Bright green spring days, warm sunshine, birds singing, and a young person's thoughts turn to . . . renovating pastures. (What *exactly* did you expect in an agricultural magazine?) Of course, we think about pastures, and, during the spring, we also think about renovating our fields. This month let's talk about what that might mean.

Let's say that we look at a field, conclude it is not "doing well," and think perhaps that we should make a major change like planting a new seed mix. So what's a good pasture mix for sheep? Whoa! Let's not jump a gun. Renovation is expensive — more than $100/acre. Before we begin plowing money into the ground, literally, maybe we should stop and carefully consider some things about this field. Afterward, of course, we can cheerfully throw money wherever we want.

The first thing we should ask ourselves is what do we want *to do* with this field? I'm talking here about the bigger picture: graze only? Make hay or silage? Make stored feed *and* graze? How does this field fit into the whole farm system? Let's take this even further: do we even *like* making hay, or would we rather shift to a full-time grazing system, minimize the use of stored feeds, and purchase any hay we need? Also, will this field be a permanent pasture or will it be a short-term temporary pasture as part of a long-term crop rotation? If the latter, maybe we would want to use it for green manure during its final year. And from a planning perspective, how much flexibility do we want to build into our choices in case we want to make management adjustments in a year or two?

These are no-nonsense questions. And we really want no-nonsense answers — *before we spend a penny*. These answers set the big picture. They'll guide our choice of seeds: annuals or perennials or short-term perennials; varieties that grow tall for making hay or low and dense for grazing. If we think that, in a couple of years, we might shift to Management-Intensive Grazing (MIG), we may not want to plant a defoliation-sensitive species like timothy or smooth brome.

Now let's turn our attention to the soil characteristics: soil type, drainage, slope, aspect (the direction it faces), tree cover, flooding potential, etc. These details can define which forage species may thrive and which may not, and when the field should be used and when it should be left alone. For example, soils in a poorly drained, east-facing field will be colder than the rest of the farm, and forage growth in that field will start later in the spring. We wouldn't want to depend on that field for early-season grazing or for anything that requires heavy equipment. Will our field receive water throughout the growing season, either from rain or irrigation? A dependable summer water supply does not jive with a forage that goes dormant in midsummer heat, like perennial ryegrass.

Then, of course, we need to be familiar with the field's soil fertility — its nutrient levels, the history of its fertilizer applications, and the history of its hay yields. Why the dual histories? Because applying fertilizer means adding nutrients to the field, and harvesting hay means hauling those nutrients away.

Most importantly, if we want to understand our soil's fertility, we *must* take a soil test. In fact, I wouldn't *begin* to think about spending money until I looked at a recent soil test. *Recent* means within the past 3-4 years. Without a soil test, I would be like a doctor attempting to treat a patient without a chart of temperature, blood pressure, and medical history.

Many laboratories report a bare minimum set of fertility values: namely soil pH, P, K, organic matter, and perhaps a liming recommendation. That's really not enough. We should also get information about soil magnesium, calcium, the *cation exchange capacity* — including the proportion of the CEC taken by each of those minerals — and also something called *buffer pH*, which tells us how much limestone is needed to increase the pH of an acidic soil. Many commercial laboratories provide this information at reasonable prices, so look around.

Another question to ask: how do we intend to graze this field? Set-stocking, or some version of rotational grazing, or full-blown MIG, where we allocate feed by adjusting the internal fence lines and stocking densities throughout the year? No single forage will excel in *all* these grazing systems, and some species will assuredly die out in some of these systems.

Notice one question I *haven't* asked: namely, "What's a good seed mixture for sheep?" (or cattle, or llamas, or whatever). Although this may be the common question producers initially ask, it's not as relevant as it sounds. *All* forages provide high nutritional quality during certain periods of their growth cycle. *All* forages will work for sheep under certain types of management conditions. It's up to us, as managers of the field, to choose the right conditions.

From an animal perspective, we are interested in forage intake, palatability, physical attributes that may influence intake, and of course, health risks. Forages may indeed differ in palatability, although when they are young and vegetative, those differences are not as much as their reputations might suggest. We really need to know about the *extreme* species: forages at the *extreme low* end of the palatability scale, like the older varieties of tall fescue and reed canarygrass, or at the *extreme high end* of the scale, like the high-sugar ryegrasses or the new varieties of chicory and plantain. Forages at either extreme of the palatability scale can be problems in a mixed-species pasture because without careful management, they will either take over the pasture or disappear from it. On the physical side, some forages like reed canarygrass can quickly grow too tall and rank for animals to consume. Some stiff-leafed forages, like grazing corn, may cause tiny facial abrasions that can increase the risk of eye problems. And some forages are associated with well-known health risks like bloat, endophyte, alkaloids, and estrogens. (Just spend an hour on the internet to see lots of scary information about these issues.)

Let's get back to our original question: if we want to renovate, what do we plant? Or — dare I say this — should we plant anything at all? If a field is not "doing well" under our current management system, then before pouring money into renovation, why not first try changing our management? We can easily do some new things: apply fertilizer and/or lime, sharpen our grazing skills, change the stocking density, etc. Then see what happens. If a year passes and we only have more moss in the field, well, then it's clear that we *do* need to plant some new seed.

But here's the catch: even if we spend the money to renovate the field, *we still must change our management*. A field is a complex ecosystem, and the plants growing in that field now are the species and varieties that have thrived under our recent management. Even *no* management is a type of management. So, if we renovate a field by spending money on seed, equipment, and fertilizer but if we don't change our management, then, after a few years, what do you think will be growing in our field?

Because if we don't change our management, that field will truly become a money pit.

First Published: May 2001
Author's Note: This is the most basic of recommendations: change the management. In some ways though, it may be the hardest, because it may mean changing a way of thinking. We can easily get caught up in the excitement of fertilizer, seed, fencing, and equipment. But changing management is the real key to success.

Section 4

Forage Growth
& Storage

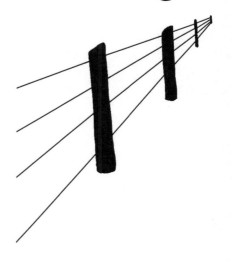

Spring Flush

Green grass at last! These first beautiful days of spring; deep blue skies, white puffy clouds, a delicious warmth in the sunshine. And look at that grass! Emerald green, three inches high, like those legendary green hills of Ireland. My pastures are really growing in this spring sunshine. It's time to get my sheep out of the barn. Finally, after all these grim winter months, I'll open the gate and let the girls out onto those pastures. The sheep will have a great time, and I'll also save some hay and finally get a chance to clean the barn . . .

Does this sound familiar? Every year there comes a day, a bright, clean, warm day in March or April or early May, depending on your area, when you just *know* that it's time to move the sheep onto that wonderful young grass. You're exhausted from feeding hay around the barn all winter. Besides, the hay or silage is running low, and the bedding is pretty thick. So you think: it's time to turn the page and move into summer mode, to trail the sheep away from the barn and move them out onto those green fields.

We've all been there. It's so tempting. But here's the rub: when we turn sheep onto that first flush of green pasture in the early spring, we are doing more than giving the animals great feed and giving ourselves relief from feeding hay. We are virtually guaranteeing we will have lower forage yields from that field, reduced persistence of our best forages, increased risks of weed intrusion, and higher expenses for the entire year.

Huh? Let's talk.

I'm not, of course, disputing the fact that grazing grass is cheaper than feeding stored hay or silage. That's almost always true — when we focus on the short-term effects. But when we look at our pastures, we need to look at the bigger picture. Grazing too early usually causes damage to our forages, and we should consider the seasonal and long-term ramifications of this.

165

What are the characteristics of these early spring pastures? Well, the earliest growth is almost exclusively grass, not legumes. This is primarily because cool-season grasses begin growing when soil temperatures reach 40°, while the cool-season legumes (clovers, alfalfa, birdsfoot trefoil) don't start growing until soil temperatures reach 50°. Which means that our early spring pastures are composed mostly of young grass plants. No surprise there, but let's think about this for a moment. Let's say that those young plants are only 2–4 inches high. Since they don't have much leaf area yet, those young plants may be still drawing nutrients from their reserves. Yes, I know that leaf photosynthesis is clearly active in this beautiful sunshine, but its rate is still much lower than it will be in two weeks because the young plants haven't produced enough solar panels yet. In a technical sense, the forage in these young fields is in the Phase I part of the growth curve, with a total mass of probably less than 600 lb of forage dry matter per acre.

This young grass is very palatable and nutritious: 20% crude protein or higher, with an extremely high digestibility. It's also relatively low in dry matter at 15% or less (hence the occasional moniker *washy grass*). Basically, our field is composed of very lush, very palatable grasses that are high in energy and protein and low in dry matter. The sheep love it, especially coming off that barn hay. Just ask them.

But now for the big issues. Putting livestock onto early pastures when the grass is only 2–4 inches high can really stress the plants. Those young grasses are just beginning to manufacture carbohydrates from photosynthesis. Their nutrient reserves are being depleted and have not yet been replenished. When animals graze those plants and defoliate them, what nutrients are available for *regrowth*? Not much, which forces these small plants to regrow slowly as they recreate more leaves.

Here's another thing: young grasses, especially annual species, will not have developed an extensive root system yet, meaning that grazing animals can easily pull these plants out of the ground. Either way, grazing spring plants too early puts them under quite a bit of stress.

Let's also consider some plant genetics. The grasses that come up first in the early spring are some of our most desirable plants. These are the species and varieties that respond quickly and aggressively to warm conditions. When we stress these plants and reduce their ability to thrive and reproduce, we are in effect *putting selection pressure against our earliest forages*. We are systematically putting these plants at a competitive disadvantage compared to species that will come up later. Therefore, our grazing management, instead of encouraging our earliest plants to thrive and provide high yields early in the season, is causing great stress on these grasses and creating conditions that favor other plant species that will emerge later and/or are less palatable.

Here's another risk that occurs during an early grazing period, especially if the stocking density is too high: the young plants can be *overgrazed*. Animals can easily damage the growing points, which are close to the ground. If left intact, healthy growing points would ultimately develop into tillers (secondary shoots), but if these growing points are damaged, the plants will produce fewer tillers, especially later in the season. Bunch grasses like orchardgrass and tall fescue rely on tillers to thicken the pasture and provide more leaf area. But grazing too early damages the growing points, which means these species won't produce many tillers later in the season. The result: lower yields, weaker plants, and more open spaces between the plants.

Speaking of open space, we know that nature abhors a vacuum, particularly in a pasture. If our early grasses cannot thrive and grow well, openings will develop between the plants. *Something else* will grow in these openings. Like weeds. And forages like the low-growing, low-yielding grasses and legumes that come up later and have growing points low to the ground — such as some of the bentgrasses, foxtails, medics, and even the bluegrasses. This results in two important consequences: (1) increased costs for weed control, and (2) establishment of forages that are less desirable and lower-yielding.

Okay, we get the idea. But still, that early green grass looks awfully attractive! If we must stay off those beautiful fields, what are some alternative strategies?

Well, the first and most obvious strategy is to wait. Stay in the barn, don't open the gate. Be patient for another two or three weeks, especially if the weather is warm. Continue to feed hay or silage, just like you've been doing for the past few months. Let that grass grow! Give your plants a chance to establish better roots, create more leaf solar panels, and begin to replenish their nutrient reserves. I know it's hard, and that pasture is *soooo* tempting. But the dollars-and-cents analysis of grazing too early is a sobering exercise. If you still have some stored feed, it's worth your trouble to feed it for another couple of weeks. If you're out of feed, maybe you can get some from a neighbor.

Another strategy is to find some alternative feeds for those couple of weeks. Are there any byproducts nearby? Old hay? Dried distillers grains? Last year's onions? Again, this is just a stopgap. Did you plant turnips last summer that are still in the field because you didn't quite use them all in the fall? If you haven't looked for alternative feeds, this could be a good chance to explore.

Here's a strategy that takes some planning: during the previous summer, identify one or two fields as your early-forage fields. Select them wisely, like fields with south-facing slopes that warm up first in the spring. Especially fields with good drainage so the soil warms quickly. These are fields that always seem to turn green earlier than the others. We usually have one or two of these fields on the farm. Then plant them specifically with forages that specialize in early growth. Your goal is to have forages that will explode out of the ground as soon as the snow melts and the soil temperature starts to rise. Every region of the country has forages that will do this: small grains like winter rye, wheat, oats, or triticale. Or annual ryegrass, or some of the Italian ryegrasses, or crested wheatgrass. Or plants that were stockpiled over the winter, like tall fescue or the forage brassicas or last fall's turnips. In any case, you need to plan this strategy in advance and plant the annuals during the previous summer or fall. The reward is that you have forages to graze early in the following spring while keeping animals off the rest of your fields for a few extra weeks.

Here's an outside the box strategy: overgraze a field in early spring *on purpose*. Why? Because you're managing that field as a *sacrifice area*. Yes, this can be a real strategy. In this strategy, you want to graze that early forage and stress those plants because you don't care about regrowth, because you plan to renovate that field later in the season or use it for a different crop. While it sounds a bit weird, a sacrifice area is a perfectly valid strategy. It can be a powerful management tool if used well.

Finally, let's think of our neighbors. Seriously. Maybe someone down the road has a field or two that needs "cleaning up." It has grass; you have sheep. Maybe you can reach a deal: you can help them out with weed- and brush-control and reduce the fire danger. You'll get early feed, your pastures get a rest during the early spring, and your neighbors get a clean field. Not bad.

Early spring is indeed a wonderful time. Those gorgeous spring days brighten your life and make you want to jump up and click your heels. So do it! Enjoy yourself in the sunshine. But keep the sheep off those fields for another couple of weeks. Your pastures will thank you for it.

First Published: April 2015
Author's Note: Grazing too early in the spring is one of the most common problems in grazing management. It's one of those perennial issues that you hear about in workshops all around the country. The universal warning is "just say no," but in practice, that's easier said than done. Nonetheless, the consequences will come back to haunt. Guaranteed.

Competition, Success, Pasture

Competition is a wonderful thing. Competition has produced Michael Jordan, Billie Jean King, and Secretariat. In a pasture, however, competition can work against a farmer by destroying clover and producing a mat of low-yielding bentgrass. Why?

A perennial pasture is like any baseball field or basketball court — a competitive arena, where instead of home runs, winning a pasture competition means survival and reproduction. Forage plants must compete for space, light, water, and nutrients. During this contest, plants must stay healthy and strong, or else they will fall away and be replaced by more aggressive, robust plants. And just like any other athletic event, the outcome can be altered by strategy and execution.

Let's look at the common practice of grazing pastures in the very early spring. A pundit once noted that throughout most of the United States, the grazing season coincides perfectly with the baseball season. Whoa! So let's focus our sports analysis on those first few weeks of pasture spring training . . .

In the early spring, soil temperatures range between 40° and 50° — warm enough for grass growth but not yet warm enough for most legumes. (In western Oregon, legumes only grow well after soil temperatures reach 50°.) Almost overnight, pastures seem to explode into that bright green color of young growth. The grass blades are small, succulent, and highly nutritious.

As we walk out to the fields after a long winter, we see the beginnings of the spring. We see the first green growth in the pastures and promptly put our animals out there to graze it. They are happy campers. They consume as much

169

grass as they can, and each day, they do it again and again and again. We are happy because our animals look good and we don't have to feed hay. We know that even the Chicago Cubs win a few games during spring training. All seems well with the world.

But many spring grasses are decidedly *not* happy. They are desperately fighting to survive. Those young plants must initially subsist on storage compounds from their seeds or roots. Only when the emerging shoots grow more leaf surface area do they begin to photosynthesize enough nutrients for the entire plant. Until then, however, the young plants continue to draw down their reserves.

And along come our hungry sheep and cattle that happily bite off those young leaves or pull them from the ground. The animals then move on, searching for more leaves. Meanwhile, our grass plants send out a fresh set of leaves and draw *more* nutrients from their reserves.

What happens if our animals stay in the same paddock? They soon find those new shoots again — after all, what else do they have to do all day? And for those unfortunate plants, the cycle goes around once more. And again, they must draw nutrients from their reserves.

Until there are no more reserves. Or until those young plants are so weakened that they die from a nematode infestation or a rust or any other stress they could normally withstand. The practical result is that, over time, plants under stress tend to disappear from the sward.

Which plants? Our best plants. When given a choice, our animals tend to graze the fast-starting, most palatable species and varieties. These are the plants that we would like to retain in our pastures. When we allow our animals to hammer them mercilessly in the spring, we create an environment that does not favor them. Weakened plants cannot compete well for sunlight and nutrients against healthier, less-palatable plants. In effect, we have designed a competitive arena that kills the wrong plants.

Meanwhile, faced with all those delicious shoots of our best plants, our animals tend to ignore the plants that are less palatable. Like, in our area, tall fescue, bentgrass, and thistle.

These species continue to grow because the animals don't eat them. As these plants mature, they become more fibrous compared with the other, younger species, and, therefore, even *less* palatable and nutritious. Their shade makes it harder for smaller plants to obtain sunlight and also creates a humid understory that encourages the growth of fungi and other leaf diseases that can further stress smaller plants.

During the early spring, some of these smaller plants are clovers because legumes begin their growth considerably later than grasses. Although clovers can manufacture their own nitrogen through the Rhizobium bacteria in their roots, they still need sunlight for photosynthesis. If a clover seedling is shaded out by the taller grasses, its ability to compete for nutrients is crippled.

Over time, the winners of this pasture competition are the less-palatable, early-maturing plants. These species successfully propagate themselves in the sward, while the other, more desirable forage species struggle to survive.

Many western Oregon ranchers routinely try to renovate their older pastures by planting mixtures of perennial ryegrass, annual ryegrass, orchardgrass, tall fescue, subclover, red clover, and white clover. These are good, dependable forage species. But after only four or five years, those fields have evolved back into stands of tall fescue, bentgrass, and thistle, with only a little subclover. Just look around.

The problem is set-stocking livestock onto early spring growth. *Set-stocking in the early spring is both understocking and overstocking at the same time. Understocking* because animals have the luxury of selecting their favorite plants and ignoring other plants. *Overstocking* because there are too many animals consuming the palatable plants, and the animals can relentlessly hammer those plants into the ground.

A solution? One good strategy is to keep animals off those very early pastures, in spite of temptation. Locate an alternative site for those animals, like a sacrifice area. Use those hooves to help replant that area, and then, when animals can finally be allowed onto the spring pastures, plant lots of fence posts. Fencing controls grazing. Move animals off a paddock when plants are grazed down to an appropriate residual mass. Controlled grazing makes animals consume all the plants to a target residual mass. That forces the less-desirable plants like bentgrass and thistle to compete directly against the ryegrasses on a level playing field (so to speak) — and the ryegrasses will usually win. The clovers will also have a better chance to flourish because they aren't shaded out. And the bentgrasses are not permitted to go to seed quickly, which slows down their establishment.

And the Chicago Cubs? I'm not sure if planting fence posts will help them win a pennant. But it can't hurt.

><

First Published: April 1996

Author's Note: As I reviewed this article before the publication of this book, the Chicago Cubs were actually in first place in their Division, with the best win-loss record in Major League Baseball. Oh well. But this still doesn't mean that we should graze our early spring pastures and ignore the consequences of competition.

Saving for Summer

Let's think outside the box about stockpiling.

Stockpiling is a well-known strategy for creating a field of high-quality forages that has been saved back for winter feed. Producers stockpile forages by closing off one or more fields during the late summer. They then fertilize those fields and let the forages accumulate vegetative growth during the remaining months of the growing season. Once winter begins and the plants become dormant, livestock are then let into the fields to graze the standing forage as a nutritious feed. Stockpiling for winter is popular in many regions of the country, but here in western Oregon, we've turned this concept upside down to fit our needs.

Stockpiling, in its broadest sense, creates high-quality forage to be used during a period when forages don't grow. Folks usually associated stockpiling with *winter* feed. Agronomically, winter is a very convenient season because forage growth during the months prior to winter is usually vegetative, with high levels of digestibility and protein. *Tall fescue* is particularly well-suited for late-summer stockpiling because its autumn growth is quite nutritious and its relatively stiff leaves stand up well under snow.

But in western Oregon on the rainy west side of the Cascade Mountains, things are different. Winter is *not* our period of dormancy. Quite the opposite. Our period of dormancy is summer. Our rainy season begins in October or November and continues until late spring or early summer. Winter temperatures rarely drop below freezing, and soil temperatures remain above 40°. In nonirrigated pastures, forages are dormant in the dry summer. They begin growing again in the fall, and growth continues slowly through the winter and then explosively during the spring.

Although winter may indeed be a hard time for feed in western Oregon, there is *some* forage growth, and there's even more if we fertilize properly. In

173

contrast, our hardest feed period is during the *summer*, when there is no rain at all, and without water, *no* forage growth. None, nada, zip. The hills and nonirrigated fields become golden and bone dry — lovely for photographs but desolate as a feed supply. Ranchers typically wean their lambs and calves at the end of spring and sell them because they have no high-quality forage in the summer.

Stockpiling could be an attractive option in western Oregon, but nature presents us with a problem. The seasons are topsy-turvy. If we tried a typical stockpiling procedure in our permanent pastures, we would close off the fields in April, fertilize, and let the forage accumulate until midsummer. But let's think about this: what happens to growing forages in the spring? Simple: they rush to maturity and then set seed. Their nutritional value plummets. By early summer, the resulting forage would be a large crop of standing straw, with digestibility below 48% and crude protein less than 6%. Not exactly what we had in mind as a green summer feed and certainly not useful for good rates of gain or high milk production. Actually, some folks occasionally create this type of forage anyway when they can't cut their hay until July. We may laughingly call it "4th of July hay," but it's not exactly a source of pride.

Our problem in western Oregon is to provide nutritious standing forage during our dry summer. How can we solve it? Let's pose this question from a different tack: what forages produce vegetative growth in late-spring and still retain that leafy green forage for weeks or months into a dry period?

Ranchers in our producer forage groups decided to address this problem and conduct a forage growth trial. Basically, they needed alternative forages. So they put their heads together and decided to try planting some nontraditional forages or use other forages in nontraditional ways. Our basic concept was to plant these forages in the rainy spring, let them grow, and hope they would still retain their green leaves into the summer. We focused our efforts on a few promising species: Italian ryegrass, winter wheat, winter oats, peas, rape and other forage brassicas, plantain, sorghum-sudangrass, and some late-maturing varieties of orchardgrass, tall fescue, and 'Matua' prairie grass.

Why *Italian* ryegrass? Because annual ryegrass genetics comes in two basic flavors, and we only wanted one of them. The two types are (1) the *Westerwold* annual ryegrasses, which are strict annuals that will always go to seed during their first year of life, no matter when they are planted, and (2) the *Italian* annual ryegrasses, which require a winter experience (*vernalization*) to stimulate their reproductive growth. If planted in the spring, the Italian ryegrasses will grow vegetatively through the first season and only go to seed at the end of their *second* spring. Sounded good to us. The same principle applies to winter wheat and winter oats planted in the spring, and so we also tried these plants.

For the past two summers, we conducted practical stockpiling trials on member ranches. These trials, mind you, did not follow strict experiment-station protocols that are based on small, tightly controlled test plots with many replications. No scientific journal will ever consider publishing our results. But we weren't trying to look at decimal places. We designed these trials to provide general impressions about vegetative forage growth, across multiple management styles and fertility levels, and with plots large enough to show practical results.

Specifically, during each spring, ranchers could plant up to four types of forages, with each forage sown in 0.5-acre nonirrigated plots as monocultures (one type of seed per plot). Ranchers had to prepare their seedbeds properly and till the soils (no tread-in methods were permitted). They had to fertilize according to their soil tests and allow unhindered plant growth into the summer. Five ranches grew plots in the first year; seven ranches grew plots in the second year. Over the course of the trial, we observed things that worked and things that didn't.

Some species didn't produce much feed: the oats and wheat and the spring-planted perennial grasses like tall fescue, orchardgrass, and 'Matua.' The large seeds of oats and wheat seemed to provide an attractive feed for the crows, but not much else. The sorghum-sudangrass did show some promise, but as a warm-season grass it also carried a special risk in a dryland situation: if planted too early, the seeds would rot in the cool, wet soil; if planted too late, the young plants would run out of moisture before they could provide any meaningful yield. But when it did successfully produce a healthy stand, that field produced *a lot* of green feed.

We observed that some forages worked quite well: specifically, the Italian ryegrasses, the *improved* hybrid varieties of forage brassicas, the peas, and the plantain. These forages had their own unique characteristics, but each provided some green feed when all the surrounding fields were gold and dry. We have photographs of trial plots that look like square, emerald-green islands amid expanses of dry yellow grass.

Our results are more than just interesting. Standing high-quality forage during the early summer gives us some marketing options that we didn't have previously. We can retain our animals for longer periods, put on some additional weight, develop future-delivery contracts for periods when the market may be better, or we can use this forage to improve the body condition of breeding stock or flush ewes for summer mating. Maybe not everyone's cup of tea, but at least it gives us more management choices.

After seeing the lush growth of some green Italian ryegrass in June, one surprised rancher asked me, "What did you put in that seed?" Nothing, really, except a little thinking outside the box. But instead of calling it just "Stockpiling," we should be more specific and call it *Summer* Stockpiling.

First Published: April 2004

Author's Note: This was one of those straightforward experiments that was relatively easy to conduct on working farms and ranches. We used large test plots and looked for obvious differences in yield and color (which were pretty easy to see — the difference between yellow and green). The result was that we gained practical information we could use in future plantings. And in subsequent years, that information was indeed used.

Dry Times, Stretching Feeds

It's been such a dry year in Douglas County that some ranchers began feeding hay in August. Annual rainfall is down 40%. Autumn pastures are tawny brown, bone dry, closely grazed. Many ranchers have already used up half their winter feed supply, and the really cold weather hasn't even begun . . .

How can we stretch our feed? Buying more hay may get very expensive — hay prices are definitely going to climb. So let's look at some options, while we still have a few left. (Just a few. My space is limited.)

Our basic choices are fairly simple: (1) conserve what we have, (2) find alternative feeds, or (3) reduce our needs. This is a good time to plan, *before* we're down to that last row of bales.

But first, a bovine caution: watch out for pine needles. Not those in the haystack, but those on the ground. Fallen needles of ponderosa pine (*Pinus ponderosa*, also called "yellow pine") can be toxic to cattle. Cows in late pregnancy that consume enough pine needles will abort. The *isocupressic acid* in these needles apparently reduces uterine blood flow, causing a premature and usually fatal birth. And that's not all. Ponderosa pine needles also contain other toxins that cause symptoms like retained placentas and kidney damage. Unfortunately, in dry autumns like this year, pine needles may be the only plentiful thing on ground. Hungry cattle often develop a taste for them. The good news is that these toxins may only be plentiful in ponderosa pine, not Douglas fir, cedar, or any other conifer. Interestingly, ponderosa pine needles don't affect sheep, goats, or deer.

Back to our situation: how can we stretch feed supplies? Firstly, we should try to conserve our existing supplies. I don't mean to feed less, but rather just

177

become more efficient. For example, it's pretty easy to unroll those big bales behind a tractor. The last time I looked, however, sheep and cattle don't just eat around the edges of that long ribbon of hay — they walk on top of it, eating here and there, stomping some into the ground, soiling a lot more. In general, unrolling big bales directly onto the ground can waste nearly 50% of the forage. That's a lot of wasted hay in times of shortage. Tossing small bales onto the ground may be only slightly less spectacularly wasteful. Economically, a 50% wastage effectively doubles the true price of your forage. Not good, unless you own stock in international hay market consortiums.

Solution: buy, build, or borrow a hay feeder (or two or three . . .). There's no problem with mud around hay feeders now — there's no water on the ground, which is why we have no forage. Hay feeders may be an old, often-repeated recommendation, but this year they may be worth more than normal. There are lots of hay feeders on the market. Blueprints are also readily available in most Extension publications, like in the series of Handbooks from the Midwest Plan Service. You might want to be careful with some big bale feeders, however, because they may have a slight design problem: they can tip over and squash lambs or calves. Ask your neighbors about their experiences with different brands.

Pelleting forages is another conservation option. This technique has pros and cons. Pelleting certainly reduces waste. It also costs money. Pelleting allows a rancher to incorporate various supplements and medicines into the pellet, thus giving more control over the ration. Pelleting may increase feed intake, but the trade-off is that it also forces animals to eat *everything* in the forage, including all the less-digestible fiber. This actually reduces the digestibility of the consumed feed. Pelleting is a case-by-case option. For some ranches, pelleting may be a practical and economical option, for other ranches, not so. A sharp pencil helps.

Another possibility: find more pasture. There are all sorts of unused fields around this county that are ripe for short-term leases: crop aftermath, old orchards, land belonging to absentee owners. All these fields need is fencing, water, minerals, stock, and a couple of signs to warn off the coyotes (assuming the coyotes can read). Small flocks are particularly mobile. You may need to ride up and down back roads and work the phones like a telemarketing agent, but you *might* turn up something. Of course that grass will be very mature — old growth tall fescue, a veritable fire danger. But it *will* provide some nutrition, especially if it is stocked lightly enough to allow animals to sort (choose) their feed. You'd be surprised how well ewes and cows can hold their condition on a mature-looking pasture, *if* they're allowed select the most nutritious vegetation. Ewes in early pregnancy or maintenance, spring-calving cows, and horses are all good candidates for this type of fall pasture. This strategy will also relieve grazing pressure on your own pastures, so your young plants will have a better chance to grow when the next rains come.

What about grain? There's an old rule of thumb: *one pound of grain can replace two pounds of hay.* But there are some limitations: This rule is based on the relative amounts of *digestible energy* in grain and in hay. Pound for pound, grain (corn, barley, wheat, etc.) generally has twice as much available energy as typical hay and is generally a better buy. But this rule does not apply to protein. In fact, most grains have *less* protein than a good-quality hay. Lack of protein can wreak nutritional havoc with ewes in late gestation or early lactation or with fall-calving cows. With these animals, you can't just willy-nilly replace two pounds of 16% alfalfa hay with one pound of 10% corn and call it good.

One solution: substitute a reasonably priced protein source for some of the grain. For example, in Douglas County, we routinely replace straight corn with a corn-pea mixture. Cull peas usually contain more than 22% crude protein. Mixing corn and peas 50:50 give us a feed of roughly 16% protein, which is usually close enough. One pound of this mixture can properly replace two pounds of good hay for animals that need the extra protein. (Recall also that grains are low in calcium. You may need to adjust ration calcium levels if you feed a lot of grain.)

And finally, can we reduce our forage needs? Sure. Most standard drought recommendations suggest that you cull a few animals. For what they're worth, here are *my* no-nonsense culling guidelines: all nonpregnant animals should go. All animals with low genetic values should go. All animals that got in your way during the year should go. All animals with political affiliations should go. And any animal that ever considered jumping a fence should go.

This way, you'll have so much extra feed that you'll be tempted to buy more animals. It's good for the national economy.

First Published: November 1994

Author's Note: I wrote this article before the internet became popular, before we routinely went online to find things like hay for sale, rentable acreage, and markets for extra animals. But the principles of dry times are still valid: conserve feed, find more feed, and reduce the need for feed. And in today's world, you can also go online in addition to making phone calls. It's progress, yes, but we still can't simply phone home for some rain.

Hard Decisions

The weather is forcing us to make some hard decisions this year. Western Oregon is famous for its tall trees, lush green pastures, and winters that are long, gray, and rainy. So famous that in the mid-1800s, more than 300,000 farmers and other emigrants trekked across the continent to settle in the Oregon territory, which was touted as the place "where the rains never fail." Every year, our rainy season begins in the fall. The skies usually dump 35–80 inches of rain across the region. By the time the dry season begins in June, the Cascade mountains are loaded with snow, and the pastures have grown lush yields of grass. But not this year.

Sure, the autumn rains began normally enough, with lots of moisture and cold weather in November and December. But in January, someone turned off the spigot. We've received only 6 inches of rain instead of the usual 16 inches since January — a 60% shortfall — and since early April it's been exceptionally dry and warm. Of course, compared to Texas two years ago or to the eastern Corn Belt last year, our situation may seem rather mild, but this season's weather forebodes some hard times for us. The pastures are maturing quickly, more than a month early. Forages are rapidly going to seed, and hay yields are down by 50%. Compared to normal water volumes, local river flows are down by more than 60%. By early July the area will be so parched that the fire danger will rise to extreme levels. In western Oregon, an extreme fire danger level for such a long period — from mid-July until the rains begin in the autumn — is a very scary prospect.

And the lifeblood of summer forage growth, irrigation, may well become unreliable this year. Water is a precious commodity in the West. Every state has a complex set of laws and traditions that control water: who can use it, how much, and when. Farmers, ranchers, urban communities, even the salmon — all have claims on water. Oregon farmers and ranchers are allowed to draw water from rivers for irrigation. But when river levels drop too low, the county watermasters begin cutting off irrigation permits, first by age of claim (newer contracts are cut off sooner than older contracts), but then, if necessary, they cut off water for everyone. This year, because the rivers are already running so low, we fear that by midsummer there may not be any irrigation water available for any farm.

As I write this in May, what can we do? A drought is not a sudden event like a hurricane or an earthquake. In a drought, the dryness comes slowly, creeping, almost imperceptible. First there are weeks of beautiful clear days, warm nights, and glorious sunsets. The changes are insidious and quiet, but folks begin to notice the pattern. Is it really a drought? The grass looks so good. Surely the rain will come soon, but things are not what they seem. When do we make decisions about this drought?

At our forage group meetings, with knowledgeable and progressive farmers and ranchers, we are discussing this situation in detail. We are weighing options and alternatives — while we still have some. Because if things progress as we fear they might, our options will become very narrow indeed.

It's all about feed and money and risk. We face some hard decisions. The basic question is: will there be enough livestock feed for the next 6–8 months? I'll share some of our options.

The main decision is about timing: should we do anything *now*, or should we wait and see if things get better or worse? Whichever way we choose, it's a gamble, a bet. If we proceed to sell sheep or buy extra feed or plant an unusual crop *now*, we're really betting that the future will bring hard times, so we need to take our losses now or spend money now. The alternative is to do nothing now and hope for the best. It's like that old Clint Eastwood movie where Dirty Harry asks, "Do you feel lucky?"

Most producers here feel strongly that doing nothing now is *not* a good choice. So, if we must act now, our decisions involve two basic strategies about livestock feed: (1) reduce the amount of feed needed, and (2) increase the amount of feed available.

Here's the first strategy: reduce the amount of feed needed: (I'll use bullet points to make my notes more succinct and readable.)

- Cull animals now. Cull much deeper than normal. If our normal culling rate is 8%, then this year we may cull 20% or more. Cull, cull, cull — now, before everyone else in the region starts selling and depresses the market further. This can be a big feed savings. If a 160-lb ewe consumes 4% of her body weight in dry matter (DM), that means she eats 64 lb DM per day. That's 192 lb DM per month. A 20% cull of a 100-ewe flock saves 2.1 tons of hay each month (= 20 ewes x 192 lb, then divide by 0.9 to convert DM to actual hay and divide by 2,000 lb to convert to tons).

- Our reasons to cull: anything. Poor production, lambing problems, inability to raise twin lambs, ketosis, hypocalcemia (milk fever in ewes), tendency to bloat, tendency to jump fences, butting, poor wool, whatever. We used to joke that some of these animals are "our best ewes." Not this year. This year is a difficult year. We need to make decisions that we would not normally make.
- Other reasons to cull: poor EPDs (EBVs) — for those producers who use careful production records and modern genetic evaluations. Also, susceptibility to internal parasites. Use the FAMACHA technique to identify animals that are most susceptible to *Haemonchus* parasites (the Barber-pole worm that sucks blood and causes anemia). A general rule of thumb with worms is that 20% of the ewes carry 80% of the parasites. We can use FAMACHA to identify those animals and then get rid of them.
- Big animals eat more than small animals. It's a scientific fact. When weighing alternatives, and all else being equal, cull the larger ewes before the smaller ewes.
- But culling animals is not all bad. It really cuts out the bottom of a flock, leaving the better animals on the ranch and effectively increasing production and efficiency.
- Accept the reality that we might make mistakes and cull some good animals. Of course, we try to minimize these errors, but unfortunately, in the face of a drought, they're really the cost of doing business.
- Wean lambs early — at 60 days or even less if you know what you are doing. Move the lambs to the best pastures or to grain. Put ewes on a weight-loss program. Unlike beef cows that are always in production (gestation or lactation), ewes have a long maintenance period before becoming pregnant again. We should use this to our advantage. Save feed with the ewes; allow them to lose body condition. But this strategy takes some good animal husbandry skills to know when to stop and how to bring them back up in condition when necessary.
- Do as much as possible to save feed *now*, as early as possible. Each day of saving feed preserves more feed for the future and increases our chances of saving the integrity of the flock.

And now the second strategy: increase the amount of feed available:

- For irrigated pastures, apply fertilizer now, especially if you have good, responsive forage in those pastures. Even if fertilizer prices are high, consider the alternatives. Fertilizing now will give a boost for the next 60-80 days. Even if irrigation is cut off midsummer, those fields will still have more vegetative feed that will last longer into a dry period.
- For nonirrigated pastures, the question is: do you take a chance with fertilizer? Probably not. Because our growing season is quickly coming to a close, and most perennial forages are going into dormancy. Unless we get a lot of rain distributed nicely during the next few weeks — a very unlikely prospect — we can expect little forage growth. Again, a gamble. Bet with the odds and use the money on other things.
- Buy hay and other feedstuffs now, as much as cash flow and availability and storage space allows. Look for oddball feedstuffs, byproducts, grains, supplements, last year's hay, etc. Prices, at least locally, will only rise as the drought deepens. We already have reports that hay supplies statewide will be very low. Sure, a record national corn crop will cause national grain prices to fall, but there are a lot of unknowns there, and those national factors are out of our control. Buying decisions are local and must be made now.
- This year, spring forage growth was so poor that there will be many local hay fields with very poor yields, especially if the owners did not apply fertilizer earlier in the season. Those owners may decide that it's not worth their time and expense to use their equipment for harvesting such small yields. But those fields may represent good opportunities for grazing, even if we've never been there previously. First, however, we should estimate the amount of feed in those fields. Then we need to judge if it's worth the time and trouble to move our animals and set up temporary fences.
- What about stock water? In this drought, we can anticipate that some springs may go dry during the summer. This could cause problems for watering sheep on some far pastures. For operations where this might occur, it may be worthwhile to graze those distant pastures earlier in the season rather than later, while stock water is still available. This decision may require flock movements that are not in the normal plan, but again, this is a year for unusual decisions.
- Grow specialized forages. If there is a realistic chance of not receiving irrigation water later in the season, we might still receive enough irrigation water early in the season for one or two water applications. We can take advantage of this by planting annual

forages that can withstand some water stress yet still provide a good yield. Our logical choices: sorghum-sudangrass or sudangrass. Plant, fertilize, and irrigate now before things get worse. Use a BMR (brown-midrib) variety, which has a higher digestibility than traditional varieties. Sorghum-sudangrass can provide *a lot* of feed throughout the summer, and we know how to manage its potential nutritional risks like cyanide toxicity and nitrates. But this family of forages may not be our only choice. Recall that there are also other warm-season, drought-tolerant grasses like teff and millet.

Our forage group discussions have been intense and very serious. Weighing options, stretching our thoughts, and carefully, so carefully, approaching decisions. These have been long sessions. In the end, our calculations resolve into a few main principles: cull, wean, find more feed, do it now.

As I sit here writing, the walls of my office seem very close. It seems like a good time to take a break. I walk outside next to the barn. It's early evening. A light, south wind ripples through the grass in the pasture. The western sky glows red and gold, pale blue overhead, with high thin clouds. Another beautiful evening, but no rain.

First Published: June 2013
Author's Note: We can learn everything possible from our books, from our classes, from our mentors, but still, nature does what it wants. We are in the farming and ranching game. We bring to the table our skills and our knowledge, but when nature runs the table and stacks a lot of points against us, we have to make choices. We make them proactively and intelligently, with knowledge. It's the best we can do.

Water Breakthroughs

Now that the growing season is drawing to a close, let's look at a "what if?" — let's look at irrigation.

I know, irrigation can be a pain. It can be expensive and time-consuming. In the West, we accept irrigation as a way of life, even for pastures and hay fields. If we want to grow any forages during our dry months, we must add water. Alternatively, we can hope that rain will fall, although in the dry western states, that is generally not a very good strategy.

On the other hand, in the East and Midwest and South, water during the summer generally comes from the sky fairly regularly (except when it doesn't). Either way, most farmers in these areas think that supplementary irrigation is an expensive luxury, *especially* for pastures. Irrigation equipment is expensive, and farmers east of the Missouri River would only consider such an investment for high-value row crops. Many university spreadsheets and budgets support this conclusion. But perhaps we should rethink this conclusion for pastures. The last ten years have seen a revolutionary development in pasture irrigation. Some new irrigation equipment is seriously changing the options and finances of using water, especially for pastures.

[Major disclaimer: I am not a company salesman. I don't make a penny by describing this stuff. It's just that this equipment works exceedingly well. It's been used quite successfully by lots of operations on the West Coast, and I think it's something everyone should know about.]

I'm speaking, of course, of the K-Line system for pasture irrigation. Haven't heard of it? Well, I'm sure you can find sales brochures and videos on the internet, but here's a brief description:

The K-Line system consists of flexible, tough, low-density plastic water hoses that can be dragged across the ground. Every 40–50 feet along the hose

187

is a plastic pod that kind of looks like a crockpot, with a sprinkler nozzle inside the pod. Hoses can be up to 400–500 feet long and contain 8–10 pods. One end of the hose is attached to a source of mainline water, and this water is pumped through the hose like any other piped irrigation system (in contrast to, say, flood irrigation). The hose is shifted every 12 or 24 hours. It's incredibly easy to move these hoses — just hook up an ATV (all-terrain vehicle, sometimes affectionately called a 4-wheeler) to the far end of the hose and drag it to the next position in a zigzag pattern across the field.

The K-Line system was originally designed by a farmer on New Zealand's South Island who was trying to create a better and more cost-effective way of irrigating his pastures. The equipment is manufactured in New Zealand by RX Plastics Ltd. There are many irrigation-equipment agents around the United States who carry and sell it. In fairness, I must add that K-Line is not the only pod-line irrigation system in existence. There are other commercial pod-line systems available, at different prices, but this is the one I am most familiar with.

One compelling advantage of a pod-line system is speed. A person riding an ATV can move all the hoses in thirty minutes. Yes, *thirty minutes*. You can move every hose in the system while riding the ATV, at a good speed, and you don't need to turn off the water. This is delightful on a hot summer day, although on a cool morning, you might want to wear rain gear.

The ease of shifting hose is actually a very big deal. It's all about labor and time. In today's world, finding and keeping good labor on a farm is a challenge. Many farm families rely on their children to do chores, but when the kids leave the farm, then what? It's getting harder and harder to find reliable workers willing to move 40-foot aluminum irrigation pipes twice each day, especially in the hot sun. But asking someone to ride an ATV for less than an hour and get a bit wet on a hot summer day — well *that's* a fun job. And instead of spending three hours each summer day moving irrigation pipe, it takes less than an hour to shift hoses. Saving two hours each day for 90 summer days . . . that's a lot of hours that can be used for other things.

These pods also have other benefits. The K-Line system runs at relatively low water pressures — around 45 psi — and requires a smaller pump, putting less stress on the fittings. During operation, the pods sprinkle the water gently, like a spring rain, which improves infiltration into the soil and reduces puddling and runoff. If the farmer has enough pods to allow shifts (called "sets" in irrigation lingo) of 24 hours rather than 12 hours, the longer irrigation period essentially eliminates the problem of wind shear — which occurs when a prevailing 20 mph wind blows the airborne irrigation water constantly in one direction, resulting in some areas of the pasture receiving too much water and some areas receiving little or no water.

Another big plus of the K-Line system is that it is expressly designed for *pastures*, unlike the big irrigation guns and center pivots. The pod-line system with its various hoses can be customized for fields of all sizes and shapes. Since short hoses can be created by using only a few pods, hose length can be adjusted to match the layout of any field, even irregularly shaped or small fields. Dragging the hose across a pasture does not damage grasses or legumes, and hoses can even be safely dragged across annual forages such as brassicas, corn, and sorghum-sudangrass when the plants are short.

There is one caveat, however: cost. A pod system is not the cheapest irrigation system available. The initial cash outlay is a serious investment. But when we look at this from a long-term business perspective, the design flexibility, its low water pressure, and the annual savings of labor and time put a pod-line system in a class by itself.

But enough sales pitch. I really want to speculate about what this system can mean for pastures.

In regions where producers rely on natural rainfall, summer water usually comes in the form of thunderstorms. Although thunderstorms may be exciting events, I would not call them dependable, at least not from an irrigation standpoint. They can drop too much rain or not enough, their path through a county can be erratic, and their timing may leave something to be desired. The rain often falls so hard that there is runoff and pooling. And every year is different, so we never know what is around the corner. But since this situation is normal in many areas, we generally shrug and live with it and hope for the best. It does give us something to talk about in coffee shops.

But *what if* we knew that we were going to have dependable water throughout the growing season? How would that change our options?

For example, if the spring months were particularly hot and dry, we could apply water early 1) to pastures so they would not dry out or go into dormancy, 2) to a new planting of grass and legumes so the seedlings get a good start and establish a thick stand of forage, 3) to summer annuals like sorghum-sudangrass so they consistently provide huge yields. How would a dependable supply of water change our options for planting different types of forages?

High-producing annuals like brassicas and sorghum-sudangrass would become more reliable; there would be less risk of losing an expensive planting or getting a small yield. The famous "summer slump" of Kentucky bluegrass — no more. We could obtain midsummer yields from alternative cool-season perennial grasses like tall fescue and orchardgrass. We could depend on legume pastures during the summer to finish lambs and beef cattle to their market weights. And in some fields, we might consider planting warm-season perennial grasses like the bluestems and switchgrass to take advantage of their high-powered summer growth.

And here's another aspect of dependable summer water. If we grew more forage during the summer, how would that reduce our need for stored feed during the rest of the year, or influence our decisions about obtaining feeder lambs or stocker cattle to graze that summer growth?

Essentially, summer irrigation might open avenues to new opportunities and decisions that we had never previously considered.

The West has depended on irrigation since the first settlers broke sod with their horse-drawn plows. Every state west of the Missouri River has developed an intricate web of laws and regulations and customs that govern water: who owns it; who uses it; how much can be used; when it can be used, etc. But in the East and Midwest and South — well, it's a lot easier to put a pump into the nearest stream and start pumping. And finally we have an irrigation system specifically designed for our pastures.

This new K-Line System is about money, of course. And risk. And opportunity. But this scenario didn't exist in the past. Now we have this new pod-line system. Maybe it's time we look at irrigation in a new light.

First Published: September 2010

Author's Note: When I originally wrote this article, the K-Line System was new to this continent. Times have changed. You can now find pod-line systems around the country, although they are not very common in many areas outside the West Coast. That, in my opinion, should change. See the next article: "Water, Water – Wouldn't It Be Nice?"

Water, Water – Wouldn't It Be Nice?

Let's talk about water . . . irrigation water. Specifically, the things affected by irrigation water: summer forage, business risks, and the possibilities for change.

Every summer, livestock producers across the Midwest and East watch the sky and hope for rain. Pastures and hay fields need water, of course, and across a broad swath of central and eastern North America, the only source is the sky. Thunderstorms are usually welcome unless they wash away the barn, and so are the occasional weather fronts that can bring a steady two-day rain. But if three or four weeks pass without rain, the ground becomes mighty dry. In addition, many cool-season forages regularly go into a *midsummer slump*, when their yields drop precipitously for two months.

You might ask: why don't we irrigate? Well, how much of a gambler are you? Supplementary irrigation comes with a heavy load of costs and risks: the cost of irrigation equipment, the cost of running the pumps, the labor to move pipes all summer, the potential high price of fertilizer, the chances of a bad market year — these are all real factors. In the past, most university budgets have shown that supplementary irrigation in these areas is a very iffy proposition at best, that for Eastern and Midwestern pastures it usually doesn't pay. So, year after year, summer after summer, we watch the sky and hope for rain.

In the West, irrigation is a fact of life. Water is limited, and entire agricultural communities are built around strict water laws: who can use it, how much, and when. Even in rainy western Oregon, the summers are actually bone dry, and nothing grows during the summer without irrigation. Farmers and ranchers here are very familiar with irrigation costs and equipment. During the past 15 years, however, the world of irrigation has experienced a revolution in supplying water to pastures.

We've seen the development of *pod-line irrigation systems.* (The most well known is the "K-Line system," but there are other brands on the market. In this article, I'll call them *pod-line systems* to avoid favoritism.) This equipment is specifically designed for pastures, even for irregularly shaped fields. These systems use less water than most traditional irrigation equipment, and they use that water more efficiently. Once or twice a day, one person on a 4-wheeler moves the pods and hoses across the field, usually in less than thirty minutes, without even turning off the water. Burying moisture sensors in the soil further increases this efficiency because you can turn off the pumps if the soil doesn't need water. Although a pod-line system is not cheap, the steady flow of low-pressure water, like a gentle rain; the ease of movement; the labor efficiency; the labor savings over time — a pod-line system is a horse of a very different color than traditional irrigation equipment.

Let's outline the situation for graziers east of the Mississippi River. Most eastern pastures contain a combination of legumes and cool-season grasses, with warm-season grasses becoming dominant during the summer months in the South. Every forage textbook depicts the forage production year as a two-humped curve: the high hump of spring growth, then a deep trough known as the *summer slump*, then a second, smaller hump in the fall, and finally the curve drops to zero after the killing frost. Every year, graziers face the issues of excess spring growth, insufficient summer feed, and the challenge of saving something in their fields for winter. But the good news is that most Eastern and Midwestern farmers may also have relatively easy access to streams or groundwater.

In light of the new pod-line systems, let's take a fresh look at the potential for irrigating these summer pastures. Farm economists scrupulously develop their analytical spreadsheets that compare forage yields with and without irrigation, taking into account the investment and operational costs of irrigation, the market value and nutritional quality of the extra forage yield, and some current prices. Spreadsheets are wonderful inventions — they rank right up there with hot showers and bowling — but their calculations tend to be one-dimensional. But grass-based livestock operations are not one-dimensional; decisions in any one part of the operation affect the *whole* operation. If we install a pod-line irrigation system into a grass-based grazing operation — opportunities and possibilities can open up that might not appear in a spreadsheet. These may be possibilities worth considering. Let's go there.

If we apply water to summer pastures, the first and most obvious result is greater yield. Which translates to more grazing days (= more livestock on the pasture for the same number of summer days), or more hay. This yield response is typically the main focus of a spreadsheet budget.

But increased yields also imply an important proviso: the forage species in the pasture *must be capable of producing increased yields during the hot summer weather.* Some fields are overgrazed and poorly managed, so they no longer contain high-producing forages. Also, some species like Kentucky bluegrass and perennial ryegrass tend to go dormant in the midsummer heat, so their fertilizer response, even with extra water, may be disappointing.

But here's where we take leave from most of the spreadsheet analyses. If you *were certain* that your fields would have water 100% of the time throughout the summer, you could really change some things. The risk of a water shortage disappears, and you can choose to do things on your farm that would otherwise seem much too risky. For example, you could purchase lots of fertilizer for those fields because you are confident that it would not be wasted.

Speaking of summer yields, you could consider making changes in the mix of forages in those fields. Instead of relying on the old standbys of bluegrass and white clover, maybe you could afford to renovate (drill, broadcast, etc.) — possibly introducing new, highly productive varieties of orchardgrass, 'Matua' prairie grass, festulolium, red clover, chicory, meadow brome, alternative legumes, and the new palatable cultivars of tall fescue (endophyte-free or novel endophyte). Lots of choices here.

Or instead of relying on permanent pastures, you might consider making a major change by planting one or two fields to high-production annuals, especially if you are confident about spending money for fertilizer to support their explosive yields. Forages such as Italian ryegrass or the new hybrid forage brassicas, etc., or forages that *really* specialize in summer growth: the warm-season grasses like sorghum-sudangrass, grazing corn, teff, or millet, along with any of an intriguing array of legumes. Again, more choices.

Having lots of forage during the summer opens up some additional possibilities. You could graze more animals on that acreage, and that translates into carrying more breeding stock or retaining weaned lambs or calves on annual pastures. If you've been feeding hay during the summer, that hay could be postponed for use during the winter, or maybe you wouldn't even need so much hay.

Here's another thought: if you had extra forage during the summer, perhaps you could sell it through someone else's animals — like making arrangements for contract grazing. Especially using a different livestock species to reduce the parasite load. Multi-species grazing by contract. For example, if you have sheep, then someone else's stocker cattle or replacement dairy heifers would do the trick. People could pay you to rent the acreage, or they could pay you on the gain. Your risk of ownership becomes zero. Alternatively, of course, you could buy additional livestock for grazing, but then you assume the risk of owning them.

Another possibility: if you are confident about growing lots of additional forage on irrigated fields, you might also save on winter feed by *winter stockpiling*. Even with partial irrigation, a good stand of tall fescue, managed and fertilized properly, could be saved back as standing feed for the winter. This is a well-known technique in many areas of the country, and on your place, irrigation might make it possible. Or if you plant one of the new hybrid forage brassicas or kale or even leafy turnips, you'll find that these plants can easily stand into the winter, again reducing the need for winter hay.

Let's think even bigger. Let's think about the entire production year. If you've always lambed during the winter but now are guaranteed high-quality forage throughout the summer, why lamb in the winter? If lambing occurred during mid-spring or later, you could get through the winter without having to worry about making and storing high-quality feed, and you could also carry more ewes in better condition during the summer. If you weaned the lambs relatively early, they could be grazed on other fields or be fed separately near the barn, and you'd have lots of good-quality feed for the ewes all summer. So you could run more ewes. Or run fewer ewes and take a vacation.

Or . . . well, you get the drift. Adding water to summer pastures can profoundly impact the operation. It changes the risks of making changes and opens a world of possibilities. Pod-line systems do more than bring water to pastures; they open doors. So, when you look at a budget for supplementary irrigation, look beyond the numbers in those spreadsheets. The old Beach Boys song "Wouldn't It Be Nice" was really about irrigating our pastures.

First Published: July 2016

Author's Note: You might say that this is thinking outside the box, or at least looking at a bigger picture than you usually see inside the box. And for that penultimate paragraph: I kind of like the idea of running fewer animals and taking a vacation. Hawaii, Tahiti, the Cook Islands — I'd go there just to check out the tropical forages, of course.

Old Hay, Good Hay?

There's a common belief that hay stored over a year old is no good — that it isn't worth very much.

Au contraire . . . Old hay can be a great value.

A few years ago, I analyzed some old hay for a client. For nearly three years, he had stored a few leafy alfalfa bales in the back of his barn. That hay analyzed at 23.8% crude protein and 65% TDN, on a dry matter basis — roughly the same protein level as cull peas with an energy density almost as high as wheat bran. Not bad for old hay.

Therefore, can we really assume that old hay stored in a barn *automatically* loses nutritional value? I don't think so.

Consider what happens when we make hay. In essence, we take a three-dimensional snapshot of the growing forage and preserve it in a stable form for future use — kind of like a very large dried flower arrangement. So when can major nutritional losses occur with this hay? Well, most losses occur either while the hay is still in the field *before* it's hauled to the barn, or when the hay is fed to animals *after* the storage period.

In the field, when the green forage is freshly cut and laying in windrows, rain can cause mold growth and loss of nutrients. In very hot weather, excessive drying or raking will cause the nutritionally valuable leaves to *shatter* (an impressive word meaning "to fall off the stems"). After the storage period, when the hay is fed, inefficiently designed feeding facilities (or put less politely, *no* feeding facilities) are notorious for permitting up to 50% wastage of the hay. Also at feeding, wind can blow away the leaves, leaving a higher percentage of poorer quality stems. Not one of these losses, however, occurs *during* the storage period when the hay is actually in the barn.

195

Now let's compare hay to its main alternative: silage. This is also a form of forage preservation, but instead of drying the forage, we pickle it. We take green or wilted forage directly from the field, stuff it into an airtight container, and let it rot. (Actually, another word for this process is *ferment*. Think of sauerkraut — made essentially by the same process.) Not much happens to the forage during the cutting and wilting process in the field, but major nutritional losses can occur *during the storage period.* Inside a silo, silage with too much moisture can lose runoff that contains soluble nutrients; a silage pH that is too high can result in major degradation of protein, not to mention an awful stench; air pockets in the silage will allow mold formation and nutrient loss; and when the silo bunker or bag is opened during the feeding process, the exposed forage will mold if the silage is not consumed fast enough. It's a dangerous world out there.

But can't hay also lose nutritional value during storage? Of course it can, but these losses are relatively easy to avoid by following two rules: (1) don't put wet hay into the barn, and (2) once you successfully put dry hay in the barn, keep it that way.

If stored hay contains more than, say, 15%–18% water, mold can grow on it and use up some of the hay's available energy and protein. But mold growth also leaves telltale evidence — a few quadzillion mold spores, a musty odor, and possibly a yellowish or brownish color that indicates caramelization. This discoloration is due to a *Browning Reaction*, also called the *Maillard Reaction*, a chemical process that converts good quality forage protein into indigestible caramel. This is the number listed in a forage analysis report as *heat-damaged protein.*

And here's a useful rule of thumb: don't cut a hole in the barn roof. Tightly packed hay that becomes damp may mold excessively, heat very badly, and cause the barn to burn down. This is not a good way of controlling excess inventory.

But if stored hay is kept dry, not much bad happens to it. It just sits and sits and sits . . .

There is, however, one minor nutritional exception — Vitamin A. Green hay contains lots of Vitamin A when it is first put up, primarily as the compound *beta-carotene.* Although nutrients such as energy, protein, and minerals are quite stable in dry hay, the life expectancy of beta-carotene is relatively short. Over time, the carotenes are destroyed by oxidation, which is nearly impossible to prevent in dry hay. The bad news is that within a year, most of the hay's original Vitamin A activity has disappeared, even if the leaves are still green. But the good news is that Vitamin A is cheap. A farmer or rancher can go into the local feedstore and buy Vitamin A in a feed supplement, mineral mix, or an injection.

If we can accept the premise that old hay in a dry barn can indeed retain its nutritional value, then we can begin to think like a bargain-hunting shopper at a garage sale. Old hay takes up storage space. A barn is nothing more than the farm equivalent of a warehouse, and farmers are like any other business people . . . they must move old inventory out of their warehouses to make room for the annual new models. Usually at a discounted price.

Therefore, all you have to do is locate good quality old hay. Shop around. When you find an attractive possibility, you can gauge the real value of that hay by doing a few things: 1) estimate the percentage of stems versus leaves — lots of stems indicate a mature forage; 2) look for the presence of legume flowers or grass seed — these suggest that the forage was harvested with a chainsaw; and 3) also look for broadleaf weeds, which could reduce palatability.

Some other tips: discoloration could indicate that the hay was put up damp. Shake some flakes or bales — do they release a lot of dust or have a musty odor? That "dust" is really a cloud of mold spores — more evidence that the hay had been put up wet. Look at the barn roof and walls — any signs of leakage or condensation? Look for rodent droppings; in large amounts, they could affect palatability. And look for signs of barn cats. Cats can carry toxoplasmosis, an abortion disease spread through cat droppings.

So . . . let *everyone else* believe that old hay has a low market value. It's a buyer's market. Stock up on vitamin A injections or supplements, look around for a barn still filled with last year's crop, use your eyes and nose, and begin negotiating a price. Bring your checkbook. You may find a very good deal.

———≺————

First Published: November 1995
Author's Note: When I talk about this topic in my workshops, audience questions come fast and furious. The belief that old hay automatically loses nutritional quality is so ingrained that many folks have a hard time believing otherwise.

Four Guys and a Barn Fire

Watch out for the Maillard Gang this summer. Across the country, these guys sneak into barns and burn them down. Official police documents may list the cause as "suspicious" or "spontaneous combustion," but the real culprit is this gang. There are four members: Amadori, Schiff, Strecker, and their leader, Maillard. They're involved in all sorts of shady deals — but they like to specialize in hay. Our hay.

I'm talking, of course, about wet hay and barn fires. There's no such thing as "spontaneous combustion." The cause is very definite and predictable — it's the notorious Maillard Reaction. Here's the story:

The Maillard Reaction is a complex chain of reactions that can occur between soluble sugars (carbohydrates) and proteins in environments like moist hay. The Maillard Reaction produces a brown, gooey substance that looks a lot like caramel. In fact, it *is* caramel. Two other names for the Maillard Reaction are "non-enzymatic browning" and "caramelization" — the same caramelization that, under the controlled cooking conditions on your stove, creates those chewy, glossy tan confections that bring back pleasant memories of summer beaches and county fairs.

Here's where the four guys come in. The *Maillard* Reaction begins when soluble sugars in moist hay combine with amino acids in that hay to form something called a glycosyl amine. This compound is rather unstable, and its atoms quickly do-si-do into an *Amadori* Rearrangement which then releases one water molecule to form a *Schiff* Base. This molecule then transforms itself in a reaction known as the *Strecker* Degradation by combining with another amino acid and losing a molecule of carbon dioxide. The resulting compounds

199

then polymerize with each other — a process similar to the making of nylon — to form something that looks like an amorphous, brown, yucky mess. This is the final product of the Maillard Reaction: the Maillard polymer.

To understand how the Maillard Reaction affects hay, we need to keep the following details in mind: Firstly, the Maillard Reaction gives off heat (an *exothermic* reaction). Secondly, the reaction goes faster in high temperatures. A rise of ten degrees will more than double its reaction speed. Thirdly, water acts as a *catalyst* to the Maillard Reaction, which means that the presence of water will increase the reaction rate. And finally, the Maillard polymer, which contains 11% nitrogen, is completely indigestible by sheep and cattle. Which means that all its nitrogen and carbohydrates are nutritionally lost to the animals.

Moist hay is prime territory for a runaway Maillard Reaction.

Let's stack some damp hay bales in a barn and see what happens (damp = 22%–24% moisture or higher). Initially, some fungi and bacteria will grow on the moist leaves and stems. This is quite normal. They break down some of the carbohydrates and give off a little heat. Everyone knows that even good hay will heat slightly when first put into a barn (it "sweats"). But here's a kicker: water holds heat. The extra water in damp hay acts as a heat trap, preventing heat from escaping easily into the surrounding air. Since this damp hay contains so much moisture, heat begins to build up in the bales.

Within a couple of weeks, as the internal temperature rises above 130°–140°, the regular fungi and bacteria die off and some heat-resistant fungi begin to flourish. These fungi use up more carbohydrates and add to the heat load in the hay. As the temperature rises to more than 170°, other carbohydrates and proteins in the hay begin to combine on their own, without assistance from any living organisms or enzymes. This is the start of the nonenzymatic browning reaction — the Maillard Reaction — which begins to generate its own heat. The bale temperature soon climbs past 190°. At that point, even the heat-resistant fungi die off. Nothing can live in those bales. As the Maillard Reaction takes over, events spiral out of control. The brown Maillard polymer begins appearing throughout the hay. Moisture accelerates the reaction, and it begins to go faster and faster, generating even more heat. Temperatures climb rapidly. 300°. 400°. At 450°–525°, the flash point of the hay is reached. The surrounding oxygen reacts with the hay. Fire. Explosive fire. Spontaneous combustion. Catastrophe.

If we can stop this process before it gets out of control — like dragging the warm bales from the barn — we'll still have nutritional problems with the hay, but we'll also still have a barn. The nitrogen locked up in that Maillard polymer is nutritionally unavailable to livestock. Which means that the hay's *available* protein is lower than its standard crude protein analysis. For example, if a heat-affected hay analyzes at 16% crude protein, and 25% of its nitrogen is tied up in Maillard polymer, the *available* protein value of that hay is only 12%. The hay will have a slightly yellow-brown tinge to it (hence the name "browning reaction"). A forage report on this hay would list the unavailable portion of the nitrogen as ADIN (acid detergent insoluble nitrogen) or ADICP (acid detergent insoluble crude protein). And we would consider this hay at 12% protein for the purposes of balancing rations.

So now what? Let's step back for a moment. The best way of dealing with the Maillard Reaction is to prevent it, so here are some basic rules of thumb: fungi and bacteria don't survive when the moisture is less than 15%. Less than 15% moisture in any hay is the best of all worlds. (Well, we can hope for good haymaking weather, can't we?) In practice, however, to be safe, square bales should *always* contain less than 22% moisture. Less is better. Large round bales should *always* contain less than 18% moisture when stored in barns because large bales naturally retain internal heat longer than square bales.

And if you're in the market for buying someone else's hay, always look at the color. If you see a yellowing or browning compared to normal hay, or, in the worst case, a blackening, steer clear. Observe the hay under natural light because bluish fluorescent light tends to mask subtle differences in color. Open up the bales. Dustiness means mold spores, and that means that the hay must have been wet enough to allow mold growth some time after it was cut.

Also look at the barn. Are there any holes in the roof that could have dripped water? And finally, is the barn still standing? If not, it's a sure sign that the Maillard Gang was there.

First Published: July 1998

Author's Note: Every now and then, as I drive down country back roads, I come across a loose pile of hay bales just outside a barn. Clearly someone had tossed them into a heap, in a hurry to move them out of the building. No additional explanation is necessary — that silent pile of hay says it all.

Pickled Forage

When we have excess forage and want to preserve it for future use, we really have only three practical choices: we can let it stand in the field or we can store it as hay or we can store it as silage. The first option means that the forage remains in the field as standing dry vegetation. Many farmers routinely do this by stockpiling late summer grass, especially tall fescue, but this option doesn't work with earlier forage growth.

If we choose to store forage as hay or silage, we must overcome two major enemies: mold and bacteria. These will grow on moist forage and use up nutrients before our animals can get to it. We can prevent this loss if we dry the forage enough so that nothing will grow on it. That's our second storage option: hay or one of its derivatives, like cubes or stacks. The third storage option is that we can enclose the wet forage in airtight containers to prevent mold growth and let it rot, so that the resulting low pH prevents bacterial growth. That's silage or one of its derivatives, like balage, haylage, or hay crop silage. We are all familiar with dry hay, but silage is a horse of a different color. Let's talk about it.

Making silage is really a process of fermentation, roughly analogous to the fermentation in a rumen, only different. The silage process occurs in five phases. (I know, I know, some publications list four phases or even six phases. But I'm not fazed. These categories overlap and authors make arbitrary distinctions, so five is a perfectly good number.) In the first phase — which scientists surprisingly call *Phase I* — we cut the green forage and stuff it into an airtight container. The plants still contain 30%–70% moisture, depending on the type of vegetation and the type of silage. Initially, the container might still contain some residual oxygen. Since the forage was green when we cut it, many plant cells are still alive and continue to carry out respiration. Which means that, for a short while, these cells will still utilize some sugar. Also during

203

this period, some oxygen-loving (*aerobic*) bacteria on the leaf and stem surfaces continue to live and metabolize. But within a few hours, all the oxygen will have been used up and the plant cells and aerobic bacteria die, signaling the end of Phase I. The forage pH at this time is 6.0–6.5.

In *Phase II*, the forage begins to rot, or should I more properly say, *ferment*. Because the container now contains little or no oxygen, the only life that can survive are bacteria that can live without oxygen. These are called *anaerobic* bacteria. In fact, oxygen may be toxic to some of them. A useful characteristic of silage is that all molds require oxygen, so by eliminating oxygen, we eliminate molds. Meanwhile, the anaerobic bacteria begin to ferment the soluble carbohydrates in the forage and produce *acetic acid*. Since a silo is a closed container, the acetic acid has no place to go, and its concentration in the forage begins to rise. This increase in acidity is reflected in the silage pH, which now drops below 6.0.

We should recognize that a silo, although it is a fermentation chamber, is not the same as a rumen, which is also a fermentation chamber. A rumen is actually a flow-through system. Things enter through the mouth and esophagus, ferment in the rumen, and then flow downstream through the rest of the gastrointestinal tract. In addition, some fermentation products are absorbed across the rumen wall into the blood. In contrast, a silo is a tightly closed static system. Once things are put into the silo, they stay there, and any fermentation products also stay there and can build up over time.

This is an important concept because within 3 days, the buildup of acetic acid causes the silage pH to drop further to around 5.0, which initiates *Phase III* of the ensiling process. The acetic acid-producing bacteria die off and are replaced by different bacteria that thrive at this lower pH — bacteria such as *Lactobacillis* and *Leuconostoc*. These anaerobic bacteria produce *lactic acid*. Lactic acid is a stronger acid than acetic acid, and as this lactic acid accumulates, the forage pH drops further. In approximately two weeks, the lactic acid accumulates to constitute more than 60% of the organic acids in the silage, which causes the silage pH to drop to below 4.5, and sometimes even below 4.2.

Which moves us to *Phase IV*: stability. The silage pH has now dropped so low that even the lactic acid-producing bacteria cannot survive. Those bacteria effectively pickled themselves. The silage has become so acidic that nothing else can live in it. Here's the bottom line: we've reached our goal. The forage is no longer losing nutrients to fermentation. The forage is stable and safe.

Unless things don't go quite right. Then the silage can slide into another phase: *Phase V*. This occurs when the silage pH doesn't drop low enough. For example, the silage might have contained too much water or maybe it did not have enough readily fermentable carbohydrates to support the lactic acid bacteria. In either case, in Phase V, the fermentation environment shifts to favor a different type of bacteria: *Clostridia.* These bacteria are not our friends. Instead of fermenting carbohydrates like the well-behaved lactic-acid producers, these clostridia bacteria thrive by fermenting protein. This, of course, reduces the amount of protein in the forage. And as they break down protein, these bacteria produce some distinctive aromatic compounds. I say distinctive because here are some names: *cadaverine* and *putrescine.* The term "stench" would be an understatement. Phase V indicates a poor silage — an unpalatable forage with significantly reduced nutritional value.

But these phases — I, II, III, IV and sometimes V — pretty much sum up the process of ensiling forage. We want to prevent the growth of molds and bacteria by making the container airtight and then reduce the pH to create an inhospitable, stable environment.

So . . . this principle opens up lots of possible engineering options for excluding oxygen and reducing the pH. A silo can be *any* airtight container, like the tall, classic Midwestern barn silo, which takes advantage of the forage weight to force out the air. Or like those big blue metal silos that can be made more airtight than traditional concrete silos. Or we can chop the forage into small pieces and pile it in a three-sided concrete bunker (a bunker silo) or a three-sided open trench (a trench silo). Then we run tractors back and forth over the forage mass to press it down and cover it with plastic and old tires. Or we can blow the cut-up forage pieces into a long white plastic sleeve like a monstrous sausage — the classic Ag-Bag.

Or we can cut the green forage as we would cut hay, let it wilt only slightly, and make large bales that contain 50% moisture — far wetter than any hay you would ever put into a barn — and wrap those bales in layers of white plastic, like mummies. This is *balage.* It's a very good technique, particularly if we keep a supply of sturdy tape in our toolbox to repair any holes in the plastic caused by moles and rocks and falling meteors.

We also have options to manipulate the silage pH. We can use techniques to make sure that the forage contains lots of rapidly fermentable carbohydrates for the bacteria. For example, in the silo, we can add some extra grain or dried whey or anything else with sugars and starch. We can also add commercial silage additives during loading to accelerate the fermentation process — like billions of extra bacteria, particularly *Lactobacillus.* Or we can add enzymes to break down the large plant starch molecules into smaller soluble sugars that these bacteria prefer. Or we can add specialized mold inhibitors to prevent, well, mold — in case the forage contains extra air pockets or doesn't pack well.

But here's a novel idea: if we want to make the forage more acidic, why not just add acid? Well, in the 1920s, someone created a system to do just that. A Finnish scientist named Artturi Virtanen devised a way to lower the forage pH to under 4.0 very quickly and thus completely avoid the fermentation process and its associated nutrient losses. He simply added mixtures of dilute hydrochloric acid and sulfuric acid directly onto the forage as it was put into the silo. The system definitely worked, and for a time it was used on farms throughout Scandinavia and elsewhere. It was, however, rather hard on equipment. The farm crews were also not thrilled about handling jars of acid. Nonetheless, in its day this method was widely known. I suspect, however, that in today's world of seatbelts and roll-bars, pouring corrosive acids from large glass jars into open silos would not be favored by most regulatory agencies.

Oh yes, Dr. Virtanen's middle name was Ilmari — Dr. Artturi Ilmari Virtanen — and he patented his process as the *A.I.V. Method* for making silage. You might not want to try this at home, but you can safely look it up on Google.

First Published: September 2008
Author's Note: The iconic tall silos you see next to barns are massive structures that require some heavy equipment, which can become particularly frustrating in subzero winter days. But as I described above, silage can also be made nicely from large round bales wrapped in plastic. This balage technique has become quite popular, particularly in grazing operations. The large white plastic puffballs you see in those fields are actually silos.

Balage in a Pickle

This spring has been one for the records. We had warm weather early and by late February, the grass began growing in earnest. When our legendary Oregon rains slacked off by mid-spring, the ranchers looked forward to a reasonable forage yield and good weather for making hay. Normally, our rains typically fade out by the end of May, but not this year. The rains came back — with a vengeance. It was rainy and cool nearly every day in May and well into June. Now we are in the second week of June, and no farmer in western Oregon has made any hay yet. The forage, of course, didn't stop growing or maturing, so most fields now boast a heavy crop of stemmy, low-quality grass.

I must confess that not all is gloom and doom. We had a four-day window of good weather in early May, and folks who had their equipment ready made some excellent-quality *balage*. That got me thinking . . . balage is a wonderful technique, a clever way of wrapping forage in a bag and allowing it to pickle into stable silage. Balage allows us to capture the nutrient quality of young forage and store it for future use, without requiring a week or more of dry weather to put that forage up as hay. Many producers around here are switching to it, but balage can also have a few problems that aren't as obvious as with hay. Perhaps this would be a good thing to discuss, so that we can avoid getting in a pickle.

But you ask: what is *balage*? Well, balage is simply a type of silage made from moist forage, either grass or legumes or any other forage that can be made into bales. To make balage, the forage is cut like hay, allowed to wilt on the ground for a day or so, and then rolled into large round bales that are far too wet to put in a barn. Then a specialized piece of wrapping equipment, typically powered by a tractor, wraps each big bale in airtight plastic, turning the bale around and around as it wraps it like a mummy. (The big, wet bales can also be stuffed into a long plastic tube, like a giant sausage. This bale sausage is sometimes called an "Ag-Bag"®.) In the airtight environment of the wrapped bale, the forage rots, or should I say *ferments*, like any other silage, until the pH of the fermenting forage drops to 5.0 or less. Then the bacteria die because they have effectively pickled themselves, and the entire forage bale is stable until it's unwrapped and fed to livestock.

Here's the question of the day: is it *balage* or *baleage*? I've seen it printed both ways. Folks have corrected me both ways. There may even be a rule in proper English that requires an "e" after the "l" (although that would be a very obscure rule indeed). So I did a critical and exhaustive investigation: I looked up both terms on Google. The search took 0.3 seconds. The result: "balage" had 85,800 hits; "baleage" had 56,200 hits. The internet has spoken: the "*a*"s have it. Balage it is.

Let's return to the forage technology. The actual ensiling process in balage is the same process that occurs in those tall silos that people associate with corn silage. The plastic wrap around the bale excludes oxygen, just like the concrete walls of a tall silo. Once the moist forage is wrapped in plastic, the living plant cells use up the residual oxygen and die, and then bacteria begin to ferment the plant carbohydrates in the no-oxygen (*anaerobic*) environment. The initial population of anaerobic bacteria produce *acetic acid*. This lowers the pH in the forage. Then a second population of *lactic acid*-producing bacteria take over and dominate the balage. The concentration of this lactic acid builds up in the balage. Within 10-14 days, the bacteria produce enough lactic acid to reduce the pH so low that even these bacteria cannot survive. In essence, the bacteria create a toxic environment for themselves. The bacteria then die, nothing else lives, and the forage remains unchanged and stable until the plastic is opened.

One unmistakable advantage of balage is that it can be made early in the growing season, when the forage is still young, vegetative, and highly nutritious. This high nutrient value means less wastage when it's fed out. Another advantage is speed: once you line up all your equipment and labor and get a short break in the weather, you can ensile *a lot* of round bales in a short period of time. The main drawback of balage, however, is that it requires specialized equipment to wrap the bales.

Making good balage depends on some basic principles. The baled forage should contain 45%–65% moisture, with an ideal goal of around 50%. Since living plants contain 75%–88% moisture, fresh-cut forage needs to wilt on the ground and lose some moisture. Generally, this takes 8–36 hours, depending on the weather. Even when there are heavy clouds with a light rain, some wilting will still occur — as ranchers in western Oregon can attest. Which means that making balage only requires one or two dry days, or even marginal weather. Unlike hay that seems to require three months of hot sunshine to dry properly, and this dry weather always seems to wait until the forage is mature enough to cut with a chainsaw.

Balage should be stored on a smooth, hard surface to prevent poking holes in the plastic wrap. For example, a Wal-Mart parking lot. Or seriously, a gravel driveway or equivalent. Although bales can be stacked two or three high if handled carefully, storing bales on pallets is not a great idea, unless you want to encourage vast populations of rodents and other critters to poke holes in the plastic.

One potential problem with balage is air, or specifically, oxygen. Oxygen allows the growth of mold and *aerobic* (oxygen-loving) bacteria. Therefore, the wrapped bales must remain airtight. So buy lots of good, specialized plastic tape because holes in the plastic can be caused by rodents, foxes, hawks, pointy sticks, sharp rocks, loose T-posts, rough-handling, etc. Every hole must be taped up quickly, or else areas of mold will develop in the bale.

Another issue related to oxygen is *dry forage*. If the forage is too dry or too stemmy, the equipment can't make a tight bale. The resulting bale will retain air pockets, which allow mold to form and prevent the pH from dropping below the critical level. The oxygen will also support aerobic bacteria which can cause the bales to overheat and lose protein value.

At the other end of the spectrum, *excessively wet forage* causes problems by altering the type of fermentation in the forage. If the baled forage contains more than, say, 65%–70% moisture, the anaerobic fermentation may become dominated by *Clostridia* bacteria. These bacteria ferment proteins rather than starch and sugars. Protein fermentation creates compounds such as *butyrate* and *cadaverine* and *putrescine*. Ugh! The result: a sour-smelling bale that most animals will run from rather than eat.

But Clostridial fermentation might cause other problems besides spoiled forage and bad odors; it can cause serious veterinary problems. For example, *Clostridium botulinum* causes botulism, which can particularly be a problem in horses. Also, balage with a relatively high pH is a good environment for *Listeria* bacteria, which causes listeriosis (also called *circling disease*).

Here's a very practical caution with balage: watch what your equipment picks up into the bale. Some toxic plants remain toxic even when fermented in balage, and unlike hay, animals are less able to sort through balage and avoid certain plants.

A few years ago, a rancher in my area made balage from a field that contained lots of poison hemlock along the fence lines. The inexperienced tractor driver didn't notice those plants, and they ended up in the bales. No one knew which bales contained hemlock, or how much. No one wanted to risk losing their cattle, so the rancher chose to leave *all* that forage in the field and use it for compost. And the problem is not just poison hemlock. Other toxic plants in our area include tansy ragwort, bracken fern, black nightshade, and poison mushrooms. Your neighborhood would have its own toxic specialties.

"In a pickle" — a nice phrase and very applicable to balage, one way or another. It's one of those pithy English phrases with its own fanciful history. The story is that one of the first writers to use the phrase was William Shakespeare in his play *The Tempest*. Shakespeare, who was really a sheep farmer who kept his farm going by writing plays, was trying to put up forage for winter feed and was worried about the effects of a violent storm on his balage. So, being a wordsmith, he cleverly incorporated his balage concern into his play. Clever man. This is true — I read it on the internet.

First Published: July 2010
Author's Note: So now, when you drive down a back road and pass a farm and see those big white mushrooms in the middle of the field, you'll know that they are just balage, not alien landing craft.

SECTION 5

Forage Quality

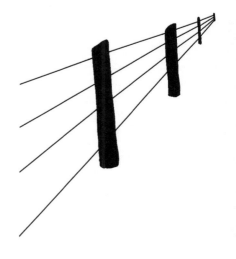

Keeping Score

We all like scores: golf scores, bowling scores, limestone scores. Single numbers that tell us volumes about complex situations. We use scores all the time. A bowling score of 300 is not just good; it's a perfect game. A golf score of 300 is, well, not. Sometimes scores go by different names. An earthquake score is the Richter Scale, where 3.2 is hardly noticeable, but 8.2 will topple buildings. Hurricane scores are called Categories, where a Category 1 storm is relatively small, but a Category 5 storm is a monster.

So, wouldn't it be useful to have a score for forages? A single number that unambiguously represents the nutritional value of a forage. We could use it to rank different forages from low to high, and even use it to evaluate market prices when we buy and sell hay.

Well, we do have such a score — it's called *Relative Feed Value (RFV)*, and it was designed to meet those exact needs. RFV has been around for years, and many analytical labs routinely list RFV in their forage reports. But RFV has some limitations that are actually quite severe. It's now being replaced by a new, improved score called *Relative Forage Quality (RFQ)*. Two scores: RFV and RFQ. Let's review them both.

First, RFV, which was originally developed in the late 1970s. The basic concept was very simple: calculate the RFV score for a forage and then compare that score to a standard reference forage that is assigned the RFV value of 100. The reference forage was defined as a full-bloom alfalfa hay containing 53% NDF and 41% ADF. (These fiber values are listed in all modern forage quality reports. *NDF = Neutral Detergent Fiber. ADF = Acid Detergent Fiber.*) Armed with RFV scores, you could go to a hay sale and easily rank the various forages and appraise their market prices. For example, if Forage X had an RFV of 110, you would know that it had a slightly higher nutritional value than the reference standard alfalfa hay. If full-bloom alfalfa hay and Forage X were both selling for $130 per ton, then Forage X would be a good buy. But if Forage X was selling at $150 per ton, then it was probably overpriced. (Of course, you would need to convince the hay seller of your logic, but that is a different story.)

How is RFV derived? By an equation. In this article, however, I won't bore you with the decimal-laden details of this equation . . . or any other equation. Instead, I'll concentrate on the main concepts and give you enough details so you can follow the equation logic. But if you still hunger for mathematical coefficients, you can enjoy many hours of them by looking them up on Google or Wikipedia.

Back to RFV. The RFV equation includes just two terms: one for digestibility and one for intake. The concept is that animal production from a forage depends on *both* the nutritional quality of the forage *and also* how much of that forage the animal consumes. In the RFV equation, dry matter intake is calculated from the % NDF of the forage. Digestibility (defined here as *Digestible Dry Matter, DDM*) is calculated from the % ADF of the forage. Researchers decided to use these two assays because NDF is best correlated with intake, while ADF is best correlated with digestibility.

In the world of alfalfa, these relationships are fairly strong, and RFV can be a reasonable score for ranking and pricing alfalfa hay. This relationship is especially useful when you are standing in a sale barn trying to compare one load of alfalfa hay to a different load of alfalfa hay.

But RFV has some inherent problems, and the concern is not just academic. Any shortcomings in RFV would translate into bias or inaccuracy. And that could mislead folks about the economic values of forages and distort their judgments about the market prices. Essentially, an RFV problem is a bottom-line pricing problem.

The most glaring drawback with RFV is that the equation does not contain a term for protein. Which means that if you have two forages A and B with the same levels of fiber — but Forage A contains 15% protein and Forage B contains only 12% protein — they would both have the same RFV. But clearly these forages are *not* equal nutritionally, and their economic values are probably different. By not including a protein term in the equation, the RFV score simply isn't sensitive to different levels of protein. Actually, the developers of RFV were not overly concerned about this problem because in alfalfa, protein levels and fiber levels are highly correlated. Well, unfortunately, this correlation is not perfect, and the relationship between these two variables might be different in different forage species.

Also, RFV was originally designed for alfalfa hay, the main, high-value forage crop that is bought and sold across state lines. (You don't see much market demand for turnip silage, do you?) Working within one well-defined legume species, scientists thought that the protein value really wouldn't make that much of a difference, and besides, crude protein is really a complex concept. The crude protein number is actually composed of many fractions. These fractions have different solubilities, different bypass characteristics, different amounts of fiber-bound nitrogen (which will show up on good forage tests as indigestible protein), etc. Trying to parse a crude protein value into its important component parts, given the technology of that time, would probably introduce more artifacts and errors than the effort was worth. Scientists knew that omitting crude protein from the RFV equation would raise some eyebrows, but they judged that omitting it would cause fewer problems than including it, considering their goals and technology. This was not a unanimous decision, I'm sure, but there it is.

But RFV has another major problem. The RFV score is poor for *comparing* forages of different species, particularly comparing legumes with grasses. *RFV tends to underestimate the true value of grasses.* The reason is rather subtle: grasses contain more fiber than legumes, but the fiber in grasses is generally more digestible than the fiber in legumes. The RFV equation does not account for fiber digestibility. When fiber digestibility is ignored, grasses don't get the nutritional credit they deserve, which tends to skew the RFV score in favor of legumes. Which means that, as an example, an RFV for a grass hay would be calculated at 106 when its true value could be, say, 118.

This drawback also affects forage improvement. Many commercial seed companies are currently trying to breed forage varieties with higher fiber digestibilities, particularly in various grass species. The RFV formula cannot distinguish among these varieties because fiber digestibility is not in the equation. So, even within the same forage species, we cannot use RFV as an accurate tool for identifying genetic lines with improved fiber fermentation characteristics. In this situation, using the RFV score is like using a chainsaw when we really need a scalpel.

So what to do? Well, we can develop something new. And there *is* a new kid on the block: *Relative Forage Quality, RFQ.*

But we're out of space. Come back next month. We'll have quality time then.

———≺———

First Published: December 2009
Author's Note: In the face of the complexity of true forage nutritional value, the RFV formula is seductively attractive because it gives a simple number. But simple is, in the end, still simple. Forage nutritional value is complex. Let's see how the RFQ equations approach this problem.

A Quality Acronym

Last month I described a popular method of scoring forages called *Relative Feed Value (RFV)*. But RFV has severe limitations. RFV ignores protein content and does not account for differences in fiber digestibility. It also distorts comparisons between different types of forages. In fact, RFV is kind of like that old barn on our farm: the roof leaks, the pillars are badly placed, the alleyways are too narrow — we know the barn has problems, but we continue to use it anyway because . . . well, because we're used to it, and also because it would take a lot of effort to replace it. But with RFV, scientists have made a solid effort to design a new barn — uh, forage score — that is indeed superior. It's called *Relative Forage Quality (RFQ)*.

The primary movers behind RFQ are Dan Undersander, a forage specialist from Wisconsin, and John Moore, a nutritionist from Florida. When they first published their proposal in 2002, their choice of the words "Forage" and "Quality" was not an accident; they were seeking precision. The words in the name of the previous forage score — "Relative Feed Value" — are ambiguous. What kind of *feed?* Hay? Corn? Dried apricots? And does the word *value* refer to nutritional value or price value? In contrast, the name "Relative Forage Quality" is precise. It's definitely about forages and nutritional quality.

But these scientists were also realists who wanted acceptance. They knew that if their new RFQ scoring system was too different from the old RFV scores, most folks would refuse to switch because, well, it wasn't what they were used to. People don't change just because "something is good for them." At least not in my world. So these researchers carefully fashioned their RFQ system to resemble RFV. Which means that most RFQ scores fall in a similar range of 70–200, and that the reference score of 100 is still based on the same full-bloom alfalfa hay containing 53% NDF and 41% ADF. All this to make it easier for

217

folks to slide into using RFQ without much concern. Good thinking. Now let's look under the RFQ hood.

Like its predecessor, RFQ is calculated from an equation that incorporates two main ideas: forage intake and forage digestibility. Basically, RFQ is a single number that combines the two concepts of (1) how much forage the animal will consume, expressed as Dry Matter Intake (DMI) and (2) the nutritional value of that forage, expressed as Total Digestible Nutrients (TDN). Each of these terms is derived from a specific equation. Like last month, I won't go into the grueling mathematical details of these equations. I'll just list the critical concepts to give you the broad overview. This also makes for easier reading. But do prepare yourself for a lot of acronyms. It's the nature of this beast.

The first thing we notice is that RFQ is calculated by *two different sets of equations*: one set for legumes and one set for grasses. This is a great start because it's clear that RFQ recognizes the reality that for forages, one size doesn't fit all.

For legumes like alfalfa, the clovers, the trefoils, etc., and also for legume-grass mixtures, the DMI term is calculated from an equation containing the % NDF in the forage and also an adjustment factor for the digestibility of that NDF. Lab technicians determine NDF digestibility by allowing the fiber to ferment in a small beaker for 48 hours under strictly controlled conditions. The amount of fiber that disappears during this fermentation period represents the digestibility of that fiber. Although this procedure entails some extra time and laboratory work, it gives a reasonable estimate of what happens to fiber in the rumen. The old RFV equation simply ignored this concept.

The legume TDN equation is rather complex. It includes five terms: (1) crude protein, (2) fat, (3) non-fiber carbohydrates (NFC), (4) nitrogen-free NDF (NDFn), and (5) NDF digestibility. *Non-fiber carbohydrates* represents starches and soluble sugars. *Nitrogen-free NDF* is the NDF value minus any nitrogen that might be caught up in the fiber. This term is included in the TDN equation to avoid counting the same nitrogen twice (i.e., once in the protein term and once in the fiber term).

Finally, the RFQ score for a legume forage is then calculated by adding the results of its legume DMI equation and its legume TDN equation.

Grasses, however, are very different. Grasses generally contain more fiber than legumes, and grass fiber tends to be more digestible than legume fiber. Also, the mathematical predictions with grasses are more complex than with legumes, as you'll see.

For grasses, the DMI term is estimated by an equation that contains crude protein, TDN, and ADF (Acid Detergent Fiber). These terms actually appear twice in the equation, with the second time being squared (multiplied by itself). You remember squares and square roots from high school, don't you?

Anyway, this complexity is necessary because in grasses, unlike legumes, the prediction relationship between grass DMI and these terms is not a straight line. In the parlance of statisticians, this relationship is *curvilinear*, which is a fancy way of saying that it is not a straight line. Mathematically, scientists shape this prediction line into an appropriate curve by including squared terms in the equation.

The grass DMI equation also contains an unusual term that is the product of multiplying ADF by crude protein. This term reflects the complex interactions between the types of fiber in ADF (lignin and cellulose) and nitrogen. Which also suggests that even if these interactions exist in legumes, they are not large enough to affect the DMI of legumes and, therefore, are not included in the legume DMI equation.

Unlike the equation for grass DMI, the grass TDN equation is straightforward. It includes the same terms found in the legume TDN equation, although the coefficients are different.

Finally, the RFQ score for a grass forage is then calculated by adding the results of its grass DMI equation and its grass TDN equation.

Still with me? I know this sounds like taking the square root of your birthday and multiplying it by the score of the sixth game of last year's World Series, but please hang in there for a bit longer . . .

For those of you with nutritional training, you may have asked an obvious question about fats because the TDN equations include a term for fat. Do these equations adjust for the higher level of energy in fats? Well, you can rest easy. Each TDN equation indeed multiplies the fat term by 2.25 to account for its extra energy. Just like in the textbooks.

But now the real question: With all these acronyms and arithmetic gobbledygook, is RFQ a true improvement over RFV? The straightforward answer is yes.

Why? In short, because RFQ successfully reflects the reality of the complex interactions among the forage nutrients. In the brief period RFQ has been available, laboratories comparing RFQ and RFV have consistently observed improved predictions with RFQ. High-quality grasses showed RFQs that were indeed higher than RFVs, sometimes by more than 20 points. RFQ is very sensitive to different types of fibers and different levels of fiber digestibility. It picks up differences between leaves and stems — just as it was designed. And heat damage, which reduces forage digestibility, concomitantly reduces the RFQ value, although it has no effect on RFV. These are all practical field situations, and RFQ seems to reflect those situations and performs as designed.

RFQ, however, still has some shortcomings. Although it nicely differentiates between legumes and grasses, it doesn't differentiate *within* those categories. Warm-season grasses differ from cool-season grasses in their fiber and protein characteristics. Temperate legumes like alfalfa and white clover differ from warm-season legumes such as lespedeza and lablab. And even corn silage may cause prediction problems because of the varying digestibilities of starch among different corn varieties. RFQ may need additional equations to account for these categories.

Also, farmers and ranchers are routinely using alternative forages like chicory, plantain, and forage brassicas. Where do *these* fit into the RFQ equations? Right now, nowhere. RFQ was not designed for these forages. (Interestingly, feed testing labs will cheerfully list RFV or RFQ scores in their reports for any forage samples submitted to them.) I see lots of opportunities for graduate student research in the next few years.

But why end there? What about farmers who routinely make hay from weeds — thistle, blackberry, nightshade, hemlock? Perhaps we could devise a score called *Relative Intake Poisonality (RIP)*. Then, by using an equation that combines RIP with RFQ, we could really claim to know our Ps and Qs.

First Published: January 2010
Author's Note: RFQ is becoming more common in the lab reports. It is indeed an improvement over RFV, but it's not perfect. Those additional equations that I mentioned above still need to be worked out. But no problem. A billion dollars in research funds should do it.

The NDF Alphabet

This month we'll talk about the new alphabet of fiber: pe, a, om, and ICP. Don't worry, you haven't wandered into an academic spelling bee. But, seriously, have you submitted a forage sample to a laboratory recently? Look closely at the report. Many lab reports now include a few codes that were not there years ago, especially concerning the values for fiber. What do those codes mean? Hang on, this may be a wild ride.

The key fiber number on which all this is based is the granddad of all modern fiber values: *NDF*, short for *Neutral Detergent Fiber*. In an NDF assay, a feed sample is boiled in a specially formulated detergent solution that's buffered at — you guessed it — the neutral pH of 7.0. The soluble compounds in the feed dissolve into the liquid, and the residue at the bottom of the beaker is the fibrous NDF, which can then be filtered and analyzed. NDF contains most of the fiber substances in the plant, particularly the major fiber compounds of cellulose, hemicellulose, and lignin, as well as some other nondigestible or inert substances like heat-damaged protein, cutin, silica, etc. Nutritionists agree that NDF is a good representation of the fiber portion of a feed, and NDF has been used extensively in equations to estimate feed intake and forage value.

But like many things in nature, this raw NDF value is not exactly perfect. NDF sometimes contains contaminating substances that are not true plant fiber. These substances do not ferment in the rumen like true fiber, and they can skew the results of ration-balancing programs that depend on NDF.

Ideally, we would like NDF to represent only the true fiber portion of the feed that is potentially fermentable in the rumen. NDF helps us better understand the microbial environment in the rumen and the large intestine. It makes ration-balancing more accurate and helps nutritionists and livestock operators manage rumen fermentation better and avoid low-fiber problems like acidosis and milk fat depression. But those pesky contaminating substances get in the way. They inflate the NDF value, which misleads us about the fermentation potential of the diet and impairs our estimates of rumen turnover times and fermentation rates. Two of the most important NDF contaminants are *dirt* and *starch*. The good news is that modern laboratory techniques can now correct for both, and the new codes in the lab reports show these results.

The first main contaminant is *dirt*, which is called *ash* (or *minerals*) in nutrition textbooks. Sure, all plants and other feedstuffs contain some minerals. Lab reports and reference books routinely list detailed values for these minerals. But the extra minerals in dirt can get into forages in many ways, like during the harvest of hay or silage, or rain splash, or contaminants from heavy machinery, etc. In any case, we don't want those minerals in our NDF; we want our NDF to be composed of *organic matter*, without the minerals. Laboratories correct for ash by cooking the NDF in an oven at 1,000°–1,200°F for two hours, thoroughly destroying all organic matter, leaving the ash. We can then calculate the amount of organic matter in the NDF by simple subtraction. Laboratories list this value on their reports as the "organic matter NDF," or *NDFom* for short.

The second main contaminant is *starch*. Huh? You probably think that starch is an easily available, easily digestible carbohydrate, more like sugar than fiber. That's true, more or less. But starch is actually quite complicated. Starch is really a large class of compounds, each with its own size and complex geometry. Some starches do not dissolve easily in neutral detergent solution, which means that they end up on the bottom of the beaker just like true fiber. These starches become part of the NDF number, even though they don't have the same fermentation characteristics as true fiber. We can, however, successfully eliminate starch from NDF by adding the enzyme *amylase* to the beaker during the initial boiling procedure. (Amyl*ose* is the scientific name for starch. Amyl*ase* is the enzyme that splits the chemical bonds.) Amylase breaks down starch during the NDF procedure, so that no starch molecules end up in the residue.

It took many years to identify a good commercial amylase product that was heat-stable and detergent-stable, but now the amylase correction is routinely used by many laboratories. Lab reports list the value of amylase-corrected NDF as *aNDF* (the "a" is for amylase). As you'd expect, this correction is more important in feeds that contain a lot of starch, like grains and certain byproducts. But when a laboratory lists the term aNDF instead of just simple NDF, we can be assured that the lab has made the proper correction for starch.

There is also a third inert substance that we should identify. This is the indigestible dark-colored goo created in heat-damaged hay and silage.

Technically, this material is a protein-carbohydrate polymer known as *Maillard Product*, after a reaction by the same name (the *Maillard Reaction* is the cause of most barn fires). This substance will not ferment in the rumen and is completely indigestible, but nonetheless its nitrogen is analyzed as part of the protein, and it also ends up as part of the NDF. But we can correct for Maillard Products by testing the NDF for nitrogen and then expressing this nitrogen as the crude protein bound to the NDF. We call this fraction *Insoluble Crude Protein* (ICP). Still with me?

In any case, feed reports will list this number as *NDICP* (= Neutral Detergent Insoluble Crude Protein). How useful is this? Very, because too much heat damage can severely reduce the nutritional value of the forage. By subtracting the *NDICP* number from the Crude Protein value, you can get the actual effective crude protein value that is available to the animals (which a laboratory report will usually list as *Available Crude Protein*).

We've covered three main interfering substances: ash (NDFom), starch (aNDF), and Maillard Products (NDICP). But before we leave this topic, we should describe one more NDF code that is important for understanding fiber and using NDF to balance rations.

The famous writer Gertrude Stein once said, "A rose is a rose is a rose." This may be a great turn of words for gardens and literary romances, but it's not so accurate for fiber. Even when corrected for contaminants, *NDF is not NDF is not NDF*. Some forms of NDF are more *effective* than others at influencing rumen fermentation, and this characteristic is primarily related to particle size. Larger fiber particles will cause more chewing activity which increases the amount of saliva. (Ruminants produce a large amount lot of saliva as part of their digestive process, much more than humans.) Saliva is very important to ruminants — it contains buffers that stabilize rumen pH. Saliva also carries nitrogen and various minerals back into the rumen as part of the animal's nutrient recycling system. Also, large fiber particles in the rumen slow down the rate of passage, affecting fermentation time and the digestibility of the diet.

How do we account for these differences? By identifying the amount of *physically effective fiber, peNDF*. We estimate this by measuring the actual size of the fiber particles. A feedstuff is passed through a series of sieves (screens) with various aperture sizes. Roughages with a high percentage of large particles are given full credit as effective fibers; feedstuffs with smaller particles are credited with proportionally lower scores. For example, a long-cut, early-bloom alfalfa hay may have a peNDF value of 40.0%. That same hay cut at medium length would have a peNDF of 36.0%. And when that hay is finely chopped, its peNDF would only be 29.0% — a 28% drop in fiber effectiveness compared to long-cut hay.

Physically effective fiber really acts like fiber in the rumen. The peNDF value listed in a forage test report gives nutritionists and farmers a more realistic picture of what occurs in the rumen.

This is not splitting hairs. In practice, we can cut hay and silage at wildly different lengths, and peNDF is a tool to estimate the effects of these lengths. For example, an extreme situation occurs when we put forage through a grinder because grinding essentially destroys the physical effectiveness of fiber, even though the uncorrected NDF value remains high. Pelleting does the same thing because pelleting is really a two-stage process: first the feed is ground, and then it is pushed through a pellet die. Grinding results in very low peNDF values. A practical consequence of a low peNDF value is an increased risk of acidosis from a forage diet, even though that same forage in long form is completely safe.

There are more NDF codes on forage reports, but let's stop here for this month. But before we leave, now that the new NDF alphabet makes a little more sense, let's use this knowledge. Let's create a doozy code that we can use in emails to our friends: *apeNDFomICP*. I have no idea what this means, but it sure looks impressive.

First Published: June 2015

Author's Note: These details may seem a bit technical and arcane, but they are really quite important. They can help you understand modern forage test reports. They can also give you an appreciation for the extra steps taken by these labs to produce meaningful numbers.

Fiber Digestion, Time, and Distance

I recently came across a magazine article about fiber that included the word "ANDFOM." Huh? What does *that* mean? ANDFOM . . . Android for Occupational Medicine? Antiquated Neural Devices for Older Mammoths?

Then I realized what happened — some of those letters should have been lowercase, and the magazine editor's spell-checker software "corrected" them by changing everything to uppercase. Progress. In any case, the correct version of this inscrutable term is "aNDFom" which means "Neutral Detergent Fiber (NDF) corrected for starch by the amylase procedure (a), expressed on an organic-matter basis (om)." A few months ago, I wrote an article describing those codes. Maybe it's time we continue this discussion and include some additional codes. The reports from forage-testing laboratories now list lots of new fiber codes. Perhaps we should learn about them before the spell-checker software tries to correct them for us.

Before we start, a brief review of my earlier article. NDF stands for *Neutral Detergent Fiber* — the fiber portion of a feedstuff. NDF consists of three main components: cellulose, hemicellulose, and lignin. NDF also may include some other fiber-like substances like Maillard Products (created in heat-damaged forages), cutin, silica, etc. In my earlier article, I covered some common codes now associated with NDF: "aNDF" for the *amylase* correction for starch; "NDFom" for the true *organic matter* fiber that contains no contaminating minerals; "NDICP" for the *insoluble crude protein* (ICP) which are the indigestible Maillard Products that are formed in heat-damaged hay; and "peNDF" which is *physically effective* NDF in the rumen, which means NDF

225

adjusted for particle size. Now for some additional codes. (Author's note: I will use the terms NDF and fiber synonymously in this article.)

The first new set of codes focuses on the rumen digestibility of fiber; namely, the amount of fiber the rumen microbes ferment while the feedstuff remains in the rumen. This is an extremely important concept in ruminant nutrition because the extent and type of fiber fermentation in the rumen determines much of the nutritional value of a fibrous feedstuff.

It's like that old Shakespearean phrase: fiber is not fiber is not fiber (or at least Shakespeare probably *would* have said it if Hamlet had been a ruminant nutritionist). Feedstuffs differ in the composition of their fiber, especially in the amount and proportion of lignin. Lignin has a zero digestibility, and as plants mature, the lignin proportion in fiber increases and thus reduces the digestibility of that fiber. Grasses generally have higher levels of NDF than legumes like alfalfa and clover, but grass NDF is generally more digestible than legume NDF primarily because it contains a lower percentage of lignin. Of course, fiber digestibility declines considerably as the grasses mature. The amount of lignin is also affected by other factors, including the species of forage, the genetic lines (varieties) within species, and environmental factors like heat and day length.

Nutritionists measure the rumen digestibility of fiber by a fairly straightforward assay: fill a beaker with rumen fluid (alive with active rumen microbes), place the fiber sample into the beaker, let the whole thing ferment for a period of time, and then measure the remaining undigested amount. Then, in the report, they put a number like 30 or 48 in the NDF code that represents the number of hours of fermentation. The full code looks something like "uNDFxx" where u means *undigested* and xx is *the number of hours of fermentation.*

One logical quirk to an expression like uNDF30 is that the resulting number represents the results of *disappearance* — i.e., the amount of *undigested* fiber (hence the "u" in the code). Human beings like to think in terms of *positive* amounts rather than *negative* amounts because we generally associate higher numbers with greater value, like ball game scores and test scores. (Let's *not* go into the sociology of golf scores here.) Therefore, nutritionists have revised the NDF code so that the trailing number presents fiber fermentation in a positive light — in terms of *digestibility* rather than disappearance. The NDF code currently found in forage reports often looks like *NDFDxx* where *xx* is the number of hours of fiber fermentation and *NDFD* is the *digestibility* of NDF for that period. For this expression, higher numbers are indeed better.

Therefore, on forage reports, you might see any or all of three standard values for NDF digestibility: NDFD24, NDFD30, and NDFD48 based on fermentation times of 24, 30, and 48 hours, respectively.

Why are these numbers important? Firstly, the value for NDFD48 is used in the equations to calculate *Relative Forage Quality (RFQ)*, a term that is quickly replacing the older *Relative Feed Value (RFV)*. Secondly, forage researchers and private seed companies are beginning to use fiber digestibility to identify superior genetic lines and develop new cultivars that provide better nutritional value in pastures and hay. And thirdly, fiber digestibility numbers are needed in some sophisticated ration-balancing software, especially for high-producing dairy cows. Forage is crucially important in these exquisitely balanced grain-based rations, and subtle differences in fiber digestibility can create major economic differences in the amount of milk produced by these cows and the efficiency of that production.

This is all fine and good, but here's an unsettling thought: all this work on fiber digestibility has been focused on *rumen* fermentation. But what about the *lower tract* (namely, the large intestine and the cecum)? Doesn't fiber fermentation also occur in the large intestine? Yes, it certainly does. Also, what about horses? Or elephants? Or kangaroos? These animals don't have a rumen, but they are professional grazers that live quite well on forages, and they probably would be greatly upset if you applied rumen-based digestion values to them.

There is, however, a potential solution — and this is the last NDF code on our docket. Since fiber fermentation takes place in the rumen and also in the lower tract, shouldn't we have a single number that represents the whole ball of wax, the sum-total digestion of the fiber as it moves from the mouth to the manure? Actually, we do: *Total Tract NDF Digestibility (TTNDFD)*.

This is a new concept that has been developed over the past ten years, primarily by dairy researchers in Wisconsin. But, interestingly, it may also be an old concept, retrofitted with modern chemistry and new understandings.

TTNDFD is a single number that describes the *digestibility of NDF across the entire gastrointestinal tract*, from beginning to end, expressed as a percent of NDF. Simply put, TTNDFD represents the percentage of NDF that disappears as the fiber passes down the entire tract.

This is a very powerful concept, and it covers a lot of bases. TTNDFD essentially incorporates four main concepts: (1) the percentage of fiber that potentially can be digested as it moves down the tract, (2) the rate that the microbes digest this fiber, wherever those microbes reside in the GI tract, (3) the rate of passage of the fiber through the tract, and (4) the actual amounts of fiber fermentation that occurs in the GI tract, both in the rumen and in the lower tract. If we think about it, TTNDFD could apply to any plant-eating species, from sheep and cattle to kangaroos.

So, what are some typical TTNDFD values? So far, these numbers seem to average around 44%, which means that NDF is approximately 44% digestible across the entire GI tract. But this is just a raw average. Alfalfa TTNDFD can range from 25%–70%, corn silage from 25%–80%, and cool-season grasses from 15%–80%. These are extremely wide ranges, and the devil is in the details. Plant genetics, soil fertility, forage maturity, heat units, level of intake, rumen pH, other feedstuffs in the diet including feed additives, and maybe even animal genetics that relate to subtle differences in anatomy — this list can get very long, which makes researchers rub their hands in excitement at all the possibilities for good research.

TTNDFD is still in its infancy. I suspect, though, that we'll see a lot more of it in the future.

But is TTNDFD truly a new concept? Well, on the surface, it certainly seems to be new. But in reality, it's the recycling of the very old concept of digestibility.

In the late 1800s, researchers made the first measurements of nutritional value by measuring nutrients that went into the mouth and then measuring the residue that came out the other end. They labeled the difference as the *digestible portion of the feed.* We now know that those numbers were inaccurate because of nutrient recycling, fecal contaminants, and endogenous wastes secreted into the GI tract, so we call these numbers *Apparent Digestibility* rather than *True Digestibility.* (There were also many analytical limitations at that time. For example, the crude fiber assay used by those researchers was not as valid an estimate of plant fiber as NDF.)

But here in the 21st Century, what are we doing? We are measuring the amount of NDF that goes into the mouth and then measuring the undigested amount that comes out the other end — for the entire gastrointestinal tract. We call it the very modern term "TTNDFD." Sure, today we have more sophisticated laboratory assays than a hundred years ago, and we have a better understanding of fiber. Unlike the old concept of crude fiber, NDF is definitely a valid nutritional entity, and its presence in the manure is not contaminated by recycled compounds.

But . . . isn't the *concept* of digestibility the same? In essence, TTNDFD is really the *true digestibility* of NDF. Hmmm. I can see some of those old nutritionists smiling knowingly. Sometimes, what goes around comes around.

First Published: December 2015

Author's Note: These code numbers are quite helpful, once you know what they mean. And TTNDFD has real potential for helping nutritionists understand the dynamics of the GI tract and also helping commercial seed companies develop forage cultivars with higher true digestibilities. Indeed, if Shakespeare had been in the nutrition field, he really could have written a best-selling play about all of this.

Sticky Fiber and Feeding Minerals

I recently saw something very odd when I observed a farm advisor balance a diet for late-gestation ewes. The advisor had analyzed the forage and trace mineral mixture and then had estimated daily feed intake. Based on these numbers, his spreadsheet showed that the magnesium intake would be only 10.6 grams per day. His reference books listed the magnesium requirement at 12.0 grams per day — indicating a shortfall of 1.4 grams. Logically, he then recommended that the shepherd should increase the magnesium percentage in his mineral mixture. The odd thing is this: he assumed that the shortfall of 1.4 grams is a real number.

Why? Because on a forage diet, mineral availability in the digestive tract is not really well-understood, certainly not enough to put decimal places on availability numbers. Forages contain high levels of fiber, and fiber can interact with minerals in ways that should make us seriously question our assumptions about mineral availability. One main reason for this is the concept of *Cation Exchange Capacity (CEC)*. I'll describe the details, but here's a gentle alert: the discussion is a bit arcane; it involves glass tubes, fruit, clay, and heat-damaged hay.

In chemistry, there is a routine laboratory procedure called *column chromatography* that is used to assay and separate chemical compounds. Column chromatography involves a long, vertical glass tube (the column) packed with some kind of gelatin-like substance. A solution containing the unknown compounds is poured into the top of the tube. As the solution slowly percolates downward through the gel, some of the dissolved molecules "stick" onto the gel particles and thus come out of the solution. This sticking — called

231

adsorption (spelled with a "d") — occurs when molecules electrostatically attach themselves to the outside surface of the gel particles, kind of like when you rub balloons on a carpet and then they tend to "stick" to that carpet. In any case, after the first solution clears the column, a different solution is slowly poured into the column which causes one or more of those compounds to detach from the gel and go back into solution. This second liquid is collected in a beaker underneath the column and analyzed. By strategically using different solutions and different gels, laboratories can routinely separate and analyze a vast array of compounds.

The important concepts here are that small molecules or even atoms will come out of solution when they are adsorbed onto solid particles, and they go back into solution only when something comes along that removes them from those particles

Let's shift our discussion to soils. Soils are composed of four main types of particles: sand, silt, clay, and organic matter (humus). (We'll ignore roots and boulders.) The surfaces of some of these particles tend to have a negative electric charge. The smallest particles — clay and humus — have the largest amounts of charge because their surface-to-weight ratios are very high. In other words, these particles have a very large surface area compared to their weight. The negative charges on these soil particles attract atoms that have a positive electric charge (*cations*) — primarily potassium, calcium, magnesium, sodium, and hydrogen. In the soil, these cations readily adsorb onto soil particles, and they are *exchangeable* — meaning that hydrogen atoms can replace the calcium or magnesium atoms.

The capability of soil particles to hold on to these cations is the soil's *Cation Exchange Capacity*. Each soil has its own characteristic CEC value that depends primarily on the percentages and types of soil particles. Soils with a high CEC can potentially hold more soil nutrients than soils with a low CEC. Laboratories can measure the proportions of each cation in a soil's CEC, and agronomists can use these numbers to help guide their crop and fertilizer recommendations. In practice, the CEC gives us an estimate of a soil's potential to act as a reservoir of plant nutrients. Again, the important concept is that individual atoms can be adsorbed onto soil particles.

Now let's switch gears and focus on the mineral nutrition for our livestock, starting with a *very* hypothetical scenario: an animal with a completely empty digestive tract. If we pour a solution of minerals into the animal's mouth, those minerals would flow down the tract unimpeded until they reach the small intestine, where a certain percentage of each mineral would then be absorbed (absorbed with a "b") across the gut wall into the blood. The actual percentage that crosses the gut wall would depend on the solubility of each mineral's compound (oxide, sulfate, carbonate, etc.) and the specific biochemical mechanisms used to transport that mineral across the gut wall. For example, if a ewe's daily magnesium requirements were 12 grams and we knew that the efficiency of absorption across the gut wall was 50%, then we could feed exactly 24 grams of magnesium and be confident that we had precisely met the ewe's magnesium requirements. So far, so good.

But we live in a real world on real farms and ranches. We don't pour simple mineral solutions into empty digestive tracts. We feed complete rations to our animals, and these rations include forages. Here's the rub: all those forages contain fiber, which is composed of a variety of large molecules like cellulose, hemicellulose, lignin, pectin, beta-glucans, and also other compounds like the Maillard Products in heat-damaged hay. These fibrous compounds all have relatively large surface areas. When animals consume forages, some fiber will ferment in the rumen and thus disappear, but some fiber particles will move through the rumen intact and proceed down the digestive tract into the small intestine. In addition, the rumen bacteria contain cell walls, which are a type of fiber from an electrostatic point of view, and when these bacteria die, their remnants wash out of the rumen and also move down the digestive tract.

Let's add one more thing to this scenario: the Cation Exchange Capacity of the fiber. This is exactly the same concept described earlier for soils. Over the past 25 years, nutritionists have determined that plant fibers in the digestive tract can exhibit a CEC, similar to the CEC of soil particles. (An interesting aside: laboratories measure fiber CEC by using the rare earth element *neodymium*, the same element used in the super magnets you can buy at home improvement stores. This obscure fact may not be particularly relevant to our discussion of mineral nutrition, but it is interesting.)

And like the different types of soil particles, each type of fiber molecule has its own characteristic CEC level. Some fiber molecules have only a moderate CEC; some show very high levels of CEC. Two types of fiber with very high CEC values are *pectin*, found commonly in fruits and soyhulls and beet pulp, and the *Maillard Products* found in heat-damaged hay. Since every forage contains a complex mixture of many types of fiber molecules, every forage has a different CEC depending on the percentages and types of fiber molecules in that forage.

Now the big picture. *We can think of the digestive tract as a flexible, living example of column chromatography.* The digestive tract is the column; the fiber inside the digestive tract is the gel that packs that column. The gel consists of the fiber molecules that pass from the rumen into the lower tract. Every diet will have its own unique mix of fiber molecules. And the liquid that moves down through the column contains the minerals that our animals require.

As this liquid moves down the digestive tract, like what happens in the glass chromatography tube in a laboratory, some of its minerals will be adsorbed onto the fiber surfaces. Once these mineral atoms are adsorbed onto the fiber, they can't be transported into the blood until they are released back into solution. If those atoms remain stuck on the fiber all the way down through the digestive tract into the manure, they are completely lost to the animal.

In practice, this situation can get even more complex. Here's an example: let's say that we feed a balanced ration of hay and corn and a good free-choice trace mineral mixture. Each mineral in this ration will have a specific availability associated with it. A few weeks after we begin feeding this ration, we run out of the original hay and replace it with a different batch of hay. But this hay had experienced some heat-damage when it was stacked in the barn. This heat-damaged hay contains a relatively high level of Maillard Products (the brown goo that resembles caramel). Maillard Products are large molecules that are completely indigestible, but they have high CEC values. Therefore, compared to the earlier hay, far more mineral atoms will be adsorbed onto this fiber which might reduce the mineral availabilities to the animal, even though the total mineral levels of the ration remain unchanged. The bottom line here is that the second batch of hay may cause lower mineral absorption than the first batch of hay, even though the total mineral levels in the ration have not changed.

From a nutritionist's perspective, the CEC of fiber adds a very big question mark to mineral nutrition. For any ration, what percentage of minerals will be adsorbed onto the fiber? Which minerals will be affected most? Under what conditions will these minerals be released back into solution? Each mineral is affected differently by the CEC, each ration contains its own combination of fiber molecules, and each combination of fiber molecules has a different impact on mineral availability. Hmm . . . how many decimal places are *you* comfortable with in your spreadsheet? There are a few unknowns here.

So, how do we cope? Well, the first thing is to ask serious questions about the numbers. When our ration-balancing calculations show only small differences between mineral intake and mineral requirements, we should take these numbers with a grain of salt. We certainly should avoid making recommendations based on decimal places. And secondly . . . well . . . perhaps we should step back, look at the bigger picture, and avoid cutting things too closely. Those mineral numbers may not be what they seem.

———✂———

First Published: September 2014
Author's Note: This issue is subtle and nuanced, with lots of unknowns. It certainly adds clouds to our mineral recommendations, which may make some folks uncomfortable. All the more reason to take it into account when we balance rations.

Growth without Clover

We've always heard that pastures need clover (or other legumes) to support high milk production and good lamb growth. Oh yeah? Then why are my lambs — notorious for ignoring my advice — growing so fast now during the early spring when my Oregon pastures contain no clover?

The question really becomes: how nutritious *are* these young spring pastures?

Some background first: grasses and clovers did not evolve over millions of years just to meet the pleasures of our livestock. Grasses and clovers have their own agendas. These plants have nutritional requirements that don't necessarily match those of our animals. It's kind of like the game of ice hockey (from the point of view of someone like me who thinks that a puck is a character in a Shakespeare play) — the opposing teams never see eye to eye. For example, our common forage plants require elements like molybdenum, which has no direct use in animal systems. Those same plants grow very well, thank you, without any iodine or selenium, which are two elements that our livestock need and feel very strongly about. We cope with these differences by periodically dumping some molybdenum on our pastures to make our plants grow better, and rigorously providing a balanced trace mineral mixture to our livestock to make them better. We do these things routinely and hope that our problems go away.

But what about the two major nutrients needed by our livestock: energy and protein? Some interesting things are happening right now in our spring pastures in western Oregon.

I could ask you, what *is* the protein level of these young pastures? The forage nutritional levels may be surprising. Depending on your background, your response will have something to do with the amount of clover in the pasture, or its fertilizer history, or perhaps if the Portland Trail Blazers have

235

won their last three games. Actually, at this time of year, clover has nothing to do with forage protein levels because there isn't much clover in these pastures right now. Clovers really don't start to grow until the soil temperatures rise above 50°F. The soil temperatures in our early spring are much lower than that. But our ryegrasses and fescues begin to grow when soil temperatures are above 40°. So, by the time our clovers are even beginning to think about commencing to start to grow, our Douglas County pastures are already in 6-inches deep in grass.

Which is not so bad, really. When grasses first start growing, they are composed of delicious young leaves that are very low in fiber and very high in protein — the typical composition of any actively growing young plant. Even the less-desirable pasture grasses like the bentgrasses and foxtails are required to be young at one time during their production cycles (if only for one week, it seems).

The practical result? Simple: the young grass plants that now populate our pastures are incredibly high in protein and energy even in the absence of clover. During a livestock nutrition course that I recently taught at our local community college, we ran some analyses on these plants. Their crude protein levels analyzed at over 20% (dry matter basis). Recall that these were just young spring grasses. The clovers in those fields were still asleep. In addition to protein, the estimated energy levels of these grasses, expressed as TDN, were nearly equal to the value of oats.

How does all this influence how we manage our livestock? Well, these numbers suggest that, during early spring growth, protein might not be a limiting factor in our forage-based nutritional universe. These numbers also mean that the energy level of our forages is pretty good. Since lambs need approximately 16% protein in their diet to support fast growth rates, our young spring pastures, even without clover, actually do the trick quite well. Which is *exactly* what my lambs have been telling me all along.

Down the road, of course, things change. How else could we begin the growing season with 20% protein pastures and routinely end it by harvesting 8% protein hay? But now, during this early spring, at least, we can luxuriate in our excellent forages and be happy that we are not trying to graze fields in Minnesota or Maine, where the current ground cover is that white stuff called snow.

First Published: April 1994

Author's Note: A short chapter, but a straightforward principle: young forages have high levels of crude protein and digestible energy. Nonetheless, I see that many managers still offer their animals high-protein grain supplements when those animals are turned out onto young spring pastures.

SECTION 6

The Science & Business of Grazing

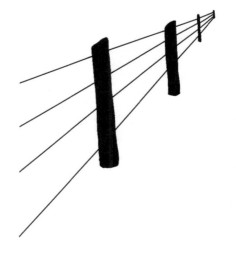

The Buck Stops Here

We are all CEOs.

That's right — Chief Executive Officers. Usually we are too buried under chores to consider anything except the next task, but perhaps we should regard ourselves like the corporate executives we are.

No, I've not been out in the sun too long (especially not during an Oregon winter). I have, however, been thinking about our role in making our operations profitable and sustainable. Farms and ranches are bottom-line businesses. A business is really a collection of resources flying in close formation and, like the people in companies such as Ford or Apple who make decisions about managing these resources, we, too, are corporate executives.

Admittedly, when I am knee-deep in spring mud, struggling to fix a fence, the image of a CEO in a three-piece suit is not exactly the first thing that comes to mind. When we work on our farms, we'd rather be outdoors, getting things *done*. The reality is that we work hard in our operations. Head down, sleeves rolled up, we dig in and get the job done — any job, every job. whatever needs to get done. We greatly respect the value of doing things ourselves. We feed animals, build fences, make hay and silage, build barns, fix machinery, doctor animals, drive trucks, and heck, we even shear the sheep ourselves. Not much different than the original yeoman farmers, the self-reliant Minutemen who grabbed their muskets in the American Revolution and helped build this country.

But the reality on our farms is this: we really wear *two* hats: the jack-of-all-trades laborer *and* the corporate-executive decision-maker. We enthusiastically embrace the first role — the exhilarating, hard field work that we love — but perhaps we should learn to value the second role just as much. When faced with a hard job, we all like to say, "well, someone has to do it!"

241

But if we step back and look at the whole picture, maybe our operations would benefit more if that someone isn't always us.

Let's recall the story of a CEO from a different era: Andrew Carnegie. Yes, the same guy whose name appears on libraries across the country. At the turn of the century (or was that *two* centuries ago?), Andrew Carnegie made a fortune in the steel industry. In his time, he was kind of like the Bill Gates of the steel industry. Carnegie lived in an era of great steel mills, blast furnaces, slag heaps, and glowing molten iron. No one would ever, even in the most extreme moments, mistake Andrew Carnegie for a sheepherder or cattle rancher. But did you know that Andrew Carnegie actually *didn't know much about making steel?* No, he hired specialists for that technical knowledge. What he did better than anyone else, however, was make the fundamental decisions that guided his business. He knew how to make money; he knew that his real role was to make good decisions about the vast industrial empire under his control. His technical people worked on the details for making steel. He decided when and where the steel would be made, who would make it, and how it was to be sold.

So, instead of viewing a farm or ranch as an endless series of physical tasks, we might try to view it from an executive perspective — as an assemblage of resources. These resources include land, money, equipment, livestock, buildings, feed, hired labor, etc. Also, some other resources that may not be so obvious, like location, history, relatives, relationships, calendars, personal preferences, and our sense of risk. And of course, *us* — our time, our skills, and our experience.

One thing that crops up again and again in farmer discussions is the monetary value of our time, sometimes even the recognition that time *is* a valuable resource. In many discussions, I've heard farmers discount their hours, as if using their time was something they could just shrug off. That's a mistake. Our time is not free. In fact, time may be one of our most valuable resources. No one is making more of it, so why should we give it away?

Here's an example. Most people accept the task of feeding hay during the winter because … well, because it's always been done that way, or because that's what we've been taught. But each decision affects other decisions. Let's examine this task more closely. Feeding hay in winter means that we must make or buy that hay prior to the winter. The farm then needs a place to store the hay and the labor to feed it out. If we choose to buy hay, we must locate a dependable vendor. If we choose to make hay — the most common strategy — we must reserve some of our best land for the crop, and that entails closing off some fields during peak growing periods. We also must obtain hay-making equipment, keep it running, and reserve our time to make that hay.

But let's put on our manager hat. We should ask ourselves, is this *really* the best allocation of resources? I can think of some alternatives: plant brassicas or stockpile other forages for winter grazing; expand the use of corn stubble; minimize our winter nutritional needs by scheduling lambing or calving for a different month; or even send our animals somewhere else for the winter (even into another county. Fiji would be nice).

A farm without hay fields? Sure. It's also a farm with more acreage for grazing, and perhaps grazing for longer periods during the year. It's also a place without all that iron equipment that depreciates year-after-year and eats up maintenance funds. And during the summers, the farm's owner can spend more time with the animals or managing the forages. It's our call. We're the CEOs. The buck stops here.

In New Zealand, quite a few skilled people make their living as fencing contractors. Most farms there are well-fenced, but often the owners did not build the fences themselves. They hired it out. One of the popular attractions in New Zealand agricultural fairs is the fence-building competition where fencing teams compete in speed and skill to build a stretch of high-tensile fence. How many professional fence-building crews can we find here? It's something to ruminate on.

Let's explore this CEO role a bit further, as not everything on a farm is nose-to-the-grindstone work. We should get paid for our efforts. If we consider ourselves as corporate executives, we should at least pay ourselves an executive wage. But, you say, we're in agriculture, not Wall Street. Who has the funds for corporate-level reimbursement? Well, let's be creative (much like some folks on Wall Street). Think of stock options. We have lots of stock — livestock. We can issue options on that stock. Maybe two shares for each ewe on the place, five shares for a cow, etc. The numbers could get quite impressive. Then perhaps we can bid up expectations and hold an IPO. The local Saturday livestock sale would become a place for day-trading. Hopefully, our stock won't split prematurely. We can even create a website. I can see it now: www.barnfallingdown.com.

First Published: June 2000
Author's Note: Seriously, a farm or ranch is indeed a business. Every week, we should reserve some quiet time, step back from the tractor and animals, sit at a desk, and think like a corporate executive. There are now ranching schools around the country that teach these concepts. The good thing is that these schools are often full.

Managing the Science of Grazing

Management-Intensive Grazing is not just a recycled version of rotational grazing. MIG is an exciting, cost-effective method for managing forages and harvesting sunlight. But most MIG information seems to come from the enthusiastic graziers who are actually doing it, not from universities or government research stations. In fact, with only a few notable exceptions, the scientific community has hardly mentioned the subject of MIG in its peer-reviewed professional literature. It might be good to explore why.

MIG is often called a "thinking person's grazing system." In MIG, a grazier establishes production goals for the livestock and allocates enough daily forage to meet those goals. He carefully monitors forage growth and responds to variations in weather and livestock needs by adjusting stocking densities and grazing areas. MIG usually entails small paddocks that vary in shape and size as animals are rotated around the farm.

A major MIG tool is pasture rotation. Animals are typically moved quite often, generally every couple of days (usually less than five) and sometimes every 12 hours, which fits the schedule of a grass-based dairy farm. Good fencing is crucial. While the perimeter fences may be permanent, the internal MIG fences are usually impermanent arrangements of fiberglass posts and electric wire or electrified netting, which are flexible and movable.

Graziers monitor pasture growth in pounds of dry matter per day, paddock by paddock. They are proud of their forages, and typical conversations involve topics like manure distribution and something called "pugging" (which is *not* a quarterback play in football). Their bedtime reading material — although I must admit that I've not done a comprehensive survey about this — will often be forage seed catalogs or fencing manuals.

Jim Gerrish, the former University of Missouri forage researcher who coined the term MIG, likes to note that MIG emphasizes *intensive management* rather than *intensive grazing*. This is important. Watch a ewe or a cow eat grass. Does she ever eat grass slowly? No, she *always* grazes intensively. MIG, on the other hand, requires intensive *management* of that grass, and also intensive management of the animals, labor, and equipment. MIG demands a day-to-day flexibility throughout the grazing season. This makes MIG quite different from traditional "rotational grazing" systems, which are cookie-cutter recipes that can be neatly summarized as "rotating every 28 days" or "15 paddocks with two days in each paddock" — uniform schedules applied across all paddocks, heedless of the changing conditions of weather and forage growth.

But here is the key: MIG is definitely *not* a cookie-cutter recipe. And science has a hard time with it.

I'll be more precise: the scientific *method* has a hard time with MIG. As do scientists who use the scientific method to conduct research and publish information. In essence, the scientific method is a very rigorous procedure for testing alternatives. Typically, a scientist phrases a question in the form of a hypothesis. He then designs an experiment to test that hypothesis against one or more alternatives. A properly designed experiment produces data that allows the scientist to reject or not reject that hypothesis. Then, based on these results, the scientist sets up another experiment with the next logical hypothesis, etc. The scientific method may be slow and ponderous, but it works beautifully with certain types of problems.

The scientific method, however, requires that each treatment be *replicated* (= the statistical term for *duplicated*). That's a problem because MIG is a free-flowing sequence of choices during the growing season, a series of flexible responses to changing conditions. Replication? MIG never heard of it. Which means that MIG is not an easy topic for scientific inquiry. Although scientists can test the *individual* building blocks of MIG — e.g., the details of forage growth rates or the consumption patterns of livestock — they find it hard to experiment with the whole, complex MIG *system*.

Let's take a different tack. Let's say that a young resourceful scientist truly wants to study MIG. She conducts a sheep experiment with four grazing areas, two using MIG and two using a traditional rotational system, and she runs the trial for two successive years. Each fall, she measures animal weights, residual forage, and lots of other variables.

The results? Although she can accurately describe the traditional rotation systems in terms of days on/days off, etc., she can't do the same for the MIG areas. Each MIG area was treated differently throughout the growing season, depending on the speed and amount of forage growth in each paddock, and the two years did not resemble each other. The MIG paddocks, therefore, were not valid replicates.

If she tries to publish the results, the editor and reviewers at the scientific journal will ask some basic questions about the MIG plots: exactly what did the animals eat? Don't know. How much did they eat and what was the nutritional value (compared to the forage that they trampled)? Don't know. Was there true replication between the MIG areas and across years? No.

Well, *that* paper won't get published, at least not in a peer-reviewed scientific journal.

For a young faculty member, how would this research affect her prospects for tenure? MIG experiments are clearly very difficult to conduct. They may take lots of time (i.e., years), and they produce messy data. Obtaining tenure still depends on the old maxim, "publish or perish," and MIG trials are notoriously difficult to publish.

What about senior faculty, who already have tenure? Well, they generally won't undertake MIG research because they already have successful research programs of their own. Why should they change? To them, MIG looks like a sloppy, ill-mannered guest who uses up resources without much hope of repayment. Staff scientists at government research stations are also in the same boat. Although somewhat insulated from the demands of university tenure, they still want to publish enough scientific material for internal advancement. To them, MIG is not a safe topic.

There are exceptions, of course, but only a few. The result is that most articles on MIG are published in the popular press as unreviewed, relatively unscientific documents.

Is this bad? Probably not. Science may *not* be the most appropriate venue for testing a grazing strategy. In the hands of graziers, MIG is really an *art built on the principles of science*. MIG is a business, a spreadsheet, an ongoing game, but it is not a scientific experiment.

First Published: June 1998

Author's Note: This was originally written in 1998, when MIG was a fairly new concept with some enthusiastic adherents but not much support or awareness in the scientific community. That has changed, at least a little. Scientists in a few institutions are now doing research on various aspects of MIG, including high-density mob grazing. And some of the MIG jargon has worked its way into academic reports and presentations. Things are moving in a good direction.

Two Cultures

It's been quite awhile since I've climbed on a soapbox. Well, maybe not a soapbox as much as a passionate examination of a controversy. In any case, I feel compelled to warn you — Dear Reader — so you can choose to continue reading the rest of this article or do something else, like check the electric fence in that far pasture. Because this month I'd like to visit about an emerging situation in the grazing world.

Grazing — good intensive grazing — is an elegant synthesis of science, art, economics, and experience. But in certain sectors of the grazing world, there seems to be a growing division between the scientific community and some graziers with lots of field experience. It almost seems as if we have two very different cultures.

The first culture is the old stand-by system of science and research. Its roots are in the formal scientific method, and its practitioners are in the agricultural universities, USDA research stations, and outreach programs of the Extension Service and other government agencies. The researchers generate technical information about forages and grazing. They design experiments, test hypotheses, analyze data, and train graduate students. Then the university faculty, Extension Agents, and NRCS field personnel distribute this information as widely as possible, often for free.

The second culture is less sharply defined, but it is definitely focused on the practical and financial aspects of grazing. This culture consists of folks who work mostly in the private arena: ranchers and farmers, field consultants, writers, and publishers of popular grazing magazines. These are very serious and astute people who practice some form of intensive grazing, usually on improved pastures. They pride themselves on producing animal products from forage — meat, milk, eggs, fiber, etc. — generally under earthy banners such as grassfed, natural, free-range, organic, antibiotic-free, and so on.

Some of this second group's production results are dazzling: grassfed cattle reaching finished weight in less than 18 months of age, grassfed lambs finishing in 6–7 months, a flock of 2,000 grassfed ewes dropping a 200% lamb crop in a 6-week lambing period, grassfed Jersey cows with a herd average of more than 15,000 lb milk, and in many instances, good evidence of vastly improved soil fertility. These graziers often push their forages far beyond any level seen on university farms, and they are routinely the first producers to use new forage species and varieties. The production responses on their farms and ranches speak for themselves.

But here's the rub. These most progressive graziers, the leaders in their field, are operating out beyond the scientific research establishment. And current university research isn't addressing their information needs, even though their financial and production achievements demonstrate that they are clearly doing lots of things right.

I can see both sides of this. When I attend some national scientific conferences — like the annual gathering of 2,500 animal and dairy scientists who share their research in more than 1,500 presentations — I am usually dismayed to see only a few good papers on intensive grazing. Oh sure, there is lots of research under the topic of "forages," but most of these projects focus on only three forages: alfalfa, corn silage, or endophyte-infected tall fescue. The problem is that the real on-farm world of grazing and forages is much broader and more complex than this.

To many graziers, the university system often seems insulated and out-of-touch. I've listened to senior scientists tell graziers that it's not possible to raise and finish cattle on grass in only 18 months. That's an interesting statement when the audience is filled with graziers who make a living by doing this routinely. I've also heard scientists say, what's the big deal about grazing — that corn is still the cheapest and least risky way to go. As if they haven't noticed the wild fluctuations in corn prices over the past few years. And in my local agricultural institution, Oregon State University, the Animal Science Department does not have a single on-campus Ph.D. scientist who is genuinely interested in forages or grazing. Also, its Department of Crop & Soil Science has only one Ph.D. professor working with forages — in a state that has some of the best grazing acreage in the world.

The flip side of this coin is that good graziers are thirsty for information. They are constantly looking for new ideas. Every year, there are dozens of grazing conferences around the country. Many are well attended, but many of these provide programs without university presenters. There are a couple of national magazines devoted to forages and grazing. And looking through them, I often see advertisements for specialized privately conducted schools and workshops for graziers. These inevitably focus on practical techniques and making money.

Graziers are shrewd observers of their fields, and their experiences have led to good questions that cry out for answers. Questions about topics like managing high-quality forages in fast grazing rotations, the use of Brix measurements to guide forage management decisions, palatability differences among forages, tissue tests from plants versus forage tests, livestock selection using grass-based genetics versus grain-based genetics, the value of extra nitrogen fertilizer in grazed forages, the most efficient ways of applying fertilizer to grass swards, etc. And in a larger sense, these questions arise from the need to fit science and technology into the shifting sequences of livestock and fences that define good intensive grazing.

Although the university research community may not be providing much state-of-the-art information for graziers, there is no scarcity of alternative sources and opinions. A vacuum doesn't last long. I've read scores of magazine articles and attended dozens of grazing conference presentations that are essentially variations of the "this-works-for-me" school of thought. No scientific references, no extensive literature reviews, no statistics. As a scientist, I shudder, but as a grazier, I am frustrated because good science has not addressed these issues.

Here's an example: I've heard strong opinions about the use of *Brix* measurements to guide decisions about pasture management. Brix is a refractometer measurement of the amount of soluble sugars in plant tissue, and it is used widely with high-sugar plants like grapes, vegetables, and sugarcane. But there is no scientific research on using it for pasture plants. Is Brix a good idea for graziers? Or are the numbers inaccurate or misleading? We really don't know. This is easily testable, and scientists should investigate it.

Another example that has made the rounds in grazing circles is the belief that only animals selected on grass should be used in grassfed production systems. And its corollary: that genetic selection using EPDs is of questionable value for graziers because EPDs are generally derived from animals fed grain. Again, this theory is testable, but the scientific analysis hasn't been done, even though EPDs are far more powerful than most people realize. Instead, strongly opinionated writers publish articles in popular grazing magazines that deride the classic EPD genetics and instead tout theories that were popular in the mid-1800s. Theories that assert that selecting the best grazing animals can be based on the width of their mouth (for increased forage intake), or on "linear measurements" of an animal's width and height, or on the appearance of the hair whorls on the head.

We appear to have two grazing cultures, and it troubles me that they seem to be diverging. A strong and vocal part of the grazing community tends to discount the science from universities, while at the same time, the research scientists are caught up in their own cloistered world and are not providing the information needed by the most-progressive graziers.

But we *can* work together. Successful graziers have made reasonable observations, and they are asking good, insightful questions. Scientists who are interested in these problems could set up experiments to test these hypotheses and generate solid information. But this strategy needs two fundamental things: (1) researchers who are truly interested in forages and grazing, and perhaps are willing to think outside the box, and (2) graziers who are willing to work with them.

I think that there *are* some scientists who are interested in forages and grazing, but they also have many other things on their plates. The grazing community should make a real effort to work with these scientists, cultivate their interests, and provide some support for them. I would be delighted to get off this soapbox. Good science results in good information. Then we all win.

First Published: May 2009

Author's Note: Over the past few years, there have been some improvements. In 2016, the Animal Science Department at OSU, for the first time, hired a new faculty member with livestock and forage responsibilities. More research papers are being published addressing the issues of stocking density, fiber digestibility, and soil compaction under mob grazing management. Small steps, perhaps, but at least they are steps.

Deciding To Rent or Pass

At a recent forage group meeting on an Oregon ranch, our discussion focused on the potential rental values for some pastures. Back and forth, ranchers discussed the pros and cons of the fields. Finally, one rancher said, "No, I wouldn't rent these fields." But across the room, another rancher countered, "Yes, there are definitely some attractive rental options here."

Whoa! What gives? Both ranchers are shrewd and experienced livestock operators. How can two people arrive at diametrically opposite conclusions about the same property?

This isn't an arbitrary coin flip. Both ranchers did indeed consider numerous factors. This is an important topic, because expanding a herd or flock often means acquiring more acreage, and sometimes it's a better business decision to rent land rather than buy it. So, what factors did those folks consider? Let's review them here. Who knows? Maybe one day you'll see a pasture and ask yourself, "Is this a good opportunity or a potential albatross?"

Location. The old real estate adage "Location, location, location" definitely applies to pastures. Is the acreage near a road? Is the road a main thoroughfare or a tiny one-lane gravel dead-end? Can you get trucks and equipment into the place easily? Is the nearest neighbor a farm down the road or a multi-dwelling housing unit across the fence? Urban, semi-urban, rural, or deep in a forest? Are the neighbors a housing tract or a pack of wolves (literally)? And how far is this pasture from your home farm? We are talking time and diesel; some folks draw a circle around their home place with a ten-mile radius. They won't consider renting anything beyond that radius. Everyone should determine his or her own radius.

Stock water. Animals need to drink. Where does the water coming from: creek, pond, deep well, rainwater, or a barn trough? How dependable is the source? Is it seasonal? How far must it be delivered? By whom? How far must the animals walk to it? If the only source is a creek, you might need to develop off-stream watering systems for intensive grazing because otherwise your animals will spend their time along the creek rather than in the pasture. The property may also have environmental regulations to consider, like salmon runs and who actually owns the water. Does delivering water require a new easement across an adjacent property or even an established easement? If so . . . well, there may be some legal issues there.

Fencing. Ah yes, fencing — one of our favorite pastimes. How good is the perimeter fence? *Is* there a perimeter fence? Any cross-fences? Are the existing gates located in the corners of the fields or in the centers of fence runs where it may be nearly impossible to convince animals to pass through them? If the perimeter fence is old, can you still make it work by installing offsets for an electric wire along the inside of the fence? Electrifying fences is usually not a problem because we now have good solar and battery-powered fence chargers, but does the field geography make it hard to design electric fencing? Does the field contain lots of heavy brush that will interfere with fencing?

Handling Facilities/Corrals. Everyone has their own preference here, but does the property contain *any* handling facilities? For which species? You'll definitely need something workable to load animals and possibly to sort and weigh them. I've seen permanent corrals built from steel road barriers. They would easily hold enraged bison without problem, but a flock of determined goats would go through them in a heartbeat. If you own a portable handling system, good on you!

Barns/Sheds. These may or may not be important, depending on your operation. If they exist, are they in good condition, or were the buildings last used when the Confederate Army marched past them en route to Gettysburg? What about hay storage? Roofs are much nicer if they don't leak. Alternatively, hay can be stored under tarps, at least temporarily, and balage can be stored outside. If there is a barn on the property, is it a magnet for veterinary problems like pneumonia and scours? How much frustration and work would be caused by a poorly designed barn? But in a larger sense, you should ask yourself if you really *need* to house animals on a rental property far from the home place. Some folks simply ignore existing structures on rental properties because the designs don't fit their operations.

Soils. Look at the actual landscape. Get a feel for the big picture and the technical details. Slope? Drainage? Fertility? Ground cover? What are the soils really like, and what grew on them recently? Any soil tests? How old are those tests, how deep were the samples, and how was the acreage sampled? Numbers can be misleading if the soil samples were not taken properly. Consider the costs of bringing the soil fertility up to your needs — both in fertilizer and limestone. The soil test buffer index will tell you how much limestone is needed. I once saw a soil test on a rental property with a pH of 5.2, a high buffer index, but a phosphorus level of 0 ppm. Yes, *zero* ppm! We visited that acreage and only saw a poor stand of thin grass and scrub. Not a surprise. The rancher wisely decided to end the lease rather than spend lots of money trying to improve the soil.

Forages. What plants are already growing in the pasture? Do you need to add forages to improve the pasture or totally renovate? How much would that cost? Or will improved grazing management change things? Is there a good variety of forage species or a good variety of recalcitrant weeds? If there are a lot of weeds, why are they in the pasture? What does the weed population tell you about previous management? What about forage density and consistency? If you can identify the existing forages, you'll know their characteristics — this will help you estimate the forage growth curve on that pasture and the potential yield of that forage. Do the current forage species dovetail into the needs of your operation?

Class of livestock. In this case, the rental price may be less relevant if the land doesn't fit your system. Which animals are best suited for the acreage? Pastures that can support dry ewes may not be good for fast-growing lambs or feeder cattle. A property that may beautifully fit the needs of a cattleman may be a disaster for a shepherd, or vice versa. Consider fences, drainage, predators, and neighbors. There are huge differences in the needs and adaptabilities of sheep, cattle, goats, and horses. The devil is in the details.

Availability of help. By help, I mean nearby, dependable labor: to check livestock when you are not on the property, walk the fence lines (and do some repairs), change irrigation pipe, treat weeds, etc. Interns, college students, high school agriculture classes — these are all variations of young, enthusiastic help. How available are they? What about retired farmers who live nearby or would like on-site living arrangements? Of course, this also depends on the distance from your home place. You might have some innovative options here.

Lease duration. One year? Five years? Ninety-nine years (like the original British lease on Hong Kong)? Lease duration depends on your needs, of course, but it also sets limits on what you can do with a property. If you want to make any soil adjustments or renovate a pasture with perennial forages, you'll need a lease of more than one year. Recall that some forages need 2–3 years to become fully productive. Would planting annual forages be a good option? What is the realistic potential for lease renewals? And realistically, if the property begins to produce more or looks better under your management, will the owner decide to take it back? Is the rental agreement in writing? Really?

Character. This item is, frankly, a bit delicate. You and the landowner need to get along. You can't define character with a ten-point checklist; it's a judgment call. What can I say about this? Not much, except that we all make judgments and choices about personalities. Can the landowner clearly articulate his needs and the rental rates? Is there something else, something indefinable that makes you feel comfortable or makes you hold back? A sixth sense, perhaps, but don't ignore it, certainly not for a long-term agreement. Business arrangements really hinge on trust between both parties, on a handshake that really means what it says. There are times when all the factors listed earlier in this article seem good, and the rental price is great, but the last item on character is, well, hmmm. Which is why, at the beginning of this article, those two ranchers came to opposite conclusions about the pastures on that farm. It all came down to judgments.

During the forage group meeting I described in the opening paragraph, one of the members asked, "What is your algorithm for evaluating a pasture's value?" A good word, algorithm. Dictionaries define it as a formula, a set of rules, a step-by-step procedure for solving a problem.

The problem we want to solve is acreage — deciding to rent or pass.

———✂———

First Published: August 2014
Author's Note: Throughout this book, most of the chapters are about technical details. This chapter, however, is about a business decision. And in the end, it's the sum of these business decisions, large and small, that really determines profit (and survival). So, it's a good thing to ask lots of questions before signing on the dotted line.

Not Horsing Around

Last spring, I visited the beautiful area around Lexington, Kentucky, and spent time looking at, well, horses. And pastures. I saw fields of early spring grass with lots of horses playing and galloping. But something intrigued me. At a couple of those horse farms, the owners spoke reverently about their forages. Actually, they talked about only one forage: Kentucky bluegrass. They said that their horses did wonderfully on it; that it was the most nutritious grass in the world; that it was the basis of their entire farms. Hmmm, I thought, what am I missing?

I don't believe in panaceas, but I also don't argue with success, especially when the successful people are such considerate hosts. So, during my farm visits, I kept my own counsel and ruminated about it for a while. I considered all sides of the issue. Finally, it came to me why Kentucky bluegrass is so important to those farms. It's not the nutritional value. It's something else, something more fundamental and profound than nutrition. In fact, the real reason demonstrates how on a farm, *all the pieces*, including the forages, must fit together to make a successful operation.

First, a textbook description of Kentucky bluegrass (KBG, *Poa pratensis*): KBG is a low-growing, sod-forming, cool-season perennial grass that grows well throughout the northeast and north-central United States, often in conjunction with white clover (*Trifolium repens*). Persistent and winter-hardy, it has long, slim leaves with a characteristic boat-shape tip. Young shoots are folded. KBG has shallow roots and spreads by rhizomes. It responds well to good fertility, although other forages like the ryegrasses or orchardgrass or timothy will generally outyield it. KBG is also rather seasonal; its main growth periods occur in the spring and fall. During its unproductive period in midsummer, commonly called a "summer slump," many other grasses will grow better, such as orchardgrass or tall fescue.

257

Nutritionally, KBG is nothing to write home about. Like any other grass, KBG is highly nutritious when the leaves are young and vegetative, but its nutritional value drops off rapidly as it matures. And recall that horses — even thoroughbred racehorses — don't have the high nutritional requirements of dairy cows or lactating ewes raising twins. Nearly any reasonable grass hay may be good enough nutritionally for these horses.

KBG excels, however, in one very critical trait: it can withstand close grazing. It will survive and flourish under set-stocking conditions. This, of course, is one of the main reasons KBG is so common on many farms around the country.

But a farm is not a farm is not a farm, and Kentucky horse farms are quite different from New York dairy farms or Oregon sheep ranches. Kentucky horse farms specialize in raising fine thoroughbred animals where horses can be worth hundreds of thousands or even millions of dollars. These farms either own their own horses or board horses owned by others. They rear these animals, breed them, train them, and sometimes, race them.

All these horse farms contain rolling pastures where horses can run and graze. The forages in these pastures must provide feed for grazing, of course, and also some hay. KBG hay is no different than other grass hays: it can range from good to poor, depending on the date of cutting and the amount of rainfall. And KBG is not waterproof — a steady rain during hay harvest will soak KBG as much as any other grass.

But let's think for a moment about the farms. What is the *real product* of these horse farms? And who is their market?

These farms don't sell hay. They don't sell feed. Yes, they do sell horses (at least the ones they own). But their real product is something that few other livestock farms can match — these horse farms sell an *image*. They sell the smell of liniment and leather; they sell the chance for a horse owner to lean over the railing at a track and watch horses run training laps, blowing steam in the early frosty mornings.

For some markets, image is nearly everything. Remember the cigarette commercials featuring the *Marlboro Man* or *Joe Camel* — two of the most successful advertising images in history? One portrayed dreams of the great glowing West; the other suggested an urban cool, the cocky boldness of James Dean. We may not all support the products presented in these images, but we can't deny that they increased sales.

So, for those Kentucky horse farms, who is their market? Investors. Investors who have lots of money. Investors who own million-dollar horses. Corporate executives, politicians, lawyers, doctors, investment bankers, professional athletes. And these folks must find places to board their horses.

They look for farms that will train their horses, run them in races, and give them the chance for a big payoff in the winner's circle.

These are city folk who will come out to the farms on weekends to "talk shop" with the trainers and watch their horses gallop through the pastures. They want to see beautiful colts and fillies playing in lawn-like paddocks. They want to buy into an image.

Here's the thing: these horse farms can provide that image. Their investors aren't interested in the technical details of "grazing cells" or intensive grazing or forage management or the cost of hay. Let's ignore the clubhouse complaints about the price of feed. These farms don't need high-yielding pastures to produce hay. They can buy any hay they need. Paying an extra $30 per ton is a trivial expense when compared to getting a contract to board a million-dollar horse.

Therefore, high-yielding forages like orchardgrass or tall fescue would not suit these farms. These are bunch grasses that require careful grazing management, something that's not easy to do with horses. No trainer would risk crowding thoroughbred racehorses tight enough for controlled grazing — the animals would hurt each other or run into fences. And using cattle or sheep to graze pastures is not an option, not on these farms, not with their image. But without good grazing management, bunch grasses would become clumpy and rank and weedy. There could be open muddy spots between the plants. Potential investors don't want to see their horses struggling through the mud of a torn-up pasture.

But Kentucky bluegrass does the job nicely.

Kentucky bluegrass forms a tight sod that will hold down the mud and withstand the pounding of flying hooves. It persists year after year even when continuously grazed by horses, which are notorious for destroying pastures. KBG can provide green, manicured paddocks even though it doesn't yield well under those conditions or provide excess nutrients for the animals. No wonder my hosts praised it. Better than any other forage, KBG helps them sell an image.

Young colts galloping on a spring green pasture. Manes flying in the wind. The promise of great races. Crowds rising to their feet as horses thunder into the final stretch.

Kentucky bluegrass.

First Published: November 1999

Author's Note: To me it was an epiphany. To see how each part fits with other parts, to look between the lines and see the bigger picture, to appreciate that the whole farming operation is greater than the sum of its disparate parts. In my graduate studies, I was trained as a scientist, Scientists strive to reduce problems into smaller and smaller parts for intense study. But as a consultant, my job is to use the information gained from those reductionist studies and apply it to functioning farms. The Kentucky in Kentucky bluegrass is a good example of this.

Optimistically Speaking

As I write this, the Chicago Cubs are contending for the wildcard spot in the National League playoffs. The Cubs in the playoffs?!? Well, if the world has gone topsy-turvy, I suppose I can write about almost anything, even a little shameless commentary.

Like about the meaning of life. And grazing.

Management-Intensive Grazing is all the rage now, at least among those who do it. But not among scientists. MIG trials are not easy. Researchers who try to measure the effects of MIG are a little like the blind men in the fable who tried to "see" the elephant by feeling different parts with their hands; they all came away with strong impressions, but no one grasped the entire picture. Graziers, on the other hand, are *forced* to see the entire picture; they must live with it.

In research, scientists routinely compare grazing animals against confinement animals by measuring production responses like growth, milk production, meat quality, etc. Surprise, surprise — MIG never looks great in research. The simple reason is because animals fed grain will nearly always outperform animals on pasture. Agronomists see equivalent results with their forage plants. Experimental plots are usually composed of a single species carefully groomed, highly fertilized, and cut at precise intervals. In contrast, plants in grazed swards face a tougher existence: they get cut at odd times, they endure greater drought and heat stress, and they get stepped on by large animals. Plant for plant, grazed forages will almost always seem less productive for longevity or yield than mechanically harvested plots.

But those research results have limited value. Like the blind men in the fable, those research results miss the whole story, and it's the whole story that matters to a grazier. MIG is more than just giving animals a daily allotment of forage and moving them around from paddock to paddock. MIG is really about sunlight — about trying to maximize the amount of sunlight captured by forages, converted to animal products, and sold for the benefit of us humans.

To successfully practice MIG, graziers must overcome a common mental hurdle: they need to think in terms of *output per pasture* rather than *output per animal*. Most research, unfortunately, evaluates treatment response as output per animal. Frankly, I can always increase animal output by feeding more grain. MIG tries to maximize production per acre, not per animal. But producing more pounds of meat or wool or milk per acre means increasing the *efficiency* of harvesting sunlight through the solar panels of forages. And from a business perspective, sunlight is cheaper and less risky than grain.

MIG is a way of thinking, *a strategy of intensively managing resources*. MIG attempts to balance the entire system. It requires skill and knowledge and a shrewd analysis of risks. It aims for a sustainable way of life, which is also a sustainable business.

Profit is a funny animal; it can be real or it can be a mirage. With a spreadsheet, I can easily devise livestock budgets that demonstrate that confinement systems will usually make larger profits than grazing systems. Animal productivity in a confinement system is almost always higher than in a grazing system. But science has unequivocally demonstrated that sheep and cattle have legs . . . and that manure and bedding do not. All confinement systems require certain tasks: *someone* must haul feed every day, and *someone* must haul the manure and bedding and find a place to put it. *Someone* must build barns and confinement pens, maintain equipment for feeding and harvesting, build structures for feed storage, and deal with the inevitable health problems caused by reduced ventilation and increased crowding. Confinement systems are like getting on a treadmill.

Similarly, on the agronomic side, I can devise crop budgets that demonstrate that annual crops — like corn or soybeans — will outyield perennial forages and will often return a larger profit. But then there is the concept of risk. How often do you have to replant corn with a short-season variety because the spring was too wet or too cold? Or fear the loss of your entire crop because of a late freeze or an early freeze or a hailstorm? These may be unpredictable acts of nature, but we know that they *will* occur; we just don't know when. Where in those crop budgets is a line item for the loss of sleep due to worry?

But as bad as these problems are, they are *not* catastrophic for grazing systems based on perennial forages like orchardgrass or tall fescue. Sure, harsh weather can cause a loss of 20% or more of a rotation's yield, but never 100%. And if weather causes some losses to our pastures, we can adjust our stocking rates or amounts of supplementary feed and keep going. Nature may be predictably unpredictable, but perennial forages will not lose everything to its whims.

Clever. And good business.

There is, however, one final thing. No successful business runs itself; it's the people who make things happen. Shrewd, skillful people who recognize a good opportunity and follow it toward the future.

For example, I know a fellow here in Douglas County, a grazier, who is really part of this future. He runs more than 500 head of cattle, a small flock of sheep, and some goats. He owns the sheep and goats but not the cattle. By not owning the cattle, he strategically reduces his risks. Every spring he receives truckloads of heifers and steers from eastern Oregon under contract — he gets paid for pounds of gain or on a per month basis. He owns or rents the land and sells the forage. In reality, he uses his land to raise forage and then sells his ability to provide high quality feed and good animal care. He moves cattle every day and creates pastures on the fly with electric fence. He doesn't own a tractor or a large barn. He runs his entire operation with an ATV, a pickup truck, two stock dogs, and a calculator. Especially the calculator. He knows his costs of production as precisely as any corporate accountant.

When he walks his fields — and I've accompanied him many times — he speaks excitedly about grazing. Not about a new piece of heavy equipment or the latest government subsidy program — but about the land itself, the pastures, the forages. He describes how his new grass varieties are outcompeting the thistles, or how the phosphorus levels in the soil are increasing, or how last year he extended his pasture growth into the dry summer by building small dikes to retain runoff water. I see justifiable pride. He is running a successful business.

This is not our traditional image of a farmer. We often think of farmers as, well . . . the kind of image portrayed by Edwin Markham in his poem "The Man with the Hoe":

Bowed by the weight of centuries he leans

Upon his hoe and gazes on the ground,

The emptiness of ages in his face,

And on his back the burden of the world.

The man in this poem was definitely not a grazier.

First Published: September 1998

Author's Notes: Risk. Yes, it's a four-letter word, but it can never be ignored. Compared to heavy-iron farming, grazing reduces risks. The skills are different; the monetary returns are different, but the life and the future of a good grazier is bright and optimistic.

One more thing: As I write this paragraph, 16 years after I penned the original article . . . the Chicago Cubs have just *won* the World Series. Life is good.

SECTION 7

I Wonder . . .

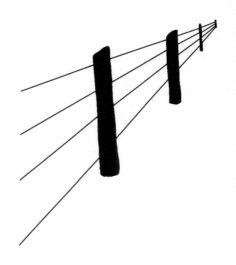

Dinosaur Dreams

We can never tell where ruminant nutrition will lead us. Start with a mundane topic like grass, and before we know it, we're into microbes and methane and fiber and size. Yes, size. That's a particularly big topic this month. Let's talk about dinosaurs, the biggest ones — the sauropods.

Were dinosaurs ruminants? We'll get to that. First let's lay some groundwork.

Dinosaurs, of course, lived more than 100 million years ago. Mostly between 230 million and 65 million years ago, when a great extinction occurred, probably as the result of a collision with a large meteor. Let's put aside the issue of meteor collisions and talk about nutrition.

I want to focus on a class of dinosaurs called the *sauropods*. These were the really big dinosaurs — the largest animals that ever lived. You know, the long-necked gigantisaurs or whatever, many longer than 100 feet. Ask any 12-year old for details. The sauropods were indeed enormous. The most massive was the *Argentinosaurus* at probably 100 tons. That's *200,000 pounds*. In comparison, our largest land animal today is the African elephant at a measly 10 tons.

Years ago, one of the finest nutritionists in the world, Peter Van Soest, the scientist who developed the NDF/ADF system of fiber analysis that forage labs everywhere use today, took an interest in species comparisons. Actually, that was quite logical, because animals are fascinatingly variable in how they address the nutritional principles of gut anatomy, fermentation rates, fiber digestion, and feed selection. Van Soest's interest in comparative nutrition led to studies of diverse species such as wombats, dik-diks, giraffes, and elephants. After these studies, it was perfectly logical to move from elephants to dinosaurs.

Which brings us to last autumn's Cornell Nutrition Conference. Amid two days of rather routine technical papers on protein nutrition, heifer development, and such, Peter Van Soest gave a lecture that was not routine at all. His topic: the nutritional issues of sauropod dinosaurs and gigantism. As Peter covered point after point, the audience became very quiet. This month I want to share some of these points with you — aspects of nutrition generally not found in classic nutrition textbooks. Here's a gentle warning: these points may not be the most practical tips for balancing your next ration (unless you raise some *very* large breeding stock), but sometimes it's just nice to kick back and dream. This is what the best scientists do — and who knows where things may lead?

Firstly, Sauropods were herbivores — vegetarians that ate plants. What types of plants? Well, not grasses or legumes — those plants didn't appear on Earth until 30 million years ago, long after dinosaurs had vanished. Scientists speculate that these large dinosaurs ate leaves and ferns and shrubs. In any case, all these plants contained fiber.

But a fiber-based forage diet has definite implications. Since no vertebrate animal today has enzymes that can digest cellulose, it's reasonable to assume that dinosaurs didn't have those enzymes either. Which means that if they consumed plants that contained high levels of fiber, they had to digest that fiber the same way today's herbivores do — by maintaining a population of fiber-fermenting microbes somewhere in their digestive tracts and then absorbing the nutrients synthesized by those microbes. Today's herbivore species have evolved many anatomical designs to solve this problem. Ruminants have a rumen; horses and elephants have a huge large intestine; rabbits and rats have a cecum. And dinosaurs had … well … something. They may not have had a rumen, and they probably didn't chew cud, but their digestive tracts had to have *someplace* that contained fiber-fermenting microbes.

Which leads directly to another item, one with tantalizing implications: fiber fermentation does not occur efficiently at low temperatures. In today's world, many industries rely on fermentation products, and for fiber-loving microbes to thrive, those fermentation vats must be warmer than 60°F. But if dinosaurs were cold-blooded, how did they maintain their internal body temperatures above 60°? Sure, the Jurassic Period was warmer than today, but the Earth still had nighttime temperatures that were cooler than daytime temperatures, and the Earth also had four seasons, as well as land masses far from the equator. A large herbivore that was cold-blooded would be at a nutritional and evolutionary disadvantage if its body temperature remained low or fluctuated greatly for any period of time.

But thanks to the laws of physics, being huge may have provided some distinct anatomical advantages for staying warm. A large animal has a low ratio of surface area to body weight, which means that a large animal has a relatively harder time dissipating heat than a small animal. If their internal metabolism generated some heat, sauropods would have had a difficult time getting rid of it. Similarly, if these dinosaurs had become warm during the day, their body size would have helped them retain heat for many hours into the night, similar to the warming strategy of today's cold-blooded animals like snakes and tortoises who lie on rocks and asphalt roads during the day. Which means, because of the principles of simple physics, that the sauropods could have been *passively* warm-blooded, or alternatively, they could have been *actively* warm-blooded through mechanisms we don't yet understand.

Either way, these animals ate forage, and they had to eat a lot of it. Let's consider our *Argentinosaurus* at 100 tons (= 200,000 lb). How much did this animal eat, and what does that imply? Well, if we assume a low rate of dry matter intake, say at only 1.0-1.5% body weight, this animal consumed *2,000–3,000 pounds of dry matter each day.* (Compare this to a high-producing Holstein cow that eats 60 pounds of dry matter per day.) If Jurassic plant material contained 25% dry matter, which is typical for living green plants, then our dinosaur needed more than 8,000 pounds of green leaves *each day.* Or if someone made hay for this monster, they would have fed at least 44 square bales each day (50-lb bales). At the very least, this level of intake implies that these animals had to keep moving throughout the day, just to find enough forage to eat. Which, in turn, implies strong legs and lots of bites.

Which brings up a technical issue: retention time. This is defined as the average time that feed material remains in the digestive tract. Retention time in herbivores is inversely related to feed intake. The higher the feed intake, the shorter the retention time. But short retention times reduce fiber digestibility because the microbes need enough hours to ferment the cellulose. Sauropod dinosaurs had to consume huge amounts of feed, but they also had to retain this feed in their digestive tracts long enough for extensive fiber digestion. But long retention times are not good either. No herbivore today has a retention time longer than four days. Why? Because after four days in a fermentation vat, some of the nutritional 2-carbon and 3-carbon VFAs (volatile fatty acids) produced by the bacteria are further reduced to the 1-carbon compound methane that has no nutritional value and is lost as gas. Our sauropods, therefore, were caught in a nutritional bind: they needed a high feed intake to support their great body mass, but they also needed a carefully balanced retention time to allow for productive fermentation. One possible strategy they might have used to cope with this quandary is to carefully select their feed, similar to the feeding behavior of some herbivore species today. It's too bad we didn't have digestion crates back then ... digestion trials with sauropods would have kept a few graduate students quite busy.

One last thing. Remember the classic picture of long-necked sauropods eating leaves from tall trees? Think about this for a moment. Some of these sauropod monsters could raise their heads 40 feet into the air. The question is not *if* they ate leaves that high; the question is *how* did they get blood and oxygen to their brains that high. Pumping blood to a height of 40 feet would require a heart the size of a refrigerator. (I know — *that* would explain how they were cold-blooded.) But there's no fossil evidence to support this anatomy. So what gives?

These animals may have had backflow valves in their neck arteries. Or they may have had special air sacks that increased the efficiency of oxygen transfer. Some of today's bird species have these air sacks. In Asia, migrating cranes fly over the Hindu Kush mountains at 24,000 feet. Cranes flying at high altitudes require lots of oxygen, but they really can't pack along their own oxygen tanks. These birds have clearly evolved a sophisticated set of air sacks to help transfer oxygen at low pressures. The tall sauropods may have had similar mechanisms.

Well, the lecture at that Nutrition Conference was classic Peter Van Soest: fascinating and definitely outside the box. But I must end here. I've decided to rent the movie *Jurassic Park*. I need to make some observations about forage intake.

―――――――

First Published: February 2010
Author's Note: The nutritionists in that conference room were not stunned into silence, nor were they sitting silent in disbelief. Not at all. As they listened to Peter's lecture, they all recognized and appreciated the opportunity to be in the presence of one of the great minds in the scientific world. The ability and willingness to think outside the box is a gift, and Peter Van Soest has shared his outside the box thoughts and insights with many people over the years, including me when I took his advanced nutrition classes at Cornell and had him as a member of one of my graduate school committees.

SECTION 8

Intensively Managed Grazing Systems
Systems
– A Textbook –

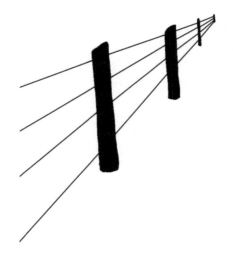

Section 8: Intensively Managed Grazing Systems – A Textbook

Author's Note & Acknowledgement

The following material is essentially a textbook on intensive grazing.

These sections were originally published as the second half (pages 212–225) of the "Forages Chapter" in the *SID Sheep Production Handbook, 2015 Edition, Volume 8,* by the American Sheep Association, Inc., ADS Publishing, Fort Collins, Colorado. I wish to acknowledge the support of the American Sheep Industry Association in this endeavor and appreciate its permission to use this material in my book.

The *SID Sheep Production Handbook* is the premier reference book for the American sheep industry. The complete "Forages Chapter" in this *Handbook* consists of two main sections: "Rangelands" and "Intensively Managed Grazing Systems." I wrote the latter section, which I am reproducing here. You may notice that the organization and writing style of this section is quite different from the other chapters in this book. This section on Intensively Managed Grazing Systems resembles the writing style of a textbook: longer sentences, mostly passive tense, multiple subsections, and a writing tone that is rather dry and detached.

But on a practical level, this section describes, in a very logical way, the principles and practical issues of Management-Intensive Grazing applied to improved pastures. It contains detailed descriptions of forage growth and grazing management. It also contains step-by-step instructions on the various techniques that you need to make decisions about this type of management.

I have, however, made a few minor editorial changes to the original text. For example, I revised some terms and abbreviations to be consistent with the rest of this book. Wherever possible, to avoid confusion, I eliminated cross-references to other chapters in the original handbook. I also eliminated two small subsections from the original material (these subsections are "Primary Forages Commonly Used in Improved Pastures" and "Health Issues on Pasture") because colleague scientists made contributions to those subsections, and therefore, that text is not entirely mine. However, you can find the complete original version of this chapter and that text in the *SID Sheep Production Handbook*.

The following sections and subsections contain a lot of no-nonsense information. Enjoy.

Intensively Managed Grazing Systems

In the broadest sense, our primary crop on a farm is sunlight. Sunlight is free, nonpolluting, and completely sustainable. We grow forages to capture that sunlight through photosynthesis, create biomass, and then harvest this biomass. In effect, we are harvesting sunlight with the use of machinery or livestock. Then we sell either the stored forage or the livestock to produce income and hopefully create a viable business. In effect, as forage producers and graziers, we are in the business of harvesting and selling sunlight. And sheep are one of the most efficient and adaptable livestock species for harvesting this forage.

Sheep are well-equipped to harvest and utilize forages. They have a rumen and a lower gastrointestinal tract that support the microbial fermentation of carbohydrates, including plant fiber. As ruminants, sheep also chew cud — regurgitated rumen contents — which increases the efficiency of fiber digestion. They also have legs that allow them to walk to their feed. And their selectivity in choosing a diet generally helps them avoid toxic or low-quality plants.

Economic analyses of sheep enterprises consistently show that more than 60 percent of their budgets is related to feeding the animals. Feed, of course, consists of more than out-of-pocket expenses. The real costs of providing feed include the following: the cash costs for feed and minerals; the costs of purchasing or renting the land for raising feed; fertilizer, machinery, and other direct costs associated with growing feed; the barns, buildings, feed bunks, and other facilities required for feed storage and winter feeding; the fencing to control grazing; the labor to harvest the stored feed, feed the rations, and haul

277

the manure back onto the fields; and all the depreciation and annual costs incurred by the equipment for handling, harvesting, and distributing the feed. If the efficiency of feeding sheep could be improved by even 10 percent, the economic effect of this change would be profound because feeding comprises such a large proportion of the budget. This improvement could significantly lower the operation's break-even price as well as allow greater financial options for the operation.

Well-managed forages, particularly grazed forages, can represent some of the most economic feedstuffs available to sheep producers. The skills to grow and manage these forages can be learned and applied to most sheep production systems, especially those that can take advantage of intensive forage management.

These pages discuss the use of high-quality forages on a farm, and how producers may use sheep in the management of these forages. This section specifically focuses on forages that can be managed intensively. These are forages that are grown in fenced fields and receive sufficient water, either from natural rainfall or from irrigation. The past fifteen years have seen a growing interest in the intensive management of improved forages, and along with this interest, a terminology has been developed for this type of management.

This section is *not* designed to be a complete course on forage production or a comprehensive treatise on grazing management. It is, rather, a short primer, a practical no-nonsense guide that outlines a framework of knowledge and skills for intensive forage management. For those producers who desire more information about this kind of forage management, additional readings are listed at the end of this chapter.

Forage Growth

To manage forages properly and efficiently and also make good decisions about grazing management, a grower must know the amount of forage in a paddock, its rates of growth, and its stage of growth. Traditionally, forage management recommendations have focused on forage height, such as, "introduce livestock into a paddock when Forage X is ten inches high and remove them when the height is reduced to two inches" or some variation of this.

However, there are two severe limitations to this approach. The first limitation relates to managing the forage. Different forage species have different physical growth patterns. Some forages, such as perennial ryegrass, gala grazing brome, Kentucky bluegrass, and the prostrate forms of birdsfoot trefoil all have a higher proportion of their vegetative growth at a lower height than upright, tall-growing species like orchardgrass, 'Matua' prairie grass, timothy, alfalfa, or red clover. Most pastures contain multiple forage species, which further complicates this height estimation. Also, forage height tells the producer little about the *density* of that forage — the amount of forage per square foot. Forage density depends on many factors, including species mix, seeding rates, stand age, fertility, weather, time of year, etc., and some of these factors usually change during the course of the growing season.

The second limitation relates to managing the sheep. Basically, this limitation involves feed consumption. This limitation can easily be demonstrated by asking two questions: (1) "How many inches of pasture does a sheep require to meet its nutrient requirements?" and (2) "How many inches of pasture will a ewe consume in a day?" Estimations of forage height do not answer these questions. The problem is obvious: nutrient requirements and dry matter intake are expressed as *amounts* of feed, not height. Forage height does not provide us with enough information to allow us to allocate the available feed in a grazing system or to alter our management properly to adjust to the changing conditions of fertility, weather, and stocking density.

Therefore, we need to adjust our approach to managing forage. We need to think about forage growth in a pasture as an amount, or *mass*, of forage. This leads us to three critical terms to describe the amount of pasture:

Total mass:	The total amount of forage above ground.
Residual mass:	The amount of forage remaining in the pasture after harvest. That harvest can be accomplished by grazing or by machines. Residual mass is the amount of forage left in the pasture when the animals are moved off that field or the amount of stubble remaining after harvesting the hay or silage.
Available mass:	Total mass minus Residual mass (= Total mass – Residual mass). This is the amount of forage that the animals can graze or that will be removed from the field as hay or silage.

All three terms are on a dry matter basis and are generally expressed as *pounds per acre*.

For example, let's consider a one-acre paddock of orchardgrass/white clover containing 2,800 pounds of total mass (of dry matter). If the producer plans to move the sheep off the paddock when the residual mass reaches 1,100 pounds, then the available feed equals 1,700 pounds.

One potential problem, especially in today's world of modern international communications via the internet, is that most other countries in the world utilize the metric system and express their values of pasture mass as *kilograms per hectare* (kg/ha). Fortunately, however, the conversion to English units is easy. Since 1.0 kilogram equals 2.20 pounds, and 1.0 hectare equals 2.47 acres, 1.0 kg/ha equals 0.89 lb/acre, which is reasonably close to 1.0. In practical usage, however, this ratio is close enough to one to allow graziers to use these terms interchangeably. Thus, for practical use, 1 kg/ha equals 1 lb/acre. This simple conversion is helpful when trying to work with international documents concerning forage mass, fertilizer rates, seeding rates, or stocking density.

Measuring Pasture Mass

How do we actually measure the amount of forage in a pasture? There are a number of different techniques. All of them, however, are ultimately based on obtaining objective measurements of pasture mass by taking small samples and drying and weighing them. Sampling technique is important because the values from the small sample areas are applied to the entire pasture. Here is a step-by-step procedure for taking and measuring a single direct sample.

Equipment needed:
- brown paper bag.
- microwave oven.
- glass of water, partially filled.
- small scale that weighs to the nearest 1.0 gram. A good postal scale will be sufficient.
- open, rectangular frame measuring 12.0 x 11.5 inches. This can be built from wood or any other convenient materials or even created from a cardboard packing box with an appropriate opening cut into its side.

1. Record the weight of the empty dry brown paper bag.
2. Lay the rectangular frame flat on the ground and clip and save all the forage inside the frame. Clip to ground level if you want to estimate the Total Mass in the sample. Take care not to include any stones, roots, soil, or other nonconsumable matter. Place all forage in the brown paper bag.
3. Dry this sample in the microwave, with the bag partially open to allow moisture to escape. Dry in short periods rather than all at once. Important: during the drying process, place a partially full glass of water in the microwave.
4. A typical drying sequence would be to dry the sample initially for six minutes, then three minutes, and thereafter for a series of two-minute bursts. Note that drying forage will give off a strong odor

that is not unpleasant but is still strong. You might want to alert other people who use that microwave about your activities before you begin drying samples.

5. Weigh the sample after each drying period and write down the weight. These weights will decrease after each microwave period. After a few drying periods, the weights will begin to level off. When the weight remains constant, the sample is dry.

6. From the final weight of the sample and bag, subtract the weight of the bag. The resulting number is the weight of forage dry matter, in grams.

To determine the mass of forage in an acre, multiply your value by 100.

$$Pounds\ of\ dry\ matter\ per\ acre = \\ (Grams\ of\ dry\ matter\ in\ sample)\ x\ 100$$

Obviously, one small sample is a poor estimate of the mass for the *entire* pasture. To obtain a better estimate of the pasture mass, you need to collect, dry, and weigh a number of samples from various parts of the pasture. The average value of all these samples is the estimated total mass of the pasture.

However, one valuable rationale for taking this single sample is to train your eye — so in the future you can look at a pasture and make a reasonable eyeball estimate of the pasture mass. To train your eye, follow this procedure: just before you take the sample in the pasture, look very carefully at that spot. Try to memorize what it looks like. If necessary, take photographs of this spot. Then, after you dry the sample and calculate a numerical value for its total mass (in lb/acre), you can associate this number with its appearance. Do this for many different samples, each time following the same procedure of carefully memorizing what each area looks like. After a few iterations of this procedure, with careful and disciplined observations, you should be able to look at a field and make a reasonably accurate eyeball estimation of the total pasture mass.

A few notes about this procedure:

1. It is important that your scale weighs to the nearest one gram, not to the nearest five grams. (Many commercial scales only weigh to the nearest five grams, so you may need to shop around.) The greater measurement sensitivity is required because the sample size is so small. An error of only one gram in

the sample results in a final calculated pasture value that is off by 100 pounds of dry matter.

2. The reason that the sampling frame is designed at 12.0 x 11.5 inches rather than one square foot (12 x 12 inches) is to permit an easy conversion from grams per sample to pounds per acre. If the frame was exactly one square foot, then the multiplier would be 95.95. The value of 100 is easier to remember than 95.95. The important parameters here are (1) one acre equals 43,560 square feet and (2) one pound equals 454 grams.

3. This sampling method is not quite exact because it incorporates a slight rounding correction. But this rounding correction is not biologically significant because your sample is only an estimate. No pasture is 100 percent consistent in its forage mass.

Other Techniques for Estimating Pasture Mass

Several different techniques are available for estimating the total mass of pasture. Most are based on calibrating the field observations with values carefully obtained from the objective microwave sampling procedure outlined previously.

Visual Appraisal. Based on "calibrating" your eye with sample values derived from the objectively measured technique as described previously. After weighing and measuring the dry matter amounts of many samples and remembering what these plots looked like at sampling, you can slowly gain a visual "feel" for the amount of forage mass that you see in a pasture. Taking and cataloging standard photographs for reference will greatly aid in accuracy and consistency of visual appraisal. For experienced graziers, the visual appraisal method can match the values of other, more sophisticated equipment. However, for each different type of pasture, the relationship between visual appraisal and total mass must be learned separately because forage height and density will change significantly due to species composition, fertility, and season.

Gumboot Method. This is really an estimation based on height — i.e., the height of the pasture when measured against the tall rubber boot that is commonly worn when walking through pastures. Although height is related to pasture mass, this relationship changes with different densities, species composition, and season. Also, the height of the top of a sward is rather difficult to determine. However, references to height are often found in popular publications, and the gumboot method is more applicable for pastures in a region that are very similar in composition and fertility.

Rising Plate Meter. A mechanical device that consists of a calibrated vertical stick on which a solid square or circular disk (or plate) can slide freely up and down. When the bottom of the stick is placed firmly on the ground, the disk slides upward until it is supported by the compressed pasture. The height of the disk on the vertical stick is recorded. A rising plate meter overcomes the problem of trying to estimate the height of the top of the sward, because it only measures the compressed height of a pasture. This compressed height is then correlated to the mass and density of the forage. To utilize a rising plate meter properly, the compressed height must be calibrated against samples that have been previously measured objectively (sampled, dried, and weighed). Also, this relationship must be recalibrated for different types of pastures because different mixtures of forage species will exhibit different relationships between density and mass. Rising Plate Meters are commercially available, or they can be constructed from common materials such as acrylic or metal or other convenient materials.

Pasture Gauge. An electronic probe device that looks like a walking stick and takes rapid and automatic determinations of pasture mass. A pasture gauge contains sophisticated circuitry in its base that measures differences in capacitance between air and forage. Its use is quite simple. The user walks across a paddock and allows the pasture gauge to take a series of readings, usually 25-30 readings or more. Upon command, the pasture gauge will then display the value for the average total mass of the pasture. The pasture gauge is then reset when a new paddock is entered. This technology has improved greatly over the past twenty years and now can be reasonably reliable. Modern units are manufactured commercially and are available from grazing supply houses.

Phases of Forage Growth

In general, the growth of improved forages can be described by a sigmoid curve that plots the total forage mass in a paddock vs time (Figure 1). This is the classic forage growth curve. Notice that this curve is not a straight line. A straight line would indicate that rate of early growth is the same as the rate of later growth. This is not true because the early and late parts of the growth curve are quite different from the central portion.

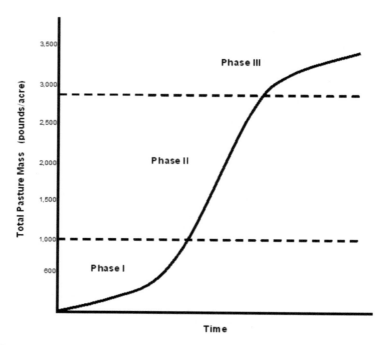

Figure 1. Forage Growth Curve

The lowest section of the sigmoid growth curve is labeled *Phase I.* This section describes the growth of newly emerged seedlings or recently harvested mature plants. In both cases, the amount of leaf area per acre is relatively small — either because the young seedling has only produced a few tiny leaves or because recently harvested forage has been defoliated to the point that only a few leaves remain. In either case, these plants only present a small amount of leaf surface area that can capture sunlight. Therefore, the absolute amount of photosynthesis occurring in the leaves of these plants is low. Although the feed value of this forage can be quite high, plant tissue accretion (growth) is also low because growth depends on photosynthetic products or root reserves. Forage accumulation is slow. In general, Phase I occurs when the total mass of the forage is less than 1,000 pounds per acre, although this amount may be slightly different for different forage species and circumstances.

The middle portion of the sigmoid curve is labeled *Phase II.* This section describes the growth of plants that are rapidly expanding their photosynthetic capacity. Note that the line rises steeply in nearly a straight line. During this period, plants are adding leaf area quickly, either by increasing leaf area on existing tillers or by adding new tillers. Photosynthetic activity is high, and if plants are provided with sufficient sunlight, water, and fertility, photosynthesis in these leaves can be producing carbohydrates at a prodigious rate. As nitrates are transported up from the roots, plants can incorporate the nitrogen into protein for additional growth. Some carbohydrates may also be translocated down into the roots for storage. During Phase II growth, forage mass accumulates rapidly, and feed value is high.

The top portion of the sigmoid growth curve is labeled *Phase III*. This section describes the period when top leaves are still photosynthesizing but lower leaves are showing senescence. The curve is flattening out, reflecting the slower *net* accumulation of forage. Plants are still adding mass during this period, but at a slower rate than during Phase II. During this Phase III period, a higher proportion of photosynthetic products are shifted from leaf growth to stem growth, root reserves, and also to reproductive growth. Plants begin to mature, and forage quality and palatability declines. In general, Phase III begins at a total mass above 2,800-3,000 pounds per acre, although this amount can be modified by other factors, including weather, fertility, forage species and cultivar, etc.

One important element in this growth curve is the junction between Phase I and Phase II. To the left of this junction, in Phase I, plants are growing slowly. To the right of this junction, in Phase II, plants are growing rapidly. The key principle for managing plant growth is to be diligent and disciplined about controlling the residual mass of a pasture. In general, efficient use of forage in a grazed pasture utilizes this junction as the target residual mass of a paddock. The amount of residual mass is a key management decision by the sheep producer. This will be discussed in greater detail later.

Types of Grazing Systems

In the scientific literature and popular press, numerous terms are used to describe grazing methods: lead-and-follow grazing, creep grazing, multi-species grazing, mob grazing, deferred grazing, strip grazing, controlled grazing, and many others. From a plant perspective, however, all these methods can be essentially described as variations of three basic types of grazing systems, which are determined primarily by the extent and quickness with which animals are allowed to harvest the forage regrowth:

Set-Stocking

Also known as *continuous grazing*, set-stocking is a system in which animals of one or more species remain in the same pasture for an extended period of time. This period of time can be as long as a full season or it can be considerably shorter. Although set-stocking is commonly associated with long grazing periods, the forage-related consequences of set-stocking can actually be induced in a much shorter period. The minimum period that would be considered as set-stocking is determined by forage species and physiology, stocking density, and weather.

The key botanical consequence of set-stocking is that animals have the opportunity to graze the *regrowth* of forage when the plants are still creating that regrowth from stored reserves. Longer grazing periods allow animals to graze regrowth multiple times, and that can have deleterious consequences for those plants. In fertile pastures containing improved forages of high growth potential, with good weather conditions and enough water, forage regrowth can begin in as little time as 3-5 days after the leaves are initially harvested (grazed). If animals remain in a pasture during this early regrowth period, and the stocking density is high enough to encourage animals to graze the same areas over and over, animals will generally prefer to consume this new regrowth because young, emerging leaves are highly palatable and nutritious.

Grazing young regrowth forces those plants to draw from their reserves to produce additional regrowth. Plants showing this regrowth are generally desirable plants in a pasture because these are the plants genetically capable of quick regrowth after defoliation. If grazing regrowth occurs multiple times — for example, if animals remain in a paddock for weeks — these plants will experience severe stress, putting them at a competitive disadvantage against other, less-desirable plants. These latter plants are less desirable in a pasture because they may be less palatable (weeds, thistles, older varieties of tall fescue and reed canarygrass) or their growing points may be below bite level (colonial bentgrass) or they may be early-maturing, low-yielding annuals that go to seed quickly (annual bluegrass, many weeds). Continuous grazing actually provides these less-desirable plants with a competitive advantage by systematically causing stress to the more-desirable plants. Thus, in a global sense, set-stocking can be considered a form of *overgrazing* because continuous grazing places some plants under stress, and also a form of *undergrazing* because the less-desirable plants may not experience enough grazing pressure to prevent them from going to seed.

Pastures managed under a set-stocking system, especially with low stocking rates, often contain areas that have been grazed heavily and areas that have been allowed to mature. This pattern is known as "spot grazing" — a common term in rangeland situations — and is the result of animals returning to the same spots to graze regrowth.

Rotational Grazing

Rotational grazing is a system in which a single pasture is subdivided into smaller paddocks, usually by permanent fencing, and animals are moved from paddock to paddock in a systematic pattern. Rotational grazing is always associated with cross-fencing and periodic stock movement. The number of days or the number of paddocks determines the shifting of stock from paddock to paddock. A rotational grazing system can be described by the number of paddocks and the number of days that animals remain in a paddock. For example, an "8 paddock, 4-day rotation" would indicate that the entire field was subdivided into 8 paddocks, and that the animals were shifted every four days, thus allowing the forage in every paddock to experience a rest period of 28 days between grazing sessions. This also means that in a 32-day period, the forages in any paddock would always experience a rest period of 28 days, or 87.5 percent of the time. Typically, the same shift pattern would be applied across an entire growing season.

The term "Rotational Grazing" is commonly found in the scientific literature. Rotational grazing systems are easy to describe, easy to understand, and easy to replicate. Scientific research about grazing often incorporates variations of rotational grazing because these standardized systems can be described precisely and replicated between years and between research institutions.

Unfortunately, the standardized schedules defined by rotational grazing systems often do not fit the physiology of plant growth, especially during various times during the growing season. These schedules are rather inflexible because they require that animals be moved according to a specific number of days (or the calendar), not according to plant growth.

During the growing season, there will indeed be periods when a strict rotational system may provide proper management to the forages, but there are also periods when such a system does not. This is because during the months of an entire growing season, so many changes occur in a paddock — soil and air temperature, moisture availability, species composition, plant growth rates, fertilizer applications, previous levels of residual forage, etc. — that plant growth is not constant, and thus there can be great variability in the total mass and residual mass in the various paddocks. This variability can easily result in inappropriate forage management for many of the paddocks, at least during certain periods of the growing season. Different forage species will be affected differently.

For example, 28 days of regrowth in the May-June period for a Kentucky bluegrass pasture will result in a different amount of forage than a 28-day regrowth period in August. However, a rigid rotation schedule throughout the entire season can result in periods of overgrazing (residual too low) or undergrazing (residual too high) or even, if the grazing periods are too long (i.e., five or more days in a paddock), some plants will be subjected to the deleterious effects of set-stocking.

Researchers attempt to address this problem by using a technique called "put-and-take," in which extra livestock are added or removed from the pastures during the season to adjust stocking density. In practice, however, put-and-take techniques are generally impractical on a farm because animals cannot be easily added or removed from a flock.

Management-Intensive Grazing (MIG)

Management-Intensive grazing is a system in which feed (forage) is allocated to the stock by fencing an appropriate area of pasture, usually within the constraints of minimizing stress on the forages and also maintaining the pastures at a high level of efficient growth and nutritional value. Jim Gerrish, formerly from the University of Missouri, originally coined the phrase "Management-Intensive Grazing." *The emphasis of MIG is on intensive management, not intensive grazing.* In MIG systems, animals are generally confined in paddocks containing only a few days of feed, but not always. The choice of grazing period depends on many factors, including the nutritional and management requirements of the animals, the grazier's intentions for managing that paddock, the goals of the operation, the time of year, etc.

Graziers who practice MIG determine how many days they want sheep to remain in a paddock and then position portable fencing (usually electric fencing) to enclose a pasture area containing the appropriate amount of feed for that period. To do this successfully, graziers must properly estimate total forage mass. Graziers must also decide upon a target level for the residual mass and then calculate the amount of available mass they wish to offer their animals. Then they place fences accordingly, so that animals will consume the available forage mass in the intended number of days. Then they move the animals to a different paddock, leaving the appropriate residual mass.

The general goal of this type of grazing management is to utilize forage efficiently and economically. To accomplish this, graziers try to introduce animals into a paddock when the total forage mass is at the top of Phase II and remove them from the paddock when the residual mass is at the bottom of Phase II. This means that grazing always occurs during Phase II growth. The consumed forage is highly nutritious, and plants are growing at the most efficient part of the growth curve. A general rule of thumb for most improved pastures is that the top of Phase II is approximately 2,800-3,000 pounds/acre, and the bottom of Phase II is approximately 1,000 pounds per acre — giving an available mass of 1,800-2,000 pounds/acre for animal consumption.

One of the most important principles of MIG is the careful monitoring and control of the residual forage mass in a paddock. If the residual is too small, then regrowth takes longer because the first days or weeks of regrowth is in Phase I, which is much slower than Phase II. Grazing too much forage from a pasture means leaving insufficient leaf area to support rapid regrowth. Forcing a pasture into Phase I translates into a lag period, which means that a longer time is required for the forage mass in that paddock to accumulate to the top of Phase II. From a grazier's perspective, this lag period is physiologically and economically inefficient because those extra days translate to higher feed costs.

Let's return to the example described previously — an orchardgrass/white clover pasture containing 2,800 pounds of total mass. The sheep producer wants to leave a residual mass of 1,100 pounds. Therefore, the available feed equals 1,700 pounds per acre. If the flock contains 230 Dorset ewes weighing an average of 150 pounds, how large an area should be fenced?

First, the grazier must determine how many days the animals should remain in the paddock. Let's assume that he decides on a grazing period of three days. Second, the grazier must determine the amount of feed required in those three days. The 230 Dorset ewes weigh a total of 34,500 pounds. If we allocate forage at five percent of body weight, then we would expect the flock to consume 1,725 pounds of dry matter each day. Knowing the number of days and the amount of feed needed, the grazier can now determine the area required by the sheep. For a three-day grazing duration, the grazier should allocate 5,175 pounds of feed. At an available mass of 1,700 pounds, the grazier should therefore set his fence for an area of 3 acres of pasture (arithmetically 3.04 acres).

A residual mass of 1,100 pounds may be represented by one to two inches of forage, which would seem very tempting for additional grazing. However, if those sheep remained in the paddock for longer than three days, they would then consume that extra forage which would reduce the residual mass to less than 1,100 pounds, which would slow forage regrowth and thus increase the amount of time before sheep could be put back onto the pasture.

People sometimes refer to MIG as *Controlled Grazing*, but this terminology is not very specific because all grazing on improved pastures is controlled, to some extent, with the use of perimeter fences. Another term sometimes used synonymously for MIG is *Management-Intensive Rotational Grazing* (MIRG), because people often automatically associate MIG with the intensive rotation of stock through small paddocks. But this association is neither automatic nor entirely correct. MIG can indeed utilize fast rotations through relatively small paddocks, but MIG also may require periods when animals are moved slowly through paddocks, as during drift lambing, or not at all, as when they are confined in a sacrifice area. The practitioner of MIG does not follow a rigidly prescribed game plan. Rather, he or she must adjust to the changing conditions of forage growth, weather, markets, etc. The underlying principle of MIG is its *resolute emphasis on intensive management, not intensive grazing*. The name of MIG has been chosen carefully to highlight this emphasis. Animals nearly always graze intensively — just watch them. The intensive part of MIG is the management — the series of active decisions by a manager who continuously monitors the forage and animal situation on the farm and strives to work with resources in an economically intelligent and physiologically sustainable manner.

The Grazing Wedge

In practice during the growing season, paddocks don't change uniformly in a linear 1-2-3-4 arrangement as if they were all neatly drawn on a blackboard. Every farm or ranch contains a multitude of different pastures. Each of these pastures has its own characteristics — soil type, drainage, slope, aspect (facing to the south, etc.), fertility and fertilizer application history, soil pH, forage species, proximity to lanes and barns, etc. During the growing season, forage in each of these paddocks will invariably grow at different rates, particularly at different times during the season. Some will grow faster and some will grow slower, and then two months later, the sequence could be reversed. For example, a well-drained paddock with a south-facing slope and early forage varieties will show rapid growth in early and mid-spring but may dry out during the heat of summer. A different paddock with low-lying heavy soils that do not dry out quickly may support good forage growth during the dry midsummer period.

Forage species also determines the grazing constraints. For example, a paddock of chicory should be grazed to smaller residuals in the late spring than a paddock containing grass and clover, to discourage summer bolting by the chicory. Another example: a paddock containing well-fertilized reed canarygrass must be grazed more often than a paddock containing Kentucky bluegrass, especially during high-growth periods of the growing season, or else the canarygrass will quickly grow into Phase III and become rank and unpalatable.

These are the realities on any forage-based farm. A grazier needs to monitor plant growth in each paddock, at least on a weekly basis, and then plan for future animal movements. A grazier must try to balance these observations with the goals of the farm, especially the goals of grazing only Phase II growth and providing high-quality nutrition to the animals. Despite having paddocks with widely divergent growth patterns, a grazier must still plan animal movement for weeks in advance, like the strategy for a chess game.

One important tool to help a grazier accomplish this is known as the *Grazing Wedge*. With the development of computers and spreadsheet software, a grazing wedge is relatively easy to create and follow.

To create a grazing wedge, a grazier first walks through each of the paddocks and records the amount of total mass in each paddock. Then the grazier enters this data into a computer spreadsheet and creates a histogram graph of the raw data. An example histogram of this raw data would look like Figure 2. The total pasture mass is represented by the y-axis; the pasture identification numbers are listed on the x-axis. The graphing routines of a spreadsheet can make this task quite simple. But notice that this graph has no discernible pattern. For example, if the sheep were currently in Paddock #3, where should they be moved next? Using the Grazing Wedge helps answer this question. The next step is that the grazier then uses the spreadsheet to sort (sequence) the paddocks in the descending order (top to bottom) from highest mass to lowest mass. Then the grazier instructs the software to recreate the histogram, this time using the sorted data listing all the pastures in descending order of total mass. Two horizontal lines are drawn across the graph — one line at the top level of Phase II at 3,000 pounds per acre and the other line at a target residual level at 1,000 pounds per acre (Figure 3).

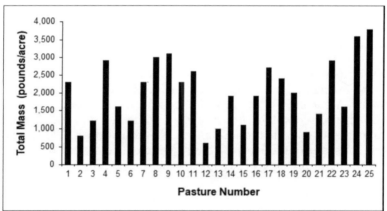

Figure 2. Raw Data from the Weekly Pasture Walk, in Original Sequence

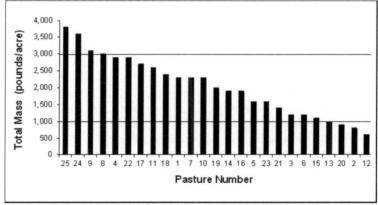

Figure 3. The Grazing Wedge, Using Pasture Observations Sorted by Total Pasture Mass

Notice the pattern of the graph from left to right — it looks like a wedge — resembling a doorstop. Any paddocks above 3,000 pounds are already in Phase III and should be topped off with a mower or made into hay or silage. Any paddocks less than 1,000 pounds are in Phase I and probably represent overgrazed areas that need time to recover and grow back. Reading from left to right gives the grazier the next sequence of paddocks to graze. Using our current example where the sheep are located in Paddock #3, Figure 3 shows us that the grazier should probably move sheep into Paddock #9 or Paddock #8. In contrast, Paddocks #24 and #25 should either be topped off or cut for hay or silage, and Paddocks #22 and then #17 are probably the next fields where the sheep will graze. Each week throughout the growing season, the grazier should walk through all the paddocks, record new pasture mass values, and update the grazing wedge after each new set of observations.

The grazing wedge is an important management tool. At a glance, a grazier can view a graphical representation of the forage status of the entire farm, paddock by paddock, showing the successes and deficiencies of a grazing strategy. A grazing wedge provides a reasonable direction for the next few stock movements. A grazing wedge, however, is only one piece of information. The grazing wedge is a good tool, but it's only a guideline. A grazier should know the characteristics of each paddock and how each paddock fits into the entire management system of the farm. These characteristics must be considered in any grazing decision. Sometimes a grazier may deviate from the suggestions of the grazing wedge because of his knowledge of the pasture specifics, as illustrated in the following examples:

Example 1. For a sheep farm in Virginia, the total forage masses displayed in a grazing wedge in mid-July suggest that Paddock BG should be grazed before Paddock CB. Both paddocks have been well-fertilized. The grazier, however, knows that Paddock BG contains mostly Kentucky bluegrass, while Paddock CB contains primarily a new, improved variety of crabgrass. Kentucky bluegrass is a cool-season species that shows a distinctive growth slump during the heat of midsummer. In contrast, crabgrass is a warm-season species that is capable of explosive growth during hot weather. Even though the grazing wedge in mid-July shows that Paddock BG contains more forage than Paddock CB, the grazier may choose to move animals onto Paddock CB first because a delayed grazing may allow its rapid growth to move it into Phase III, while delaying the grazing of Paddock BG will cause little harm because the bluegrass will be growing slowly anyway during midsummer.

Example 2. This example describes the use of a grazing wedge during the late spring, when most pasture plants are growing at peak rates. During this period, a grazier may want to graze some paddocks down to much lower residuals than generally recommended. Instead of leaving 1,000 pounds per acre, a grazier may decide to graze some paddocks down to 600 pounds or even less. Which paddocks? Probably those paddocks containing forage species capable of good summer growth, like orchardgrass, tall fescue, and white clover. The reasoning is straightforward. By grazing those paddocks down into Phase I, the regrowth rates in those paddocks will be slower, as described in the forage growth section earlier in this chapter, and those paddocks will show a lag period before they reach the top of Phase I. Under normal conditions, that farm typically experiences more forage growth during late spring than the animals can consume — a common problem — and by slowing the regrowth in some paddocks, the grazier is trying to balance or equalize the forage growth patterns across a longer period of time. To accomplish this goal of balancing forage growth, however, the grazier must be intimately familiar with the species composition and fertility characteristics of each of these paddocks. Paddocks dominated by plants such as Kentucky bluegrass or perennial ryegrass would *not* be good candidates for this treatment because these species typically show a summer slump in hot weather anyway. Overgrazing them during late spring might simply cause a significant loss of forage growth in those paddocks rather than just shifting that growth to a later period.

Additional Things to Consider

Managing pastures to produce high-quality forage in an economic and sustainable system requires considerable skill and knowledge. In addition to understanding the basic principles of plant growth and pasture measurement, a grazier must become proficient in many other aspects of forages. Some of these aspects relate directly to the soil and forage, and some relate directly to the sheep. This section covers a variety of principles and techniques that affect good forage management.

Grazing Period

This is the number of days that animals remain in the same paddock. Although the choice is ultimately up to the grazier and may be influenced by many economic and weather-related factors, one basic principle must always be considered — when will the animals consume any new *regrowth* of the forage? In fertile pastures containing actively growing plants, high-quality forage plants will begin to show new regrowth of the leaves within 3-5 days of being grazed. Regrowth consists of young, tender leaves, which are highly palatable and nutritious. If given the opportunity, sheep will seek out and graze these young leaves in preference to other forage in the pasture, even if that other forage is in Phase II growth. This grazing behavior forces those regrowing plants to draw more from their reserves and ultimately puts them at a competitive disadvantage, especially compared to other species such as weeds, thistles, and less-palatable forages (for example, the older varieties of tall fescue). This leads us to a basic principle — *The 5-Day Rule*. Specifically, this rule states that animals should not remain in the same paddock area for more than five days or else they will begin to graze regrowth. Of course, if plants are dormant (i.e., stockpiled forage in late autumn in most of North America, or residual brown forage in the dry midsummer in California and the Pacific Northwest), then there is no active regrowth, and the 5-day Rule would not apply. Also, if a grazier planned to renovate a pasture and therefore wanted to remove all the forage, plant stress would not be a consideration, and he would intentionally keep animals in the pasture for longer than five days.

Stocking Density

Stocking density is defined as the amount of animal biomass per unit area at a specific instant of time. It is essentially a biological snapshot of the grazing intensity in a pasture. Although many farmers like to talk about *yyy* sheep per acre or *zzz* cattle per acre, stocking density is a more precise term for intensive grazing systems because it describes the amount of biomass actually confined in an area of forage and is best expressed as *pounds (of animal) per acre*. Describing grazing in terms of stocking density, rather than in terms of numbers of animals, allows comparisons between different livestock species and different types of operations, and also facilitates MIG computations on forage mass and grazing interval. For example, if a two-acre paddock contains 400 ewes that average 160 pounds, the stocking density would be 32,000 pounds per acre. Similarly, if a 0.25-acre paddock contains 25 ewes that average 220 pounds, the stocking density would be 22,000 pounds per acre. Knowing the values for stocking density allows different producers to compare grazing techniques and also enables a producer to monitor and adjust grazing strategies over time, especially as important characteristics of the operation change, such as stock numbers, forage species, and soil fertility.

The term Stocking Density is usually used in conjunction with non-supplemented animals on pasture. The feeding of supplements to grazing animals distorts the value of stocking density because supplements generally alter the rate of forage intake. Stocking Density is sometimes used synonymously with the phrase "*grazing pressure*," although the latter terminology may be somewhat ambiguous.

Stocking Rate

Defined as the number of animals in a grazing unit over a period of time (usually assumed to be the growing season). In the United States., stocking rate is usually expressed in terms of "Animal Units" where an Animal Unit (AU) is equivalent to one 1,000-pound cow (dry or with a calf up to 6 months of age) with a forage allowance of 26 pounds of dry matter per day. Five ewes are equivalent to one cow. Different terminology is used in other countries. For example, stocking rates in New Zealand are expressed in terms of "Stock Units" where one Stock Unit equals the annual metabolizable energy requirement of a 121-pound (55-kg) ewe raising 1.05 lambs.

Stocking Rate is often used to describe the number of animals that a farm or grazing unit can support over time, as in six ewes per acre or three ewes per acre or as in one cow per two acres. This terminology can be very useful in range environments. In practice, however, the term "stocking rate" is less useful for intensive-management situations than the term "stocking density" because the number of animals that an area will carry (stocking rate) can easily change over time, but the amount of grazing pressure (stocking density) is a precise number that is determined at a single point in time. The stocking rate of a farm or field can change radically with forage improvements, changes in fertility, changes in water supply, changes in weather or season, or the use of supplemental feed. If the forage conditions in a pasture or farm changes during that period of time, the term "stocking rate" becomes ambiguous because the feed amount in the forage area has not been held constant. This is particularly true if animals receive any supplementary feed such as hay, silage, or grain. For example, if the "stocking rate" on a farm is increased dramatically because the farmer provides 30 percent of the energy and protein requirements as supplementary grain, then what is the value of the number represented by the term stocking rate?

Sacrifice Area

A sacrifice area is a relatively small paddock where animals are confined long enough to consume forage below the normal residual mass. A sacrifice area is useful when a grazier, for any reason, does not want to graze the other paddocks on the farm. A sacrifice area can be any area on a farm, or even a rented pasture, and each year it can be a different pasture. A sacrifice area is particularly useful when none of the other areas on the farm contains sufficient mass for grazing or are too muddy for grazing, and the grazier wants to wait before putting animals back into the improved paddocks. Graziers often strategically select a sacrifice area to fit into the overall management of the farm, such as a paddock that will undergo renovation or an area that is heavily populated with weeds or brush.

Dry Matter Intake

Allocating feed in a MIG system requires the grazier to do three things before placing the temporary fence: (1) estimate how much feed the sheep will consume each day, (2) estimate the amount of forage in the pasture, and (3) decide on the target residual mass and grazing period (while complying with the 5-day Rule). The second and third items have already been discussed in this chapter. The first item requires a knowledge of the animals and a working understanding of feed consumption.

As a starting point, general guidelines for estimating the dry matter intake (DMI) of sheep can be obtained in many reference books (for example, in the Nutrition Chapter of the *SID Sheep Production Handbook,* from its table on Daily Nutrient Requirements of Sheep). These reference values are based on body weight and stage of production. In practice, it is easiest to work with DMI values that are expressed as a percentage of body weight. Graziers should recognize, however, that reference values for expected DMI are not as precise as reference values for required nutrients such as energy and protein, especially for animals on pasture. Experienced graziers using high-quality forages generally add 20-30 percent or more to these DMI values to allow for variability, trampled forage, etc. On high-quality pasture, graziers often observe that DMI may be considerably higher than the reference values, as measured by the disappearance of forage mass when the sheep graze. Low-quality forages, of course, contain higher levels of fiber that will correspondingly reduce DMI. Setting the grazing area in a MIG system is essentially a balancing act between estimating the amount of forage in the pasture versus estimating the daily DMI of the animals in that pasture. Graziers should always monitor the disappearance of forage, especially with new pastures or new animals, and adjust their allocations accordingly. Over time, experience will help guide decisions about DMI.

Water

The basic principle for good grazing management is to move water to the animals, rather than allowing animals to move to the water. Ideally, a good water distribution system should permit water delivery to every paddock on the farm, including all temporary grazing areas within each paddock. This design gives the farmer full flexibility to adjust to changing pasture conditions, erect temporary fences in any area of the farm, and effectively manage forage growth. Allowing stock to drink water directly from streams or ponds should be avoided because this requires animals to move to the water source (rather than vice versa) and also may not be in compliance with local or national guidelines on water quality.

For farms with small acreages, water can be delivered through flexible garden hoses, sometimes connected together to create long tubes. Larger areas require permanent or temporary main pipes combined with risers or other joints to attach lateral hoses. Buried mainlines are ideal, but water lines should not be buried until the grazier is familiar with the forage growth patterns on a property. A typical well-designed system would include buried mainlines, with below-ground couplings for attaching lateral pipes or hoses. Vertical risers are also popular, but if they stick up above the ground surface, they could be damaged by tractors and other equipment.

For small flocks, water troughs can be small and portable. Larger flocks might require more permanent facilities. At certain times of the year, particularly when forage is lush, sheep may not consume much water. However, it is always wise to supply water to the animals in pastures. Changing conditions can cause major shifts in drinking patterns. Lactating ewes and growing lambs are particularly sensitive to inadequate water.

Pasture systems in which animals must travel to large, centralized water troughs (or ponds or natural streams) result in inconsistent and inefficient forage management. Areas adjacent to central water troughs tend to become overgrazed, while forage areas at any distance from the troughs are often inadequately grazed. Once height (and mass) differences begin to appear in paddocks, subsequent plant growth only exacerbates these differences. Some areas of pastures will continue to grow into Phase III while other areas struggle in Phase I growth. Sheep walking to central water sources will preferentially graze the more palatable forage in Phase I regrowth, thus compounding the problems of managing the forage properly.

Placement of water troughs is critical. Many producers like to put water troughs near trees to provide shade to the animals. During hot weather, unfortunately, this arrangement encourages livestock to congregate around the water and lie in the shade. Since animals tend to deposit manure and urine near their resting areas, this arrangement also facilitates movement of soil fertility from open paddock areas to areas under trees. When deciding upon trough placement, graziers should consider the factors of heat, humidity, and nutrient transfer. Humid heat is more stressful to sheep than dry heat, especially if the sheep are in full fleece

Regardless of the type of system design, stock drinking water should always be clean.

Minerals

Providing supplementary minerals (including salt) on pasture follows the same principle as providing water on pasture. In every paddock, sheep should always have access to an appropriate mineral mixture. Sheep should not be required to walk long distances to obtain minerals. Providing minerals in each paddock is usually easier than providing water because mineral feeders can be small and portable. A pasture mineral feeder does not need to be expensive or elaborate. It should be designed to protect minerals from rain and wind. Since it remains in a pasture and animals always have free-choice access to it, a mineral feeder does not have to be big, even for large flocks. For MIG systems, a mineral feeder should be large enough to supply a few days of minerals to the animals, yet small enough to be easily portable. Larger flocks can utilize small portable mineral feeders that can be dragged behind an ATV. In any grazing system, a large centralized mineral feeder can create the same forage management problems as a centralized water system.

The composition of the mineral mix will depend on the geographical region of the farm and many other factors. Check with your local Extension Agent, nutritionist, or veterinarian for recommendations about the specifics of mineral mixtures for your area.

Free-choice mineral intake is difficult to predict and is also quite variable. Mature ewes will generally consume 0.25-0.50 ounces of salt daily, but their actual intake of a mineral mixture can range from zero to many times that expected level. High intakes often occur if the mineral mixture contains highly palatable ingredients, such as molasses. In general, mineral intake is higher from loose minerals than from mineral blocks. However, many factors influence mineral intake, including weather, forage composition, animal activity, production stage, the palatability of the mineral ingredients, block hardness, and the availability of salt from alternative sources.

Fencing

Good fencing is essential for good forage management. Simply put, without good fencing, a grazier cannot properly manage the defoliation and regrowth of his forages. Many advisors like to use the phrase "plant fence posts" to describe the relationship between good fencing and good grazing.

There are essentially two types of fencing: (1) perimeter fencing, and (2) internal fencing. Perimeter fencing separates the farm's pastures from roads and other nonfarm areas. Perimeter fencing must always be constructed from materials sturdy enough to keep animals in and keep animals out, without significant risk of failure. In general, perimeter fencing for sheep is permanent fencing built of various long-lasting materials, including standard woven-wire, high-tensile woven-wire, high-tensile electrified fencing, or high-tensile wires, with solidly-constructed corner and brace posts, etc. This fence must keep sheep from straying onto other properties or onto roads and must protect sheep from predators. Good perimeter fencing is essential for peace of mind and smooth operation of stock. It essentially is a kind of liability insurance and should always be maintained properly. The use of barbed wire must be mentioned here. Although barbed wire can be successfully used for cattle, it can only be used for sheep when placed as the top wire *above* a woven-wire fence (high enough so that sheep cannot reach it) to allow that fence to also be used for cattle, or as the bottom wire next to the ground *beneath* a woven-wire fence, as a deterrent against predators. Regardless of how barbed wire is used in any fence system, for any species of livestock, *barbed wire must never be electrified.* Electrified barbed wire is a serious safety threat to humans and animals.

Internal fencing, on the other hand, is designed to keep stock within specific areas of paddocks, and it can be constructed from temporary or permanent materials, although a temporary fence allows for more flexibility. Temporary electric fencing is very effective for sheep. This type of fencing can be achieved by strands of electrified plastic (usually two or three strands for sheep, although trained adult ewes can be restrained by a single strand if the grazing pressure is not great), or electrified plastic netting. The plastic netting is popular because its self-contained, self-standing design is light, portable, and doesn't require additional fence posts.

When first designing the layout of internal fencing, avoid constructing permanent internal fences — because once permanent fences are built, the grazier must live with them, good or bad, even if the forage situation on the farm becomes radically altered. Permanent internal fences built in the wrong places become a hindrance to smooth farm operation. They can prevent easy machinery movement and may severely complicate stock movement. In general, producers should defer building permanent internal fences until they are certain about best placement, after at least a couple of years of experience of managing pastures on that acreage.

Electric fencing is very effective at restraining sheep, and sheep can be trained to an electric fence. Compared to other livestock, sheep in fleece are less sensitive to electric fencing, and full-fleeced sheep require at least 5,000 volts in the fence for reliable containment. One common technique to train sheep is to confine the animals in a relatively small area enclosed by an electric fence and place a small amount of grain under the fence. Sheared sheep are easier to train than wooled sheep. Occasionally, an individual sheep may resist this training and should be culled.

Effective electric fencing for sheep requires one or more good, modern low-impedance chargers, a properly engineered grounding system, and a well-designed method of transmitting the charge across the farm. A grazier should always have a voltage tester to monitor the system and detect problems. Detailed fencing information can be obtained from many sources, including the Extension Service, workshops, commercial companies and their catalogs, grazing groups, and the internet.

All new graziers should make it a priority to learn to use fencing quickly and effectively. The fencing equipment currently available is far superior to the older equipment. The last fifteen years has seen an explosion of new commercial fencing equipment for graziers, and a multitude of new fencing items and gadgets are now available that were unknown years ago.

Soil Fertility

Forage can be a high-value crop for a sheep producer, and like any crop, good yields depend on good soil fertility. The only accurate way of determining soil fertility status is to take a soil test. A good soil test provides information on a large array of soil characteristics, including major plant nutrients (usually phosphorus and potassium, also known as potash), microminerals, organic matter, cation exchange capacity, pH, and an indication of the resistance of acid soils to changes in pH. A soil test can also be a valuable report card on nitrogen usage. Knowing these values, a producer can then make wise choices about which fertilizers and other soil amendments might be necessary. Soil tests also provide excellent information that can guide renovation efforts and seeding choices.

All paddocks should be tested at least once, and it is a good practice to repeat the test every three or four years. Annual soil tests for pastures are generally not necessary. For any pasture, however, its soil test should be taken during the same month as its previous soil tests because some soil characteristics such as pH and certain mineral levels might fluctuate naturally during the year. Taking soil tests at different times during different years may give in misleading results. For example, if a pasture is tested at different months in different years, and the fertility values differ between the tests, the grazier does not know if those differences are due to real changes in soil fertility or are simply due to natural seasonal variations.

It should be remembered that harvesting hay and silage from a field removes considerable amounts of fertility from that field. For example, if a legume-grass hay contains 14 percent crude protein, 0.25 percent phosphorus, 2.1 percent potassium, and 0.25 percent sulfur on a dry matter basis, harvesting three tons of this hay (at 90 percent dry matter = 5,400 lb of dry matter) removes from the soil 121 lb nitrogen, 13.5 lb phosphorus, 113 lb potassium, and 13.5 lb sulfur. To support future crops, some of this nitrogen may be replaced by actively growing legumes that fix nitrogen from the atmosphere, but the rest of the nitrogen and all the other minerals must be replaced from breakdown in the soil or from fertilizers.

In contrast, grazing does not remove many nutrients from the pasture, except for small amounts of minerals incorporated into the meat, wool, or milk created while animals were in the pasture. Grazing recycles nearly all minerals through manure and urine. Manure also provides the additional benefit of adding organic matter to the soil.

Although most producers use commercial fertilizers to improve soil fertility, those producers who sell lamb in the "organic" market must work within the constraints of rules that certify them for that market. These producers must only use soil amendments approved by their state organic board. These boards do not permit the use of many common commercial fertilizers. Organic producers need to keep up-to-date with their state rules for fertilizer usage, as these rules are often revised.

Pasture Renovation

Renovating fields with new seed is an expensive undertaking and should not be done lightly. Each field in a farm has a unique set of characteristics and circumstances and should be viewed as an individual situation that is part of the entire farm operation. Before renovating any field, a grazier should complete three steps:

First decide what goal is to be met by a field — hay, silage, grazing, or a combination — and how that field may fit into the framework of the entire farm operation. For example, will the field need to provide early spring pasture, or mid-summer grazing for feeder lambs, or be the main source of hay for the farm?

Then obtain information about soil fertility levels, including pH. Knowing how a field will be used and its fertility status will provide a framework for deciding what species to plant and how much it would cost for seed and fertilizer.

The third step — choosing appropriate species and varieties — should only be done after the first two points have been addressed. Unlike planting an annual forage (such as annual ryegrass or forage rape) or even a biennial forage (such as red clover), planting a perennial forage is truly a long-term decision because a grazier must live with and manage that forage for many years. When choosing seed, carefully consider the advantages and disadvantages of each species. Consider the major types of forages — grasses, legumes, herbs, or other species — and how each would fit into the management of that pasture and the entire farm. Within each species, there are often many genetic lines, called varieties (or cultivars). Over the past fifteen years, public research stations and private companies have developed a wide assortment of new forage varieties. These newer varieties may have quite different characteristics than the older ones. Although "total yield" is the bellwether trait that most people traditionally measure when comparing varieties and species, graziers should also be aware of other forage characteristics that are very important to good forage management. Recent genetic selections have expanded their criteria to include economically important traits for graziers, such as palatability, winter hardiness, date of maturity, seasonal growth patterns, persistence in the stand, speed of recovery after defoliation, disease and pest resistance, reduction of metabolic toxins, ease of establishment, and physical growth patterns (upright, prostrate, etc.).

Variability among varieties within a forage species may sometimes be greater than variability between species. Before selecting new seed, graziers should research these choices carefully. Some varieties may provide much better combinations of characteristics for a farm than others.

On the other hand, an expensive pasture renovation may not always be an appropriate response to the problem of low forage production. Strategically changing the pasture management and increasing soil fertility can often obtain a major productivity response. In many situations, this option should be explored *before* deciding to completely renovate a pasture.

A final note about renovation: Any producer who is thinking about solving a pasture problem by renovation should recognize that the existing forages in a pasture are the cumulative result of current management. Those species have been *selected* naturally to survive and thrive under the existing management. Remember that "no management"— i.e., continuous grazing with no fertility improvements — is a kind of management. Changing the forage by planting new seeds may indeed show a dramatic improvement initially, but if the forage management does not change, that pasture will soon revert back to the original problem situation. Therefore, any pasture renovation should be accompanied by a change in management of that pasture.

Multispecies Grazing

This is the use of more than one species on a farm for grazing. For example, many farmers run sheep and cattle, or sheep and goats, or they keep horses on the farm pastures in addition to the sheep. Recently, the use of South American Camelids (SACs — primarily llamas and alpacas) has grown in popularity, either for predator control or the production of alpaca fiber. Over the years, the topic of multi-species grazing has been the subject of quite a lot of research. Multispecies grazing can have at least two different meanings: (1) the different species are grazed on the same farm but always in different paddocks, and (2) the different species are grazed together in the same paddock, at least for some of the time.

Much significance has been made about species differences in grazing preferences — that sheep and cattle and goats have different preferences about plant consumption, and that combining livestock species will sometimes provide a better utilization of forages. From a forage management perspective, these observations are more applicable to grazing systems where pastures contain many different plant species and the stocking densities are low enough to allow animals the luxury of selecting their feed. This situation certainly occurs in range operations and also may occur in pastures where animals are lightly stocked.

However, from the perspective of managing improved pastures, the difference in grazing preferences between livestock species implies a form of set-stocking, because animals grazed in high stocking densities and moved often do not usually have the luxury of selecting a preferred forage species. From a marketing perspective, however, running more than one livestock species in an operation may increase marketing options and may have excellent economic ramifications for the farm. Grazing multiple species on the same farm also may provide methods of controlling internal parasites because many parasites are species-specific.

Regardless of which combination of livestock species is utilized on a farm, the grazier should always remember the basic principles of forage growth and regrowth, residual mass, length of time on a paddock, and stocking density. Keeping these in mind, here are a few guidelines for grazing with multiple species:

- Sheep tend to consume legumes in preference to grasses.
- Cattle tend to graze grasses in preference to legumes.
- Cattle tend to graze plants that are higher in the sward — for example grasses that extend above the height of the rest of the plants. Cattle can be often used to clean up paddocks and help maintain an even pasture mass.
- Horses cannot be confined in pastures in high enough stocking densities to allow for MIG.
- High-quality forages may cause digestive problems with horses.
- Goats tend to prefer a higher percentage of forbs in their diet to grasses and legumes. Goats like to graze upward rather than downward. Goats also require fencing that is well-designed and well-maintained.
- Sheep are more susceptible to chronic copper toxicity than cattle, goats, and SACs. In many regions of the United States, cattle and sheep should receive different mineral mixtures on pastures, although there are also some regions where copper is deficient. This topic is complex. In any situation, check with a knowledgeable nutritionist or veterinarian.

Selected References

(Author's note: These are not all the references listed in the original *SID Sheep Production Handbook*, but these are ones that are particularly useful for the topic of "Intensively Managed Grazing Systems")

Cheeke, P.R., 1998. Natural Toxicants in Feeds, Forages, and Poisonous Plants, 2nd Edition. Interstate Publishers, Inc., Danville, IL

Gerrish, J. and Roberts, C. (eds.), 1999. Missouri Grazing Manual. MU Extension, University of Missouri-Columbia, MO

Gerrish, J., 2004, Management-intensive Grazing: The Grassroots of Grass Farming. Green Park Press, Ridgeland, MS

Murphy, B., 1998. Greener Pastures On Your Side Of The Fence, 4th Edition. Arriba Publishing, Colchester, VT

Van Soest, P.J., 1994. Nutritional Ecology of the Ruminant. 2nd Edition. Cornell University Press, Ithaca, NY

Voisin, A., 1959. Grass Productivity. Island Press, Washington, D.C.

Acronyms and Abbreviations

ADF	Acid Detergent Fiber
ADIN	Acid Detergent Insoluble Nitrogen
ADICP	Acid Detergent Insoluble Crude Protein
AIV	Artturi Ilmari Virtanen (A.I.V method of making silage)
aNDF	Amylase-Treated NDF (corrected for starch)
ANR	Apparent Nitrogen Recovery
ARG	Annual Ryegrass
ASI	American Sheep Industry Association
ATV	All-Terrain Vehicle (aka "four-wheeler")
AU	Animal Unit
AUM	Animal Unit Month
BLM	Bureau of Land Management
BMR	Brown Midrib (genetic mutation)
C3	Cool-season grass(es)
C4	Warm-season grass(es)
CAFO	Confined Animal Feeding Operation
CEC	Cation Exchange Capacity
CEO	Chief Executive Officer
CP	Crude Protein
DDM	Digestible Dry Matter
DM	Dry Matter
DMI	Dry Matter Intake

EBV .... Estimated Breeding Value (for genetic selection of livestock)
EE .... Ether extract (assay for fat and other ether-soluble compounds)
EPA .... Environmental Protection Agency
EPD .... Expected Progeny Difference (for genetic selection of livestock)
FAMACHA .... acronym of "FAffa MAlan CHArt." A technique for evaluating parasite-caused anemia in sheep and goats, developed in South Africa.
FANG .... Forage And Nutrition Group
FIU .... Feed Intake Unit
GI .... Gastrointestinal (as in gastrointestinal tract)
ICP .... Insoluble Crude Protein
KBG .... Kentucky Bluegrass
MIG .... Management-Intensive Grazing
MIRG .... Management-Intensive Rotational Grazing
NDF .... Neutral Detergent Fiber
NDFDxx .... NDF digestibility after xx hours of fermentation
NDFom .... Organic Matter NDF (corrected for minerals)
NDICP .... Neutral Detergent Insoluble Crude Protein
NDFn .... Nitrogen-Free NDF
NFC .... Non-Fiber carbohydrates
NPN .... Non-Protein Nitrogen
NRC .... National Research Council
NRCS .... Natural Resources Conservation Service (of the USDA)
NUE .... Nitrogen Use Efficiency
peNDF .... Physically Effective NDF
PRG .... Perennial Ryegrass
psi .... pounds per square inch
RCG .... Reed Canarygrass
RFV .... Relative Feed Value
RFQ .... Relative Forage Quality
SAC .... South American Camelid
SD .... Stocking Density
SID .... Sheep Industry Development Inc.
SMP .... Shoemaker-McLean-Pratt. SMP Buffer method for estimating lime requirement
SR .... Stocking Rate
SRM .... Society for Range Management
SWCD .... Soil and Water Conservation District

TDN .... Total Digestible Nutrients
TTNDFD .... Total Tract NDF Digestibility
uNDFxx .... Undigested NDF after xx hours of fermentation
USDA .... United States Department of Agriculture
UVFSG .... Umpqua Valley Forage Study Group
VFAs .... Volatile Fatty Acids
WVGANG .... Willamette Valley Grazing And Nutrition
Group

Index

Editor's Note: Common forage terms and phrases have not been indexed, as they occur with great frequency throughout the book. These terms include forage, grass, legume, root, leaf, blade, hay, soil, soil fertility, fertilizer, nitrogen, cattle, sheep, ruminant, vegetation, etc.

About the Author

Woody Lane is a nationally known expert on pasture management, sheep and beef cattle nutrition, and grazing techniques. His passion for sharing his knowledge comes across in all he does, including his writing. Laypeople who have read this work on forages say they will never look at a field the same way again.

Earlier, he published a book on nutrition, *From The Feed Trough—Essays and Insights on Livestock Nutrition in a Complex World.* That book and this one are compilations of his monthly column "From The Feed Trough..." for *The Shepherd* magazine. He has published hundreds of popular articles and fact sheets on cattle and sheep production and grazing, and he has also written more than twenty-five research articles in peer-reviewed scientific journals.

Woody earned his PhD and MS degrees in animal nutrition from Cornell University. He now owns and operates Lane Livestock Services, an independent consulting firm based in Roseburg, Oregon. He can't look at a field without wanting to improve it. Woody enjoys public speaking, and he has often been featured in many of the top workshops and conferences across the United States and Canada. He also teaches practical courses on forage management and livestock nutrition. In addition, he facilitates three innovative forage discussion groups for farmers and ranchers in Oregon.

Originally from New York, Woody's interest in livestock management stems from two years as a Peace Corps Volunteer in Sarawak, Malaysia, and then six months working on farms in New Zealand. In the 1970s, he worked on the well-known Allegheny Highlands Project in West Virginia. This project, which delivered information to farmers to promote rural development, was the groundbreaking prototype for the Integrated Resource Management programs that are used throughout the livestock world today. Woody joined the faculty of the University of Wisconsin in the 1980s as the State Sheep and Beef Cattle Extension Specialist.

He and his wife, Jeri Frank, migrated to western Oregon in 1990. When he is not working with livestock and pastures, Woody enjoys dancing and calling contra dances and square dances. But that, as they say, is a very different field altogether.

Made in the USA
Thornton, CO
10/17/23 21:25:10